Melanie McGrath

is the author of one previous
New Age in the American Desert (
Llewellyn Rhys Prize for the Be

from the reviews:

'Thanks to the strands of auto
novelistic density and narrative c   ultimately
it is rather moving, something of a novelty for books about the Net.'

JIM McCLELLAN, *Guardian*

'McGrath writes with intimacy and her astute portrayals of people, conversations and encounters give the book its edge. This is a story in which everything grows up, old, or at least used to the digital world. What begins as an alien culture, young and seductive, becomes familiar routine and far more diverse by the end of the book. First waves of enthusiasm give way to the reflective waters in which the book so elegantly swims . . . It is a compelling parable, and McGrath is perfectly poised to record the unique qualities of this slice of history.'

SADIE PLANT, *The Times*

'In a candid travelogue, McGrath recounts her romance with the nebulous world of the digital generation and her encounters with the newbies, hackers, sippies, slot freaks and virus writers who inhabit it. She travels to isolated new towns in England and Wales, the former Eastern bloc, freezing Reykavik, sketching in the real world with its intense smell of gasoline and eucalyptus, and the virtual world full of caffeine clichés, vampire lifestyles and astounding innovations. Throughout, McGrath is a sharp and convincing observer.'

EITHNE FARRY, *Time Out*

'Meditations on the digital generation and how technology reconfigures our notions of intimacy, friendship and even personality itself. McGrath travels the world meeting hackers, e-mail junkies, skip raiders and virus writers, piecing together an alien culture. Anecdotal and discursive, this is the book which opens up the electronic frontier to those still left out in the cold, the volume McLuhan would have written were he to be still surfing the Nineties.' *Arena*

further reviews overleaf

'McGrath is a funny and intelligent writer.'

TERENCE BLACKER, *Mail on Sunday*

'In a brilliant passage Melanie walks through California's ancient Muir Woods with her American friend Nancy. They pass a Redwood tree with its age rings marked out to map human achievements since Christopher Columbus and – in that quiet clearing where the first frontiersmen came, just a few miles from the present Silicon Valley – Nancy talks of California as the epicentre of the American spirit and dream, the place where the old and new frontiers collide.

That new frontier is an equally hazy illusion. Nancy says that "the first frontier was never some fixed thing . . . first it was the Appalachians, then the Missouri, the Great Plains, then the Rockies. It's the same with high tech. There isn't a single technological frontier. The minute one boundary is crossed the dream moves on."

A travel writer and explorer, writing of an unchartable and possibly illusory world, McGrath sets out to stake her claim to this ever-changing digital age, perpetually on the move between Britain and America, with stops in Iceland, Russia and Germany. Yet like any good travel writer, her perspective is always more powerful for the fact that she remains somehow an outsider to that world. It's an ideal standpoint to produce this personal memoir and guide to the follies and revelations of the electronic frontier. It's not always an attractive new world, it's not a particularly brave one either, and little enough of the information saturating the superhighway is real. But maybe the word "real" will never be the same again. Reading *Hard, Soft & Wet* one cannot but feel that you have received a vivid, quirky and shrewd insight into a frontier, the possibilities of which are just starting to be explored.'

DERMOT BOLGER, *Tribune Magazine*

'You can disagree with McGrath. But you can't fault the quality of her observations or her writing.' WENDY GROSSMAN, *New Scientist*

'*Hard, Soft & Wet* provides many provocative glimpses of how people are faring in our modern techno-wilderness.'

SCOTT BRADFIELD, *TES*

'The slyly contrapuntal structure of the book points up the redundancy of human travel. She herself might be an e-mail, shuttling around the globe, except that such items rarely go climbing with the local techno-geeks or witness their absurdly fractured conversations . . . [McGrath] is clever, poised and attentive.' MARTIN CROPPER, *Daily Telegraph*

HARD, SOFT & WET

the digital generation comes of age

MELANIE McGRATH

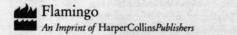Flamingo
An Imprint of HarperCollins*Publishers*

for Alex and Daniel

Flamingo
An Imprint of HarperCollins Publishers
77-85 Fulham Palace Road,
Hammersmith, London W6 8JB

Published by Flamingo 1998
9 8 7 6 5 4 3 2

First published in Great Britain by
HarperCollins Publishers 1997

ISBN 0 00 654849 0

Set in Monotype Bembo and Chicago by
Rowlands Phototypesetting Ltd,
Bury St Edmunds, Suffolk

Printed and bound in Great Britain by
Caledonian International Book Manufacturing Ltd, Glasgow

'I could tell you my adventures – beginning from this morning,' said Alice a little timidly; 'but it's no use going back to yesterday, because I was a different person then.'

LEWIS CARROLL,
Alice's Adventures in Wonderland

Contents

all this began some time ago

i: IN WONDERLAND

THERE'S NO EXPLAINING why Nancy and I have stayed friends over the years. We don't have much in common any more. Not much you could put your finger on. But friends we are, strung together by our few similarities and by the thin, tough mesh of our small shared past.

The airport train unzips to let a couple out, then zips back up and hums away from the station, picking up speed and rediscovering its riff. Beating out the same syllables on its tracks: Am-er-i-ca, Am-er-i-ca. A squall of tunnel air scatters them. Am-er-i-ca. Am-er-i-ca. It's been fourteen years since I first stepped out of the plane at San Francisco. Now I'm going back. Nancy will be standing at the barrier on the other side waiting for me. Nancy with the troublesome eyes, the air of insouciance, the panoramic humour. Nancy of the good dream.

Out on the other side of the tunnel the rhythm tugs on, a restless, sexy hiss of noise. Am-er-i-ca. Am-er-i-ca. Mad, fat, brave America. Am-er-i-ca. The sound of redwoods big as mushroom clouds, of cream soda cans trapped in cooler bags, of blanket smog tricked out as coastal cloud. Am-er-i-ca. A sway of pricking notes, like liquorice powder on the tongue.

We met in a borrowed apartment on Venice Beach. She was a couple of years older than me, nineteen I think, but assured and at home in herself even then. I thought she was the girl from Ipanema on loan to Los Angeles; tallish, with a swing of a walk and sharp brown hair. We watched TV together, roaring at the re-runs of *The Partridge Family* and after we were done laughing, we skipped down to the beach and played. She dazzled me. I hung on her words and practised their pronunciation. Bayzil, leeshure, parsta, lootenant. We had all the usual Anglo-American spats, who came first at what.

Later, Nancy's brother saw me off at the Amtrak station and promised to catch up with the train on his motorbike at Santa Barbara or thereabouts. The last I saw of him, he was standing in a field next to the track, waving and smiling as the train sped by, too fast for him to be able to make out my carriage or me. He moved to Canada some years later, but I was always touched by that gesture. I was seventeen and everything was ripe with meaning.

SAN FRANCISCO, CALIFORNIA, TUESDAY
Apple pie

Nancy was there at the barrier as I'd expected, her hair shorter and still beautiful, with tracings around the eyes. We rumbled along highway 280 into San Francisco, past the industrial centre, past the university and down into 19th Avenue, chirping like caged birds, our heads darting about and our tongues full of this and that. The city was looking just so in the afternoon sun.

'When Brezhnev came, he asked if people had to pay an extra tax to come and live here,' said Nancy.

'Well it's not cheap.' We'd already stopped off for a long shot of latte. I'd noticed the prices of a few things.

'No, but it's pretty.'

And with the broad light showing off the pastel-coloured porches and bougainvillaea flowers strewn along 19th Ave, it was pretty. Fine and pretty.

As we crossed the Golden Gate Bridge I turned in my seat so as not to miss the view of the Bay with the Transamerica building shining like a chunk of Toblerone still wrapped in its foil and the rocky bubbles of Alcatraz and Angel Island. Coit Tower was murky red against the haze with Pacific Heights and Nob Hill behind and North Beach at the other side, the lot piled up against the hills as rumpled as a plate of pastel berries, or maybe a volcano cast in scumble glaze. I began to smile. The car tyres continued tocking over the metal stress bars of the bridge while Nancy and I fell silent and happy.

At Strawberry Point we dropped down onto the slip road and lost sight of the city. Fuddled with pride, Nancy turned to me and said in a choked-up voice:

'Shall we get something to eat?'

'Yeah,' I replied in an instant. 'McDonald's apple pie.'

And now it is the middle of the Californian night, and I'm sitting on the bed in Nancy's spare room listening to the crack of the cedar shingles and the distant mechanical blur of traffic running along the Golden Gate Bridge and into the Waldo tunnel. A sweep of light from a passing car flares against the books pinned up about the room. Four shelves on the history of science, two more on computing, a small collection of modern novels, software guides and a couple of teach yourself programming manuals, all smelling of must and chemicals.

Somewhere below the house, at the water's edge along the rim of shingle, a nightbird caws.

America. Here I am once more.

FRIDAY

By the time I wake Nancy has left for work. A note in her familiar hand lies on the table:

'Sweetheart. I'll be back early so we can go for a walk in Muir Woods, OK?'

Muir Woods is my favourite spot in the whole of Northern California. It is where the Spanish moss hangs from the branches of thick red trees as old as gunpowder.

Over the past couple of years Nancy has been marketing software for a company in Marin. We've never spoken about it much. Our friendship isn't based on long shared experience, but on some intangible, timeless affection. Whenever I think of my friend, I am haunted by those impressions of her that were first imprinted on my memory when I was seventeen. Sunny brown hair, a restless air and a wide confident swing. We don't have to know much about the everyday run of one another's lives, to love one another all the same.

Down in Strawberry Village at lunchtime my eye is drawn to the '$3.99 high-tech burrito special' on offer at the local taqueria. A regular-looking burrito arrives: flour tortilla, beans, cheese, shredded lettuce, sour cream on the side.

'What's the high-tech part?' The waiter looks at me darkly.

'I don't know, lady.'

He fills up my glass so hard that waves of iced water explode from the rim and wet the table.

Along one of the main trails in Muir Woods, just beyond the visitor centre, there is a slice of redwood tree with its age rings marked out in years of human history. Christopher Columbus' discovery of America is marked on a ring about three-quarters of the way in, the Declaration of Independence is three-quarters of the way out and the American Civil War is so new that it's almost set into bark. Each time Nancy and I have been out to Muir Woods together we've had the same conversation standing in front of that piece of tree. It's a ritual. Nancy says something like: 'Look at the huge gaps between markers until you get to the twentieth century, which is all backed up, like more has happened in the last hundred years than in all the other centuries combined.' And I generally reply with some platitude like: 'Yeah, it makes you think, doesn't it?'

Dry weather has brought up the dust in Muir Woods, thickening the stems of bright sun bursting through the trees. A few jars wheeze under the canopy and the air is big in stillness.

'This place feels like a contradiction of America,' I say, as we meander along the river bank towards the mouth of the canyon. 'So quiet, untouched.' A small shadow falls over Nancy's face.

She stops in her tracks, gazing at the sky as though reading some message from an aerial autocue.

'But this is *exactly* America,' she says. 'The America of the first frontier.' She flips an insect from her arm. 'Northern California is the one place where the old and new frontiers collide. It's at the epicentre of every dream America ever had. The old frontier,' she waves at the trees, at the key of light through the leaves, 'and the new frontier a few miles down the road in Silicon Valley. The high-tech frontier of chips and virtual worlds'. We wander on a few paces, locked in thought.

'All those books in your spare room,' I begin. Nancy waves the question away.

'I haven't read them *all*. I'm trying to keep up is all.' She returns to her own bright thoughts. 'You know, the first frontier was never some fixed thing. It was kind of mutable. First it was the Appalachians, then the Missouri, the Great Plains, then the Rockies. It's the same with high tech. There isn't a single techno-logical frontier. The minute one boundary is crossed, the dream moves on.'

We stop at a tangle of furze marking the mouth of the canyon and prepare to turn back towards the visitor centre past the slice of redwood tree. I'm wondering why I chose to come to America now, with nothing particular to do and nowhere particular to go. I'm thinking that somehow, subconsciously, I must have sensed a new beginning here. And I must have felt the need to join in the game, to stake out some territory that might fill up the empty hours and the meaningless, shifting days of my adult life.

'You know, Nance, I'd really like to be in on this new frontier, if that's what it is. Will you teach me?'

'Sure. I thought that was why you came.'

'I don't know why I came,' I say, laying down part of the truth. 'I just wanted to be in America.'

After supper, Nancy introduces me to her clippings box and pulls out a copy of an article she cut from some magazine a few months before.

'What I love about all this high-tech stuff', she says, handing me the paper, 'is that no one really knows how the hell it's all gonna turn out.'

The article is a list of all the technological predictions ever made in print. Marconi prophesying that radio would only be used for telegrams ship to shore, Alexander Graham Bell supposing the phone was destined for nothing more than piping concert music from one place to another. And in 1977 the Chairman of Digital Equipment Corporation saying: 'There is no reason for any individual to have a computer in their home.'

MONDAY

Nancy is back at work, leaving me time to think about the days just gone.

I spent much of the weekend taking my first frail steps along the technological frontier in Internet Relay Chat. Nancy said she'd show me how it worked if I made her a trifle, so we drove down to Strawberry Village shopping mall and picked up some eggs and spray-on cream and while the custard was still hot Nancy sat me down in front of her machine and instructed me which keys to press first to set the modem dialling out and then to access IRC.

'IRC goes like this,' she said. 'You dial up a channel, like ham radio, and then you type in whatever you want to say to whoever else is on the same channel. You have to choose an on-line name, but it's not called a name, it's called a handle.'

I chose the handle Fish 'n' Chips. Nancy said she'd watch, brown hair pinned back out of the way. And since I really didn't know what I was doing, she started me off on the newbie channel, and told me just to type in whatever seemed natural to me, so I typed

<Hi everybody.

And within the wink someone with the handle Rosebud had typed back

<Hi Fish 'n' Chips!!!!!

And it felt as though I'd made contact with some creature in another world. I clattered feverishly at the keys
‹ **I'm new to this**, smiling at the absurd, the really wonderful idea of Rosebud sitting at a desk somewhere distant, waiting those few miniature moments while her screen filled up with me.
‹ **Hey**, she typed, ‹ **this is the newbie channel. We're all new!!!!!!**
There were twenty-four of us on the newbie channel, each feeling about for an electric self as though made suddenly blind in an unfamiliar territory, equipped only with the feel of the keys and the breath of the screen. Nothing else to go on but discovery. It was captivating.

Nancy and I ate the trifle for lunch, although it wasn't quite set and it wasn't quite lunchtime. Nancy explained it all to me, every part of it; the bleeping din of the modem as it reached for another of its kind, the innocent pause while machines far distant exchanged their pleasantries, the secret switch of passwords, the blank blink of the cursor awaiting commands, the flim-flam of lights passing ones and noughts to and fro, and all of it winding up on the dumb, fixating screen, slave of keys and mice and human hands.
And as for the voices, Rosebud and Fish 'n' Chips, as for the contact of one stranger to another, as for the chitter chat and the spread of words, well that felt something like the touch of spirits, the broad and speechless song of being human.

After lunch Nancy suggested we play around in a new virtual reality chat space she had heard about where you play a three-dimensional character and interact with all the other three-dimensional characters representing real people sat at real computer terminals just like yourself. We chose to be a fish with a Buddha's face and we floated around until we found a room of other avatars, an artist's mannequin, a witch, a disembodied smiley and a panda bear.
› **Hi people**, we typed, but no one answered. They were busy exploring the room with their avatars. Nancy and I took a look

around ourselves, guiding the Buddha about with the mouse. Grey walls, a few posters hung on one of them and a fountain in the middle. Then Nancy instructed me to carry on while she went into the kitchen to fetch us some iced tea.

>**Hi people**, I typed, but still nothing came back.

'Nance, am I doing this right?'

She wandered in from the other room, checked the screen.

'Yeah, sure.'

'I can't get anyone to talk to us.'

'I dunno, Sweetie, try again.'

>**Hi people. Does anyone want to chat?**

A message from the artist's mannequin appeared.

>**Hey, fish, cool avatar.**

We drove out to Nancy's office on the edge of Tiburon, a few miles round the peninsula from Strawberry Point, in a complex of offices housing high-tech businesses. Very smoked glass and chrome. We didn't talk much about her job; she seemed satisfied just to have shown me where she did it. I think I must have bored her with my froth of new-found enthusiasm, because she remarked very dryly as we got back into the car that I'd have to be prepared to come down off the high in a week or two.

'Bob was *just* like this when he first started.'

I didn't ask who Bob was. Nancy has a habit of talking about people you've never heard of as though they were the world's best friends.

Sunday was rainy. We stayed in and skimmed through magazines all morning. I discovered from an old copy of *Scientific American* that in 1946 a three-minute transatlantic phone call cost the equivalent of $600 and had to be booked two weeks ahead.

Later in the day, as a result of watching too much TV (though I don't know why TV and not some other excess), the conversation got onto the subject of kids. I seem to get onto that particular subject a great deal these days. Thoughts about kids prowl about my head so often I sometimes feel as though my brain has sprung a brood. When I admitted as much to Nancy, she said:

'It's the age. You and I are an invincible brew of roaring hormones. I should know because I'm even older.'

'But what I mean,' I added, 'is have you thought about, you know, actually *having* any.' It was a stupid question. No woman reaches her thirties without turning over in her mind whether or not she might have children.

Nancy hesitated, crunching up her eyes to give her better access to her thoughts and stared through the TV.

'You hear such stories, twelve-year-old rapists and I don't know what. I'm not so sure I really understand kids these days,' she said.

'We don't seem to like them much any more.' I looked at the TV for a moment. 'Why is that?'

Nancy shrugged and flicked back her hair. The rills around her eyes deepened, leaving tiny crevasses, like cracks opening up in drying clay.

'I dunno. Envy, maybe?' she asked in an exploratory tone. 'When *we* were kids in the sixties and seventies there were so many worlds still to be invented or discovered or imagined whereas these days . . .' She tailed off and we sank into a gloomy kind of Sunday funk, tucked up on the sofa together while the TV bled its way through prime time. Some sort of animal connection passed between us, but I couldn't put my finger on it. I thought of the children I might have, and wondered whether I'd ever comprehend the world they would inhabit, thirty years on from my own dimly recalled childhood, when colour TVs were still a novelty, and no one had ever heard of a VCR. Eventually I broke the silence.

'You know, Nancy, if this high-tech thing really is the new frontier, then it's the kids who are going to be settling it, not us.'

'I guess.' Nancy seemed suddenly to have lost interest in talking about kids. I wondered vaguely if I'd touched on some painful secret, but ploughed on regardless. 'In twenty or thirty years' time it'll be today's kids who will really be feeling the impact of the

Net, the Human Genome Project and virtual reality and nanotech and all that stuff.'

I went to bed that night with the sense that some immense gate was opening up ahead of me. I knew I was about to pass through it and I hoped that when I did I wouldn't find myself walled off from the world I'd left. I thought about the people behind the IRC handles Rosebud, the panda bear and the artist's mannequin and wondered if I'd ever come across them again. As I was about to fall asleep, Nancy slid into my room clutching something to her chest. She sat on the bed, looked about her at the library of books and began to wonder in a wistful tone whether we were just part of some transitional generation, unconvinced by the old myths but incapable of absorbing the new ones either, condemned to cling on to a fifties B-movie future of personal commuter jet-pods, clingy silver suits and robot pets which we knew to be a fake.

I could tell by the droop in her voice that she was struggling not to believe her own predictions. She handed me the paper she'd been holding to her chest, a computer print-out of a name, a phone number and an e-mail address.

'Hey, if you're really interested in kids, you should visit this little guy. He's the youngest kid ever to hang out in virtual reality.'

'That's sweet.' I imagined a little boy in a baggy romper suit tumbling round in a set of VR goggles, and felt a sudden strong purpose and a sense of knowing.

'Let's hope so,' Nancy said.

Sitting in bed in Nancy's room, watching the shadows play about her books, I decided to give myself a mission. I would hunt down the future, starting with the everyday intimations of tomorrow – the games, gadgets and consumer fads – that were already an invisible part of so many young lives and I would work my way up to the networks, which will, in their turn, become a mundane part of the lives of those children's children, and perhaps also of my own children. If digital culture was going to be the new frontier, I had an urge to become one of its pioneers, to comprehend it from the inside, to feel less like an observer and more like a participant. To be truly honest, I wanted to be sure there would be a future – of almost any sort.

Click and something happens

Three days later I'm driving back across the Golden Gate Bridge towards San Francisco admiring the heaped up pile of the city stretched silver white across the bay. Streaks of sun are beginning to slice through the morning mist on the ocean side and the weatherman at KCBS radio has promised it's going to stay sunny and dry until the weekend. Traffic stammers along at 19th Avenue, stop-starting and banging about for breath, before picking up speed south of the city and unwinding into two skeins at the exit to Silicon Valley and San Jose. America feels ordered and uncomplicated today.

Alex Rothman and his dad are expecting me the other side of lunchtime.

Twenty miles further on at Millbrae the mist is all burned off. By the time I've reached the Valley town of Redwood City I'm popping the first of the morning's root beers and thinking about how the world must have been when I was three, the same age as Alex. I say must have been, because all I have by way of memory from that time are vague impressions of age-long days and months, spiked at regular intervals with odd intrusions of anxiety and our neighbour Mrs Ivan's treacle toffee. I remember my dad buying me a clockwork duck when he won the football pools and I can taste the toffee apples Mrs Ivan made on fireworks night. But of the larger world around about I can recall almost nothing.

The events of the year spanning '67 and '68 when I was three passed me by. While the Paris uprisings raged, Woodstock rocked, Vietnam was plundered, my generation was regardless, too busy being fed and formed by our mothers and – maybe – our fathers too. Too busy with Alphabetti Spaghetti and *Top of the Pops*, the

TV and David Cassidy and all our clockwork ducks and toffee apples.

So I wonder what Alex will remember of now, of this week, this month, this year, of this day even, in twenty years from now?

Somewhere in Palo Alto I take a wrong turn and end up driving around the suburbs before finding myself by some miracle back at Page Mill Road from where my directions begin again. With the map spread out on my lap I head west towards the Santa Cruz Mountains. Up at 6000 ft on Skyline Road a wispy grey foam appears to have crept back over the Valley, hinting at rain, but the radio weather reports continue to promise a dry day. I wonder if the mist might be a smog cloud spilled over from San Francisco or San Jose, if such a thing ever happens. By the time I reach Boulder Creek my head feels as thick as a plate of dumplings left to boil too long.

I explain to the man in the Boulder Creek General Store that I have a migraine coming on.

'That'll be a thunderstorm, I expect,' he replies, wrapping a packet of painkillers in a brown paper bag with a missing persons message on it, then dumping the change on the counter. I mention that the weather reports are insisting it's going to stay dry.

'The two most unpredictable things in this world are weather and women,' the man says, turning away.

Boulder Creek was a logging town until the Silicon Valley suits started moving in, and though it still has some of the tarry con-servatism and pine-needle neighbourliness left over from those days, the racketing confidence of new money runs through its veins.

In the driveway where Alex lives a woman is loading bags into a station wagon. She looks up at me, wary, and gestures with her arm towards the porch but before I've reached the door a man has already opened it and ushers me in, muttering, 'My wife is running into town to pick up some supplies because friends of theirs think there's going to be a storm.'

•

Alex's father, Peter, is one of those gently cumbersome, ursine men peculiar to North America; a biter on life, a big-eating, big-earning human Panzer tank. According to Nancy, he develops virtual reality software for financiers and the US military, through which connection they are on waving terms at industry parties. His job is to write code so complex that it can trick a person into imagining he's moving through a stock exchange, or crouching in a bunker and surveying the horizon, when all he is really doing is processing data projected on to a screen and held fast in front of his eyes by a helmet.

Wasting no time on niceties, the human Panzer waves me into an armchair, surges over to a cupboard by the kitchen, dives in and comes up for air minutes later with a black strip of a thing trailing cables from its sides. Plugs it into a computer on the table.

'This,' he announces, 'is a total immersion VR helmet.'

The thing in his hands shines like a black ball of insect eyes. He urges me to put it on. Inside the helmet a blue room rises. For a moment it feels as though I'm in a deep sea diving bell, listening to the steady purr of my breath and drinking in the first view of a newly discovered territory.

'It's great isn't it?' Peter tips me very gently with the ridged track of his palm. 'Look, when you move your head, the computerized world of images inside the helmet moves with you.' I glance down at the depths, and look up at the heights. All blue. Too blue to belong to for long. I lift the helmet from my face to find a little boy watching impassively, marking time in the way that children often do. This is Alex. A regular-looking three-year-old. Matt brown hair, Bermudas and a sweat shirt, nothing like the grinning future-creature I'd envisaged at the weekend. I'm shamefully disappointed.

'So, Alex, buddy,' says the father to his son, 'say hello.' He gestures towards me.

'Hello,' obeys Alex, inching forward. We cross gazes for a moment then I open with a question.

'What's your favourite colour, Alex?' I'm imagining that it

must be blue. VR blue. But Alex merely looks at me, turns tail and toddles back to his room. He returns with a Bart Simpson doll.

'Bart Simpson, great,' say I, taking the doll, 'but you play with computers, too, don't you Alex?'

The boy scampers back to his room. Returns with a Bugs Bunny wind-up toy. Winds it, sets it pacing and begins squealing in time with the clockwork.

'Do you have any electronic toys you could show me, Alex?'

Alex contemplates, snatches Bart Simpson, flees back to his room. Five minutes later he comes running out clutching a Power Ranger.

'Look,' says Alex, sprawling on the carpet and using the Power Ranger's face to shovel out some of the shag pile. 'Cool.'

'So it is,' I chirp, then more sly, leaning down to whisper in the boy's ear, 'but I bet it's not as cool as the games you play with Dad's computers.'

Alex pushes my head away in disgust. The head incidentally which is booming along the temples in time with my breath and pulse.

Peter returns from putting away the VR helmet. 'Alex first wore one of those things on the fourth of July 1992, when he was just over a year old. The youngest kid ever. He loves it. Navigates through buildings, whole star systems in virtual reality. Doesn't even know the alphabet yet. Now, Buddy.' Peter turns his attention to his son and lifting the boy onto his knee, silencing the squeals, whispers 'tell us what you put on when you're playing special games.'

'A head-mounted display,' returns the boy, unimpressed.

'And what does that do, Bud?' Peter backs up into his seat, then manoeuvres his body forward again at a different angle, as though he were the driver of some intractable piece of plant.

'Oh, you know,' the boy follows Bugs Bunny crawling across the carpet. 'You get to see things, and when you move . . .' Tails off.

'Yeah,' says Peter. 'And what happens when you move, Bud?'

'Uh, you get to see more things,' confirms Alex, clambering down from his father's lap and running away. He returns from his bedroom with a Tonka toy.

'This is heavy,' he says, holding it out for me to feel.

Peter shoots me a look of mock despair, mixed in with a chesty heave of involuntary pride.

'I was thinking. A while ago a German film-maker guy came over and took some film of Alex wearing his virtual reality helmet. He was a baby then. We've got it somewhere in the den if you'd like to see it.' He motors off, tagging Alex, who has discovered a bamboo cane and is waving it to make whizzing noises in the air. Peter finds the tape and fast forwards it to a shot of a baby, naked except for duvet-diaper and VR helmet, blind to reality, grappling with his hands for something in the virtual world behind his eyes. Peter giggles with recollected affection for the Alex that was, while the Alex that is prowls about the room, as yet a shadow of a person made bright with temporary definition.

Just then the wife bursts into the room, registers the video, smiles to herself and at Alex and shakes some dampness from her hair.

'It's raining already. I think it's going to be some big storm. The forecasters are going crazy.' She stares at me with a doubtful eye. I feel myself returning the look, and we catch each other's eye, exchanging hints of competitive pride and a resistance to the other's unoffered pity. Rain begins ticking on the window panes.

Alex, oblivious to all this, toddles about happily brandishing his bamboo cane. His father pulls him close, thundering into his ear.

'Tell us how you use a computer mouse, Bud.'

'I click and something happens. I click and something turns on.' The mother retreats from the room and switches on a radio somewhere. Peter ignores the music and rumbles ahead:

'Alex has been playing this game I wrote for VR, called Neo-Tokyo. Actually, we play together. You're the renegade pilot of a high-speed police hovercraft, and you have to steer your vehicle through the city, shooting out billboard advertisements. It's cute.'

'Everything breaks,' remarks Alex, unasked. 'I shot a window and I shot a sign.' He dismisses the light stick and climbs up into his father's lap.

'You were going everywhere, Dad, and you were shooting.'

'Yeah,' says the father.

'And there were some bad guys and I got them.' He looks up at his father for a reiteration but the father merely smiles and raises an indulgent eyebrow.

'No you didn't, Bud, there aren't any bad guys in NeoTokyo, remember?'

'*Yes there are*,' says Alex, emphatically. 'I shot them.'

I suddenly realize that my little game is going to be harder to play than I had first imagined.

Out on the road leading back east to Palo Alto, the rain is punching fierce cold fists, drumming at the windscreen and emerging in dirty great geysers at the side of each wing mirror. The radio hisses in and out of non-stop country hits, overlaying Kenny, Tammy, Dolly, Garth and the rest with the dim waves of a news flash from some other station announcing that a state of emergency has been declared around San Jose.

It's times like these that an alternate reality would be really handy. And not just a blue VR room, either, but a place with substance, in other colours. You could plug into a beach there and wait until it's all over. On the other hand, there is something so absolutely American about blustering, muscular weather like this that you'd have to be a fool to want to escape it. Great, roaring weather it is, as big as the forty-eight.

A captive stick begins to whirr its way round the front nearside wheel arch, spinning rainbowed water onto the bonnet. Underneath the chassis, the four low tread tyres skate along on a meniscus of grease and every so often the suspension bumps over fallen branches and other dead things, sending the car sidling towards the silt-laden river by the side of the road. I'm wondering whether I should stop at the first big town, find myself a pay phone and call Nancy, but I can't make out any exits off the highway.

The police have set up a road block at Mountain View. I pull up and leave my headlights burning. A cop with a torch runs over, hunched against the rain. Leans into the car.

'We're about to close 101. There are some nasty holes opened up five miles north of here. Is your journey absolutely necessary, ma'am?' Shouting against the beat of water on the blacktop.

'I'm going home.'

'And where is that?' I consider how to answer this, think of Nancy.

'Marin County.' The cop lifts his hand to cut me short, shouts something into his cop phone, then leans back in again. A rope of rainwater bungees from his hat, blackening the upholstery.

'When did you begin your journey, ma'am?'

'At nine o'clock this morning, give or take.'

The cop checks in over the phone, waves me forward.

'We'd have turned you back if you'd known there was going to be a storm, but we're gonna let you go through this time 'cause no one saw this thing coming. Stick to the far lane and you'll miss the holes. Go slow, now.' I nod, and switch the window up. Only the weather seems to know its own future.

Nancy is sitting at her computer reading off her e-mail.

'Some storm,' she says, checking to see I've taken my shoes off. 'Erica was saying that quite a few folks in Marin don't have any electricity.'

Naturally I've no idea who Erica is, but in this case, it doesn't matter.

'How was Alex?'

'Sweet. Normal. I mean, I don't know, I haven't really had time to think about it.'

'I tell you,' says Nancy, 'Silicon Valley is like one big proto-type-farm right now. Some kind of mutant factory. They're turning out new patents down there fast as McDonald's turn out burgers. Software prototypes, business prototypes, chip prototypes, even prototype kids.'

I snicker, expecting Nancy to join in the joke, but she surprises me by tossing out one of her super-serious looks:

'You'd better believe it, Sweetheart.'

THURSDAY
Vote now!

The sun is back this morning, burning off the rainwater and leaving a crust of dried mud, twigs and storm debris on the blacktop of the 101 freeway running south from Marin. In the queue for the post office in Sausalito the talk is of the neighbours' broken shingles and the sleepless night, and the air down at the houseboat pier fronting onto San Francisco Bay still smells as strongly of static cling as the upholstery on rental cars. And all this some four or five hours after the final lightning strike.

Nancy has given me a list of groceries to buy at Mollie Stone's and a book – the first published guide to the Net, signed by the author, an acquaintance of Nancy's from her college days. She makes me swear on a carton of Ben & Jerry's not to lose it.

The inside of Mollie Stone's feels more like a provisions cathedral than a supermarket. Along either side of the aisles sweet indulgences dazzle the nose and promises of edible heaven line the shelves. At the fish counter the whole of the sea bed from San Francisco to Patagonia lies outstretched and odourless upon its icy lilo. Trial titbits of this and that lie in wait round each corner to assault your senses and dizzy you into a purchase. A sales clerk lurks about to take your money while your eyes are still in reflex action. There are six varieties of sun-dried tomato, twenty-four styles of chocolate biscuit, spaghetti in seven flavours. In the fruit and veg section organic Guatemalan mange tout fight for space with Napa Valley chanterelles and things I've never heard of. There's no lettuce, as such, only Batavia, Butternut, Beet leaf, Romaine, Radicchio, Rocket and Stone's special selection, all ready to go. The whole store reeks of money. Northern California reeks of it.

★ ★ ★

Turning left at the end of the Oakland Bay Bridge I find myself in Emeryville, a strip of waterfront warehouses, malls, parking lots and golf driving ranges looking out over the black quays of Oakland to San Francisco. *Mr Payback*, billed as the world's first interactive movie is playing at a specially converted theatre in the United Artists multiplex just round the corner.

A typical matinée crowd of truant teens, retired couples, students and lonely housewives beats about the ticket counter chewing popcorn and waiting for friends or for the start of their movies. Further inside the overactive air conditioning blows the smell of estery butter sauce out through a series of metal vents into the larger space of the foyer. TV screens show clipped versions of the new releases to a scattering of people sitting on the padded benches set around the walls. An atmosphere of quiet separation prevails, lending the building the genteel air of a public records office with all its dark secrets locked up in mysterious boxrooms off to the sides.

While my eyes are still adjusting to the shade in theatre five, six Chinese boys press past, heading towards the screen, murmuring, 'Hey, cool,' at their first sighting of the modified seats, each fitted with a joystick carrying three buttons in green, orange and yellow. I check my ticket, move down the steps to row L and settle myself into a seat behind the boys. The speakers begin to spew out soft rock numbers by Bread and Captain Beefheart. Within seconds of finding their places, the boys have already mastered their joysticks and are lost in a thick din of clicking thumb candy. Aside from myself and the boys, huddled together into two rows, the theatre is empty.

I sink into the velvet scoop of L14 with my coat about my legs to ward off the air conditioning, and position three of the fingers of my right hand on the green, orange and yellow buttons of the joystick in front to get the feel of it. Each button gives to pressure with a handsome poot and a wiggle of resistance.

'Maybe it's like the orange button is BLAM, and it offs the bad guy and the green just puts him in jail for life,' speculates one of the boys, pounding his joystick.

'Like, who, man?'

'The *bad guy*, asshole.'

And the row of boys begins clicking as if their thumbs had evolved precisely for the purpose.

Voice-over and a red Testarossa on the screen: 'The world is digital, fibre optic, cellular, but still there are assholes, jerks and scumbags around.' Dissolves into the Title Sequence. The voice-over says 'When you see the "VOTE NOW" message press the orange, yellow or green button on your joystick to make your selection. The film will then follow whichever selection wins the largest number of votes.'

Barely a minute in, before the stain left by the opening credits has fully faded from my eyes, the words 'vote now' appear in flashing dayglo, and an involuntary surge of adrenaline darts through my right hand speeding the fingers into a rise and fall. A multitude of clicks. I'm caught short by how much it matters to press down and win.

'Vote orange, orange, *orange*.' One of the Chinese boys in the row ahead is shouting. I can taste the concentration carried on his breath, the thrashing excitement, can feel the throb of clicks coming up through the fabric of the walls like some universal pulse.

The film slips seamlessly beyond the vote into the next act. A familiar smell of static rises from the seats. I've no idea exactly how I've voted, but it hardly matters, since it wasn't so much a vote in any case as a series of miniature acts of incursion. Press, press, press, tap, tap, tap, click, click, click, the will of the flesh bearing down onto a lifeless ring of green and yellow buttons.

The high of the moment quickly passes and I'm left staring through the gloaming at the row of stiffened necks and knotted hands belonging to the boys in front. Whatever thin narrative is flickering across the screen is irrelevant. Only when the next 'VOTE NOW', the insistent call to arms, appears will our heads rock and our fingers bounce and the spells leak out from our bodies and animate for a few seconds the dead passage of the square of light ahead of us.

We don't have long to wait, for within a matter of a few moments the words 'VOTE NOW' are flashing on the screen and my lungs begin to demand their breath in shallow shots, tapping out the rhythm of the next click, the next hammering vote, the clueless choice, the next small pulse of power that will electrify the web of nerves running along my arm and pull at the muscles of my right hand and finally set off the cushion of cells along my fingertips.

Thirty minutes after it first began, seven brain-dead people stagger out of theatre five into the foyer in a kind of ragged trance.

One of the boys says it was cool. Another says it was galactic.

Back at Nancy's house I unpack the shopping in a daze, reminding myself to squirrel away a few of my more creative impulse purchases such as the slab of dried Greenland halibut and the packet of cream of tartar behind the tins in Nancy's store cupboard. I'll confess to my product promiscuity the next time I find her in a particularly good mood. Meanwhile, a few remaining extras will have to be consigned forever to a dark spot under the bed in the spare room. I'm not sure even Nancy would be able to forgive Japanese pickled strawberries and black finger fungus.

With an hour to kill before she's due back I flip through Nancy's manual of the Net, but soon find myself struggling for comprehension through the pile of abstract, dreary jargon: ftp, tcp, pop, ppp. I mean, what *is* all that? It sounds like radio interference.

FRIDAY

As she's leaving for work, Nancy invites me to a talk on education and technology being held this evening in the Valley.

'You're interested in the future, right?' she says.

'Well, yeah.' I look up, uncertain of her tone, but the expression on her face has already moved on.

'Sweetie, education and technology are the ways the future gets made,' she says.

And with that she jumps up from the table, swings back that clot of brown hair and transforms immediately into Nancy the software marketer.

'Why don't you go browse my clippings box? Also there's a big crate of articles and whatnot in the garage.'

In the garage it looks as though the San Andreas fault exploded over everything. Where the clippings crate might be among the heap of basketball nets, broken toasters, project files, back issues of *Cosmopolitan* and *Wired*, and beaten-up old software packages is anyone's guess. Eventually, following a half-hour excavation I dig out the box from under a fortress of old *Vanity Fairs* and flipping through the disintegrating leaves of newsprint read the following:

> *28% of teenagers are screen addicts, 24% grey conformists.*
>
> *Annual US spend on entertainment and recreation reaches $340bn, only $270bn for elementary and secondary education.*
>
> *$800m spent every year in US on TV ads to children. Deyna Vesey, Kidvertisers' Creative Director, says 'the general rule of thumb is, once a kid is three, you can go after them on TV.'*
>
> *American kids under twelve spend $8.6bn, 13–18 year olds spend $57bn.*

And so it goes on, an avalanche of abstracted facts, public opinion surveys, vox pop statistics, flow charts, graphic predictions, trend tables.

The Sausalito Library's catalogue of books lists a handful of titles under the category 'adolescence', including:

*The Power of Ritalin: Attention Deficit Disorder among
    Teenagers*

Educating the Disturbed Adolescent

Suicide Among Adolescents

Coping with Teens

*The Handbook of Adolescence, Psychopathology and
    Anti-Social Deviancy*

It seems adolescence is treated as some kind of disease rather
than a normal part of the human life cycle these days, but we feed
on images of it still, like a flock of ageing carrion birds.

Nancy picks me up at six and we drive down to Mountain View
for the education and technology talk. Inside the conference room
at the Hilton a couple of hundred people in power suits with full
shoulder extensions, sprayed hair and pigskin attaché cases flutter
about with their business cards like tickertapers on VJ day. It's all
so *eighties*, somehow.

'Where are the teachers, Nance?' I ask, looking through the
suits.

'This meet is more for Valley types,' says Nancy, fingering
an Evian spritzer. 'You know, software providers, consultants,
techno-visionaries, wizards, that kind of thing.'

I flash Nancy one of my disgruntled looks.

'I thought it was supposed to be about education.'

'It is, but so what? We're talking about a whole new technological revolution in the classroom. Kids won't need teachers any
more. They'll need software supervisors.'

'Jesus, Nancy.'

'Look, Sweetie,' Nancy is already moving off into the crowd,
'I have to keep ahead, OK? It's my job, if that's all right with
you.'

Nancy finds me after the talk.

'Sorry,' she says, 'I had to network. What did you think?'

We spin through the smoked-glass doors and out into the evening. The question bothers me, although I'm not quite sure why. A wave of defensiveness beaches itself at the front of my mind and I realize I'm reluctant to admit what I'm actually thinking, since it contradicts what I'd *rather* be thinking.

'I dunno,' I say by way of reply. 'Ask me later.'

We decide to stop off for dinner at 'the place everyone in new tech is talking about', the Icon Byte Grill in the SoMa district of San Francisco, or Multimedia Gulch as it's becoming known. Nancy, multimedia glamour puss that she is, was invited to the opening party, but it was so full of movie types cooking up white lines and special-effects deals that she couldn't get inside the door. She had no choice but to turn around, go home and eat a tub of Ben & Jerry's instead.

'We're going to have to go, Nance,' I say, spotting the themed menu. 'I refuse to ask for circuitboard chips, or whatever.'

'Aw, c'mon,' says Nancy, looking peevish. 'It's no big deal.'

'I hate themes. They're so, oh I don't know, *undignified*.'

I hear myself whining to go to McDonald's, like some sullen teen.

'McDonald's? Like McDonald's is *dignified*?'

'No.' I'm stuck in some impenetrable psychological groove. 'McDonald's apple pie is though.'

This is the final straw for Nancy. Some weird, dark corner of her psyche launches into a white-hot diatribe about how little right I have to complain, and what a conservative little snob I am, and so on. Blah blah blah.

'I can't believe it,' she says finally, calming down. 'You're in complete denial of the wave of change going on here. In any case, a touch of theming is like, so what? Big deal.'

To save the peace I cave in and adopt a humbled air. We agree to stay and Nancy orders for me, but the evening isn't exactly what anyone might call a pile of fun. And I still think themed menus are ridiculous and humiliating. But one thing is for sure and that is whatever is awry between Nancy and me, a themed menu is the least of it.

SATURDAY
Completely pointless detail

Walnut Creek, California. No walnut trees and no creeks, only row after row of Contemporary Mediterraneans with yard pools and mulberry trees backed up along the suburban streets.

Nancy refused to come. Says she hates the suburbs. Strawberry Point, where Nancy lives, is not a suburb, despite looking suspiciously like one, but rather a spread of coastal brush with occasional urban fill-in. Personally, I don't care what she calls home. I've nothing much against suburbs anyway. They appear bland, but that's just surface skim. Underneath, they're the same heaving mess of calamities and cock-ups as everywhere else. Besides, I have a little mission these days. To explore new worlds and seek out new civilizations. To boldly face the future, as it were.

And to that end I'm sitting in the Virtual World Entertainment Center on the main street in suburban Walnut Creek, waiting my turn to be entertained, and making conversation of sorts with my two new friends, Todd and Jim, to pass the time. Todd, a boy of about seventeen, thin and angular, with the jawline of SS officers in war movies, is doing his damnedest to impress.

'C'mon, Todd,' I say, faintly wishing I were somewhere else, 'you're too young to have been in the marines when they stormed Grenada.'

Todd appeals to the boy next to him.

Jim, six inches shorter and still ablaze with shyness, shrugs in a noncommittal way. 'Whatever.' And with that he dunks himself back in the Virtual Geographic League *Battletech Manual* lying on his lap.

Todd throws back his Coke, addresses himself to me:

'So you're a rookie, huh? First time?'

'Uh huh.'

'Ha,' laughs Todd, shaking his head. 'Rookie!'

I smile back.

'Yeah, ha,' I say.

We sit in silence. A perky little grin spreads over Todd's face, indicating a fresh idea for conversation.

'Hey.' He grabs my wrist, registers its small size then drops it, embarrassed. 'Hey, see this flight suit?' He smoothes an out-sized palm across his chest. 'Genuine Foreign Legion it is, I swear.'

I smile back and nod indulgently, thinking that if Nancy were in my place right now, she'd be having one of her fits about suburban militia enclaves full of inbred NRA types stashing away semi-automatics fast as Imelda M clocks up kitten heels.

'I sent off for it in the *Survivalist*,' continues Todd. 'I wear it for luck.'

The *Survivalist*?

'Listen,' I scan the bar, trying to find an excuse to escape, 'I think I'll just take a look around.'

'Yeah,' says Todd, ignoring me. 'This'll be my fifty-fifth mission.'

'No kidding?' The Americanism tumbles from my tongue without anyone else noticing. It feels awkward and sly, like using a lover's nickname for the first time, but good all the same. No kidding. Neat.

'Hey,' says Todd, pointing to his circle of bar snacks. 'Want one of my Tesla Coil fries and some Solarian salsa?'

I'm not sure Virtual World Entertainment Centers exist as yet in Britain. But they will. In Britain and all over. Give it a year or two and there'll be Virtual World Entertainment Centers in every major city from Uzbekistan to Angola. Since Tim Disney, nephew of Walt, and his partners took over the Virtual World Entertainment company a couple of years ago, centres exactly like this one have spread out over suburban America as fast as prickly heat, 'and now constitute one of the peaks of the suburban entertainment landscape,' according to Nancy's memory of some article in *Marketing America*.

A strange sort of nostalgia pervades the room, running along-side the futurism. The walls are clad in fake wood panelling with brass wall lights; grim Victorian-style armchairs dominate a space presided over by yawing prints of Howard Hughes, Amelia Earhart, Sir Richard Burton and Charles Lindbergh. Old-time heroes.

Back at the bar, Todd has turned his attentions to Jim. 'I still say that the T6 is the übermech. People go out in Loki5s because they can't handle the idea of hand-to-hand combat is all. The Loki5 is a chicken's machine.'

I take up my stool again, feeling slightly foolish since it's perfectly obvious that Todd and Jim are just two lonesome Joes looking for a life, like a zillion other teenage boys, and really not the crazed splatter-brats I'd momentarily imagined them to be.

'What *is* a T6? And what's a Loki5?'

Jim looks up from his manual, puzzled and faintly disgusted. Todd just gives me the eye and says:

'Like, *hello* . . . ?' in a tone hinting at disbelief.

'Well?'

'*Mechs*, robots, you know, the things you fight in.' He slaps his forehead with the palm of his hand. '*Man*. Rookies! Listen, all you need to know at this stage is to select a Loki5. They're easiest to handle. Then remember to keep your crosshairs on the black spots and don't go up the ramps.'

'Why not?' I ask, returning the gaze.

'It's *dangerous*, man,' says Todd, raising his eyes to the heavens. 'Read the manual.'

> The year is 3050. Man has colonized the universe. The one great Star League has degenerated into a corrupt feudal society riven by petty rivalries. Life is cheap. War is constant. Mercenaries equipped with futuristic two-legged

tanks called BattleMechs drift from planet to planet fighting for whoever offers the most cash.

Like the jousting tournaments of old, war in the 31st
century has also been ritualized into sport. Mechwarriors
from far and wide gather on the desert planet of Solaris
VII to test their mettle against the best the universe has
to offer. Now you can join them.

At the cash till, Andromeda, a qualified Virtual Geographic
League Briefing Officer, recites the mission plan.

'For nine dollars you'll be entitled to a mission briefing where
you'll learn about your destination of choice, followed by translo-
cation to a virtual world with a group of other adventurers where
your mission will commence. After that there will be a full mission
debriefing and a pilot's log. It's a total twenty-five minute adventure. From ten to a hundred missions, every tenth mission is free.
Take part in three hundred missions and you can become part of
the Inner Circle.'

'Which is the bit where I actually play the game?' I ask, pulling
a ten-dollar bill out of my wallet.

Andromeda looks uncertain.

'You mean the mission?'

'Yeah, which is the mission bit?'

'It's all an adventure,' says Andromeda, handing me my ticket
and a plasticized paper card. 'Trust me.' She advises me to choose
a call sign for the mission.

The line of explorers requiring mission tickets begins to build
up behind, forming a vaguely threatening mass.

'Let's see.' Andromeda struggles to assist. 'Variations on death
are always popular along with pets' names. Nexus14, for example?
Zombiewoman? Driller killer?'

My recent online adventures come to mind.

'How's about Fish 'n' Chips?'

'There you go,' toots Andromeda. 'We'll enter you in the
log . . .' she types a few letters into a PC '. . . as Fish and . . .
Chips.'

''n' Chips.'

'Sure, 'n' Chips. It'll be about forty minutes. Take a seat in the Explorers' Lounge and you'll get to meet some great people. We at VGL believe that one of the most satisfying aspects of interdimensional travel is the people you meet en route.' Resigned, I hold my hand out for change. Andromeda shakes her head and waggles a finger.

'Nine dollars for the adventure plus a dollar for the one-off pilot's fee.'

'Which means?'

'You're now an Associate Member of the Virtual Geographical League. Caveat Emptor!'

'Right.' I smile, vainly struggling with the creeping canker of disillusionment.

Back at the bar, Dave and Todd are still drinking Martian Coke and bantering over their Mech strategies.

'The software aces at VGL Research Labs changed the rules so a Mech can be damaged if it bumps into a stationary part of the Solaris VII landscape, and not just if it impacts with another Mech. Did you read that in the stats report? Man, it's gonna change free-for-alls forever,' says Todd.

I resume my place at the bar and order a beer, and, remembering the Icon Byte Bar, some Tesla Coil chips and Solarian salsa from 'The Briefing' menu.

'Listen,' says Todd, turning to me, 'They'll put you with some other rookies, so you'll be OK. I mean, you'll get reduced to rubble a coupla times, but nothing you can't survive.'

'Want some advice from me?' adds Jim. 'Read the Battletech op manual, and when you're in there aim for the black spots on the other guy's Mech and don't forget . . .' he pauses to dunk another Tesla Coil chip in salsa '. . . experience is a man's best teacher.'

Battletech team messages are pinned to a noticeboard in the pool room:

Ⅹ Ⅹ Ⅹ

```
[TO] DON'T SHOOT
[FROM] CAPTAIN CRYBABY
[MESSAGE] WE ACCEPT YOUR 3 ON 3 CHALLENGE
ON ONE CONDITION: WE PLAY 2 ON 3. US
BEING THE 2. CALL 555 5173 AND ASK FOR
JOHN. WE'RE KIDS, BUT YOU'LL STILL
GO DOWN IN AGONIZING, MERCILESS FLAMES.
```

```
[TO] BLOOD ANGEL DEMISE
[FROM] CLAN GHOST TIGER
[MESSAGE] YUPPIE DEATH

WE THE MEMBERS OF CLAN GHOST TIGER WISH
TO THANK BLOOD ANGEL DEMISE. SUCKS BE TO
YOU SLACKERS FOR AN HONOURABLE AND FUN
BATTLETECH MINOR LEAGUE TOURNAMENT.
```

Ⅹ Ⅹ Ⅹ

In the hour or so since I arrived, the Virtual World Explorers' Lounge has doubled its occupancy. More families, more kids, more packs of teens and more men with shiny heads and brown moustaches lining up obediently for their mission tickets.

Jim lends me his copy of the *Battletech Operations Manual*. Byzantine! Thirty-three different types of Mech robot to choose, each one with a specific armoury and a top speed and a heat quotient, four battle arenas drawn out on grids, notes on heat sinks and dissipation units, a stack of tables covering controls and weapons and tips on weapons configuration strategy, light and weather manipulation and heat management, and finally, a list of ten tips for rookies. Totalling forty pages of graphs and tables and handy hints amounting to complete hierarchies of knowledge. It could take a person a couple of months simply to absorb all this stuff.

Forty-five minutes later, Andromeda calls out my tag, along with six others, belonging to a party of two adults and four kids with handles Stallion, Princess, Animal, Warrior, Wad and Sakan. Stallion, Animal and Wad admit to having played before, but the rest of us are virgins.

'Decided on your terrain and your Mechs yet?' enquires Balthazar, our Virtual World Mission Briefing Officer.

'Loki5s, Nazca-24,' pleads Animal.

'Anyone have any other preferences?'

And with that all six of us are shut into large black pods and left. My night vision's so bad I'm still attempting to locate the joystick when the action starts and the screen lights up and I find myself rumbling around in the middle of a desert on another planet with a school of marauding robots. My instinct tells me to white out everything I've learned in the *Battletech Operations Manual* and concentrate on pumping the joystick. A spear of green pixel bullets whooshes through the screen towards the horizon and a robot lumbers into view from my right, the radar showing it approaching at full speed with ready guns. The adrenaline rises in my stomach, leaving behind it a faint tang of nausea. The robot is bearing down on me now, firing from machine guns in its arms. Green bullets trailing fiery electric tails begin to whistle past. Ferocious clicks on the joystick get me nowhere. The enemy robot remains undimmed. Making a strategic decision to run away I reverse and bang almost immediately into Animal, who deposits some green pixel bullets into my thorax and reduces me to rubble. An amber alarm throbs through the pod, but seconds later I have magically remorphed as a new Mech stashed high with lasers and am eager to pile back into the action. It's plain bad luck that Princess reduces me to rubble again before I've had the time to engage my spatial co-ordinates and begin firing. The amber alarm begins to throb once more. I remorph stashed with lasers and give all I've got to what turns out to be a rock. A few moments later, some intriguing spots begin moving about on the screen's horizon bar. The radar is blank. A red alarm begins to pulse. For a moment I am confused, then it occurs to me to check my co-ordinates which serve to prove that I have been travelling full speed in reverse for the last four minutes and am currently about ten kilometres from the battle arena. I push down hard on the throttle and head once more for the epicentre of the battle, the black dots on the horizon accreting into fellow Mechs, and I'm suddenly right in the middle of it all, opening my guns and pouring green electronic lead into anything moving. And then the lights come on and two seconds later I'm translocated back to planet earth.

Seven personalized copies of the mission debriefing scroll out of a printer back in the Explorers' Lounge. Sakan wins with 2836 points, Stallion comes second with 2720. Fish 'n' Chips scores −1. I appear in the battle log a total of three times. At minute 2:34 Animal reduced me to rubble, at minute 4:56 Princess reduced me to rubble, and on the third occasion, in minute 9, with two seconds of action left to go, I opened fire and punctured Wad's right upper leg.

Todd and Jim have been watching the action on the Explorers' Lounge screen.

'You were totally remedial, man,' says Todd, looking over my shoulder at the mission debriefing. That hurts, actually.

'It was unbelievable. You weren't even in the battle arena,' adds Jim.

'Look,' I carp in my own defence. 'I decided to take a break, OK? It's a tactic.'

'That is the fuckin' lamest tactic I ever seen,' adds Todd, turning back to his Martian Coke.

I discover the real flaw in my tactic some minutes later: it has left me buzzing but boastless. I have nothing to talk about. OK, I pressed a few buttons, fired a few shots. But with no approach, no angle, no line. Stallion by contrast, is talking himself up to a group of teens, and Animal and Warrior are standing at the pool table sparring over their respective performances with the particle projection cannon, and the only thing I've got to contribute is what it really felt like to be stuck behind a rock ten kilometres away from any of the action. I feel a sudden pang of loneliness. It's suddenly clear how Buzz Aldrin must have felt as he watched Neil Armstrong thud onto the surface of the moon. Only now it's too late do I begin to see that the real point of Battletech is the buzz and thrall of camaraderie clinging to the players after the main event is over, when the outcome is clear and none of it matters too much any more, those five or ten minutes of grand and shared intensity, the minutes for which all of us stood in line and drank tepid Martian cola and made stilted pre-mission conversation. Those five or ten minutes of fraternity, the tiny splinters of intimacy, the fleeting alchemical moments, which turn Tim Disney and his ilk into multi-millionaires.

SUNDAY

Nancy and I take a picnic up to Muir Woods. Rain has fallen during the night, softening the air and stirring up the smell of leaf mould. Nancy is wearing blue shorts which set off her hair and make her look a decade younger than she is.

We climb up the path through the woods towards the clearing, from where the Pacific Ocean is visible, creating the illusion of a tiny island of woods drifting unnoticed towards Japan.

'Karin says . . .' begins Nancy, gazing down at the leaf mould and forgetting her next thought.

'Who's Karin?' I ask and she darts me a strange look, as if puzzled by my tone, then, realizing the question is genuine, shakes her head and waves it away. I'm touched by this habit of hers, this assumption that everyone leads the exact same life as she does, has the same set of friends, the same job, the same taste in food. It's so intimate and self-involved and scatty, which three possibly contradictory qualities Nancy possesses in equal and lavish abundance.

'I always think the weirdest thing about Battletech and all those geeky games', she follows, changing the subject, 'is the mountain of trivia you have to absorb to make any sense out of it at all. It's such a boy thing. Lists and specs and reams of completely pointless detail.'

'Yeah, I guess.' I try out another Americanism. 'But, you know, once you've done it, there's this amazing feeling of shared experience. I can't really explain it. It's like any ritual. Church, waterskiing clubs, trainspotting, whatever.'

Suddenly the trees fall away, and we are out on the grassy plateau, overlooking the ocean.

'Sweetheart,' says Nancy, adopting a wheedling tone. 'About the other day, at the education and technology meet . . .'

I stop her with my hand, anxious not to spoil the atmosphere, and conscious also that whatever passed between us that day probably doesn't brook too much explanation or analysis. But Nancy is eager to talk it out. She's so Californian that way.

'I mean, I think you're right. Information isn't the same as knowledge. You can fill every classroom in the country with a thousand computers and link them all up to the Net, and you won't have taught anyone anything.'

'Is that what I said?' I don't recall saying any such thing, though I remember a similar thought passing through my mind.

Nancy carries on walking along the plateau, gazing down into the water as if draining her breath from it.

'Data doesn't mean anything on its own. You have to be able to interpret it, relate it to the real world.'

We find a spot to sit, and pull out a couple of cans of Coke from our picnic bag. I try to drag Nancy away from the subject, introduce the topic of wildflowers, the sky, pretty much everything, but she won't be drawn. Some nudging gobbet of resentment sticks in my breast. I'm not *ready* to be disillusioned, dammit. Give me hope.

'You put future education policy in the hands of the computer industry and they're going to come up with something involving truckloads of computers, obviously.'

'Oh well,' I say, blandly, 'it's early days yet.'

Nancy wheels round, looks through my eyes into the dark recesses of my head.

'Why the hell are you trying to defend them?' she says, voice suddenly dark with anger. I adopt an ameliorating smile. Them? Us? Them? By her own account. Nancy *is* one of them.

'Rome wasn't built in a day,' I say, determined to protect my new-found future.

'But the networks will be,' cries Nancy in return. 'They already are. In a year's time you'll hardly remember life without them.'

I've never seen her in this mood before, so hellbent on sabotaging her own bullish optimism, so bent on spoiling the game. It's so unlike her. So un-American.

THURSDAY, FOUR DAYS LATER

Nancy has flown off to COMDEX, taking her mood swings with her, and leaving me in charge of the house at Strawberry Point. Yesterday, a tomcat came in through the open window and sprayed the kitchen herbs. Mint, flat-leafed parsley, chives all died, thyme survived. Driving out this morning to the plant nursery to replace them before the weekend I realized I hadn't left the house since taking Nancy to the airport early on Monday. Not once. Three days and nights have passed without my collecting the mail from the mail box, or the *San Francisco Chronicle* and *New York Times* from the driveway. Three days and nights without opening the door out onto the deck to watch the city across the Bay, without removing the trash, picking up the phone, taking a shower, sleeping in a bed. Three days oblivious to the squabbling din of the redwings in the cypress trees outside, oblivious to the breeze of traffic on the freeway, to the lazy slap of water on the pebble beach below, to the barks of the neighbour's children, or the tickled hum of the air conditioning. Three days and three nights floating about in the weightless breadth of the network, almost a century of hours with only the owlish whine of the modem, the rushing of lights and the glow of growing words for company.

The first night after Nancy left, it must have been Monday, I pored through the Net manual but didn't get very far. Towards dawn, though, I found a dissertation on a computer at Duke University in North Carolina and managed to download it to Nancy's hard disk. It turned out to be someone's thesis on genetic reprogramming, which made little sense to me, but the point was that I'd ventured out on the wires and captured something strange and brought it back undamaged and I felt the same satisfaction in that feat as I had in collecting caterpillars twenty years ago. Afterwards I slept for a while on the sofa, then rose again on Tuesday afternoon and made a pot of coffee. I must have been dozing on and off through most of that night, and by the morning I hadn't accomplished much more than the previous day. A few more files added to the hard disk was all.

I passed Wednesday on the Whole Earth 'Lectronic Link, the WELL, a bulletin board and computer conferencing setup based in Sausalito. Nancy's been a member since the electronic Pleistocene, about two years. It's one of the things you do if you live in Marin, along with hot-tubbing and baking biscotti. She left brief instructions plus a list of WELL gods, the network VIPs, pinned up on the wall beside the computer, saying, 'When a WELL god posts, people listen. Show respect, OK? But nothing tacky.' So I passed the day – yesterday – typing out my respectful thoughts and considered pearls in the hope that others would read them and type their pearls and thoughts back in return. I dipped in and out of politics, music, the future. After a time I gathered sufficient confidence to begin my own discussion topic in the future conference, and by the end of the day there were twenty-three replies, twenty-three earnest, considered, respectful responses. There we all were, sitting at our keyboards, unknown to each other in any real-life way, chattering into our screens and feeling that each new word meant something beyond itself.

Too tightly wound to go to bed, I dozed for a while on the sofa and woke just as the light was beginning to break through the cedars outside. A pot of cold coffee was sitting on the table next to the computer, so I warmed the bitter brown liquid in the microwave and toasted a couple of muffins and ate my breakfast waiting for the computer to boot up and pass me back out into the dark space of the network, which was beginning to feel more substantial to me than the room around, and as full of enchantment and tricks as a fast-hand conjuror.

In the early hours of the morning, I circled the globe. A listing of stock prices in Singapore, software files in Rome, the welcome screen of the University of Pretoria information service, a dissertation archive in Hong Kong, four tourist guides to Queensland and New South Wales, some incomprehensible jargon housed at Lawrence Livermore, a list of new releases from EMI in London. And on around the world again, with the same perfect, fearful freedom a lone sailor must feel when out of sight of land, my only navigation tools a keyboard, a mouse and a set of instincts.

Eventually, I fell onto the sofa and slept without dreaming until nine, when I got up and made some more coffee. In a few minutes from now, I shall pull out the plug on Nancy's computer and lock myself in the spare bedroom and sleep until the weekend. Otherwise, I'll still be sitting at this table when Nancy returns, eyes buggled and stiff as a piece of metal soldered to the screen.

SATURDAY

Nancy says I should get in touch with a boy called Isaac, who runs the conference for children at the WELL. The word is that he's the kind of person our kids – if we ever get around to having kids – might turn out to be. Another futuristic prototype, like Alex.

I'm relieved to say she has returned from COMDEX in fine spirits, having met *everyone* of *any* importance in software plus an old (male) friend to boot, who just *happens* to be living in the area and just *happens* to be swinging by for lunch tomorrow. Nancy emerges from her bedroom some time late in the afternoon, with a casual kind of air, humming some old James Taylor number. Neither of us remarks on the fact that she's been locked up in there for four hours testing her outfits and teasing her hair into different shapes. Following a short inspection of the living room, she wanders into the kitchen and begins rearranging the jars of antipasti, the squid ink pappardelle someone gave her for a birthday present and sun-dried tomatoes in front of all the instant soup and chocolate pop tarts. Suspecting that three might be a crowd, I mail a message off to Isaac, asking if he'd mind a visit. A response arrives almost instantly.

>I'll have to ask my mom.

And then a few hours later:

>Mom says it's OK. We live in Long Beach.

'How far is Long Beach from Marin?' I ask Nancy, when the worst of the clatter is done.

'Oh, a ways, about ten hours' drive,' she says, disappearing into her room and re-emerging with a brochure.

'I just remembered. I picked this up at the trade show. The Fifth Annual Digital Hollywood Exhibition. "The Media Market-Place where Deals are Done™." Thought it might interest you.'

So I flip through the first couple of pages and read:

'Somewhere between the zirconia-obsessed and the hackers on the Net with electronic credit to burn, there is a mega world of virtual shopping and marketing in the ethernet. Some day there may be more retail dollars to be spent in the virtual marketplace than in the domain of the current retailing mall culture . . .'

'It doesn't even make sense,' I protest, hurling the thing onto the coffee table, from where Nancy rescues it, saying in a firmer voice than ever she intends:

'That's why I thought you'd be interested in going, sweetie. Say, *tomorrow?*'

SUNDAY

The foyer of the ten-screen multiplex in Culver City, Los Angeles, is already full of teenagers just out of school, waiting for the late afternoon showing of *Streetfighter – the Ultimate Battle*.

I wander back into the mall, pick up a root beer and an apple pie in McDonalds and sit myself next to an off-duty security guard with a face full of freckles and hands all knotted up like vine stems. We make awkward small talk for a while. He mentions that Culver City was recently voted the second most desirable neighbourhood inside Los Angeles city limits.

'It just looks like a hatch of freeways joined by shopping malls to me.'

'Nothing wrong with that,' returns the guard, offended. 'You should see this place for example, first thing in the morning. The folks from the Culver City senior citizen's mall-walking club come in around ten. Perfect behaviour. It's clean and quiet till lunchtime and then these mall rats –' He gestures towards a group of teenagers lounging round McDonald's drinking Coke. Two tough-eyed girls glower back – 'begin drifting in and the whole atmosphere of the place . . .' He holds his hands up to the heavens, then begins to twist a waxed burger paper into a candle, forcing it inside an empty carton of french fries. 'I just wish they'd find someplace else to go.'

'Like where?' I say, trying to catch his eye. He looks up from his carton crunching and there's meanness written on his face.

'I don't know, Tallahassee for all I care.'

I was seventeen when I first saw Los Angeles. Staying in a borrowed apartment in Venice, I spent my days boogie-boarding and watching TV and playing beach volleyball with Nancy. I thought everyone in California lived that way then. I was naive and I wanted to believe it.

★   ★   ★

A pay phone outside Footlocker.

'Is Isaac there?'

'Uh uh.'

I check my watch and see there is nearly an hour and a half before we're due to meet. An almost inaudible sigh trickles down the phone line.

'Are you his father by any chance?'

'Stepfather, why?' I explain that I've arranged to see Isaac later on.

'That can't be. Isaac had his mother drive him up to San Francisco last night on a business matter.'

I hang up. What the hell kind of fourteen-year-old makes last-minute twelve hundred mile round-trips on business?

WEDNESDAY

Isaac mails to say he's very sorry not to have kept our appointment, but if I'm ever down in the Los Angeles area again . . .

SATURDAY

Brain machine

Nancy's COMDEX friend Dave brings his brain machine and an ounce of crystal caffeine around. He says that crystal caff is the drug *du jour* among programming types, and I suppose he should know, since he is one, all the way from the Dead Kennedys T-shirt to the lightly sprinkled dandruff. After spending Sunday in his company, Nancy told him as sweetly as she could that in spite of the fact that his qualities were manifestly overwhelming, she wasn't ready for a relationship just now (which is actually a bald-faced lie, albeit a tactful one), but she'd like to be 'just friends'. I suspect the truth is she doesn't think Dave is glamorous enough for her. Nancy is always chasing the unattainable at the expense of the possible, whether it be some greaseball zillionaire in a sta-prest suit, the state of permanent perfect happiness, or the latest must-have body-shape.

We set up the brain machine and toss a coin to see who goes first. The machine reprograms your moods by flashing a series of lights into your retina and changing the pathways of your neural impulses. I win the toss. Having selected my chosen mood – exhilaration – from the mood menu, I settle down on the sofa, cover my eyes with the special glasses and flip the on button.

At first nothing happens. Then, a few seconds later, some strange pulsing music starts up, followed by flashes of light which gather into a pattern of green helixes inside my eyelids. For a moment the whole thing feels like a bad trip, but the next I know, Nancy is tugging on my shoulder.

'Sweetie, it's time to get up.'

I remove the glasses from my eyes.

'Did I fall asleep?'

Nancy nods. 'Twenty-five minutes ago.'

'That's pretty amazing for an insomniac.'

'Except you were supposed to be exhilarated.'

And then Nancy takes her turn, chooses 'speed learning', picks up a software manual and is asleep within seconds.

Later, we pipe a little caffeine while Dave tells us the story of his six-toed cat, Arnie, who is a direct descendant of an identical six-toed cat found stowed away on the *Mayflower*. After that we sit around in benign but awkward silence; then Dave, smiling, makes his excuses and gets up to go. He's picked up the thought waves passing between me and Nance and feels excluded. Besides, there really is no follow-up to Arnie, the six-toed feline Pilgrim Father, is there?

SUNDAY

Unwelcome thoughts of home crowd round the breakfast table.

Sorting through Nancy's clippings box I find the following:

1980s see 19,346 US teen murders, 18,365 suicides.

150,000 young Americans on missing persons register

20% teenage unemployment rises to 40% for African Americans

*One in four young African American males in prison, on
    probation, parole*

At lunch, an uneasiness sets in, somehow connected to Dave's visit.

'Don't all those gloomy statistics about kids get you down?'

'Uh huh.' My friend pushes aside a half-eaten pop tart, takes some ice cream out of the freezer. It occurs to me that Nancy's clippings are as much a part of Nancy as her fragile insouciance, whereas for me they're just statistics strings.

'So why d'you keep them?'

A bottle of olives appears on the table, followed by some Oreo cookies. She tries a spoonful of ice cream, an olive, a bite of pop tart. Looks unsteady.

'Pandora's Box.' A muffled sound as the other half of the pop tart follows an olive. She scrapes some Oreo filling onto her teeth.

'It's my only weapon against the bio-clock. Just to concentrate on what a shitty world it is out there for kids.' I watch her removing an olive stone and inserting a spoonful of ice-cream.

'Nancy. You're not . . . ?'

'Are you *insane*?' she looks at me with her eyes in that crepey position. 'I don't even know a friendly sperm bank.'

I remind her of Dave.

'Oh yeah, like the world really needs another programmer geek in diapers.'

'That's harsh.'

Nancy pauses to think for a moment.

'You're right. And anyway, it's untrue. The world needs all the programmer geeks in diapers it can get right now.'

Muir Woods has become a weekend routine. At Nancy's request a Japanese tourist takes a photo of us marking off the start of the digital age on the slice of redwood trunk, at the very edge where the bark begins to flake away. Climbing up onto the plateau, a weight of sadness falls. I look out over the ocean towards Japan, trying to think myself back to the blue of that wide water. Almost before I'm aware of it, salt tears have begun to scratch at my contact lenses.

It dawns on me that I'm not a part of the grand technological experiment that is Northern California right now, nor a part either of those older dreams it has come to symbolize. I don't belong to the redwoods, to the frozen yoghurt stands or the piney air. I've found myself a project here precisely because I am not *from* here. There is so much about this new digital world that is alien to me, but utterly familiar to Nancy. I am deflated and left behind, made spare by the sheer pace and scale of the change. I feel like a dazzled rabbit caught in headlights, a mere witness to the ballooning din and flux that is digital America, a self-indulgent stand-in. And as I watch Nancy striding across the plateau towards the woods again, I see she's given me a vivid fragment of her life to take away and make flourish somewhere else. And I'm overcome by the stillness of understanding. What Nancy has known for a while and has patiently waited for me to discover is that the time has come for me to return to England, though that is where I least belong.

ii: HOME & AWAY

Lost in the blizzard of youth culture

Saturday night has begun early in the Trocadero at Piccadilly Circus. Samantha, fourteen, breath as short as a running dog, scrapes back the rope of her hair and turns to say something. Behind her, in the belly of the arcade, a swell of pubescent boys fuels the games machines and fills the room with the jangle of defeat and Samantha's words are obliterated in the greater noise.

Today I'll come clean. I'll confess. I feel lost in the blizzard of youth culture.

Samantha, Samantha, oh please tell me do.
How shall I be young again, as young and hip as you?

We break a path across the floor, unnoticed. Me under cover of her.

'Chopping through the enemy,' says Samantha. She is through to round four of the Streetfighter II South of England Turbo Tournament. The only girl. This is what it takes to rise through the ranks, according to Samantha: 'Guts and loads of practice.'

We remove to a bank of Streetfighter consoles pitched up against the back wall of the arcade. Samantha leans into the central deck, opens her callused baby hands, flips the supple wrists, stretches the finger clumps and lets them fall onto the joystick like a final act of homecoming. She closes her eyes for a moment, entertaining some thought, then smiles.

'Double-jointed, ambidextrous Streetfighting champion,' she says of herself, not having won the championship yet, but having ambitions.

And so there I am, loading tokens into a Streetfighter deck, about to lose to some peppery girl almost half my age while she waits nerves akimbo for the call-up.

'I've actually never played Streetfighter,' I say, suddenly aware of how it feels to be one of those antique judges for whom the Rolling Stones is a description of a chain gang.

'Yeah, I can tell,' Samantha replies. 'But that's all right.' She winks at me and pushes her hair back again. 'I ain't gonna hammer you straight off. Wouldn't be sporting, would it?'

Apparently Sam and I inhabit the same real-life world, but you wouldn't know it.

Outside in the foyer a line of Streetfighter decks has been set up for the competition, alongside a sound system, a string of mikes and an outside broadcast unit. A computerized scoreboard hangs suspended from the escalator. About fifty kids, boys, are lined up along the row of decks, hands on joysticks, arms beating out the moves of the final leg of the third round. Behind a cordon another six hundred teens await their call-up for the fourth round. And behind *them*, so distant you can't see their faces, another eight or nine hundred folk watching, tip-toeing to catch glimpses of their sons, brothers, nephews, grandsons, step-sons, whatever.

A boy with pudding-bowl hair detonates from the shadow of the arcade, looks Samantha almost in the eye, mumbles:

'I got fucking mashed, man, and now I ain't got no more money.'

'You see my pockets bulging, man?' asks Samantha in return, hard, with her hands on her thighs, calluses pressed in.

'*This* is my brother. Jez.' Her eyes fill with mock impatience.

'Sisterly love,' grins the brother, hair part-concealing a face crazy with electric messages.

Sam and her brother came specially for the tournament, but Jez got knocked out in the second round by a Chinese boy from an arcade in Oxford Street. She hadn't seen him since. She says he's not a good loser, but it's his own fault. He gets too cocky and doesn't practise enough.

'Why don't you play and I'll pay.'

'Oh no, man, you don't have to do that.' Samantha's voice sings high with guilty insincerity.

'I can't play anyway,' I insist. 'I'd rather watch. It'll be like training.'

'Wicked,' says Jez, moving up to the console. 'You going down.' This from Jez, his right palm levitating over the start button, tongue coiled against lower lip in anticipation. 'Which character?'

'Ken,' says Sam.

'Man, you're always Ken.'

'I got the expertise.' So Sam plays as Ken, the karate beach punk, and Jez plays as Blanka, the mutant Brazilian. Jez toggles the setting to a beach in America. Adrenaline drifts around them like heatwaves off sand. Jez raises his palm, holds the position as if startled into it, brings the force of his hand stamping down on *start*.

'You dead man, dead,' Jez's voice twisted with the moment.

'No, *you* dead, right?' replies his sister.

A second's stillness, like a snarl-up in a projection room, and brother and sister bear down on their joysticks with a series of spastic jerks and swings, closing in on the screen, elbows pumping like pistons. Jez flaps his tongue against his chin, then moves back from the console, eyes momentarily drifting across the room, but sightlessly, with a kind of narcoleptic thrill written on his face. Sam stays close in, rocks slightly. Two ghosts competing for the machine.

A boy wanders up from behind, comes to a standstill and fixes his stare on the deck. Jez, sensing his presence, chooses not to acknowledge the boy, maybe doesn't know him. All over the arcade, pairs of stiffened kids are hanging over a console with an array of onlookers beside, by turns bored and in the thrall of it.

'Spike it, give it some wellie.'

'Combo Combo. Block, block, block.' The boy uses his fists to scrub canals into the seams of his baggies.

'C'mon, twist it, man,' says Jez, keyed up and trying to control Blanka with a series of hops and piston movements.

Sam moves Ken in, charges Blanka with a close-range round-house kick. Blanka is in trouble.

'Head butt him, Blanka,' squeals the boy, thumping his thigh.

Too late. Sam and Jez slip from the console like drowned hands leaving driftwood.

'I mashed you, man, first round over.' Samantha leans back, unlocks her shoulders, breathes deep and smacks her lips in a sly way. Jez has had an idea.

'Replay,' he spits, wheeling round, glaring at the boy. 'That boy fucking put me off. Unfair disadvantage.'

'You just a bad loser,' replies his sister.

'C'*mon*, man.' Jez holds his arms close to his chest, eyes grinning at me.

I shrug and smile off the appeal.

'Replay, no way,' says Samantha.

Round four opens with the star player, a boy from one of the Chinatown arcades with control-pad buttons for eyes, who has won all fifty of his games. A block of twitchy adrenaline he is, buoyed up with Coke. A couple of dozen nervous kids, Samantha included, scout the electronic running order, in search of their numbers, hoping they're not pitched against Button-Eyes.

The constant flow of kids from the tournament consoles to the practice machines in the arcade leaves a matt stain from their sneakers across the linoleum. Sam's number, 437, appears on the electronic call sheet.

'You been to America?' Jez has followed me out into the foyer.

I narrow my eyes to slits and nod.

'Yeah, but I never met Michael Jordan, or Michelle Pfeiffer or Pam Anderson or Mickey Mouse or anybody anyone's ever heard of.' The words burn up in the acrid atmosphere of my remembrance. Whenever America is mentioned I feel sour and fondly protective, like a child forced to lend out a treasured possession.

'Did you get a go on the Sony Playstation?' Jez has not noticed my sullen mood. 'They got them all over America.'

'They've got everything in America.' Jez ignores me, lost in some internal reverie.

'I'm getting the import version', he says. 'The official English version's bound to be slow speeds.' Then, in a righteous gush of consumer patriotism, 'It's *sick* how they rip the English off with slow speeds.'

A queue gathers around one of the Streetfighter decks, and the boy in the baggies is there, egging on a teen combatant. It's pretty quiet now. A party of Arabs sits in a row at the camel-racing booth. Next to them their bodyguards. Shift changes at the token counter. Brazilian hands over to Brazilian, smiles at the bouncer, heads for the black matt door in the black matt wall marked 'Staff Only' in black gloss paint. There is no sign of Samantha.

Jez is moving around in the small knot of people standing by the entrance to the arcade. Looking about for his sister, maybe. Seeing me instead, he flashes a wide, young smile and makes his way over.

'You seen Sam?'

'Nah, she'll be all right,' replies the brother.

Seven p.m. The smell of baking rises from the food court down-stairs. Six hours after it began, Button-Eyes is declared Supreme Champion of the South of England Streetfighter Turbo Tourna-ment, first prize a full arcade version of Streetfighter II Turbo. A DJ in Kiss FM uniform jogs onto the makeshift prize-giving podium, raises his mike, waits for the on-air cue from the sidelines. Tips the words out:

'A totally wicked contest, man, completely *MEN-TAL* . . .'

'Congratulations.' The DJ pulls Button-Eyes towards the mike, peers down at a piece of paper. 'Whasyername.' He smiles and gives the boy a comedy punch.

*　　*　　*

It is seven thirty and the Streetfighter tournament consoles are open for the free use of whoever remains. Six and a half hours after the first closed their palms round their joysticks, a row of arms begins to beat in front of the screens, like fleshy pistons.

'C'mon, I'll buy you a McDonalds,' I say.

'OK,' says Jez. He wouldn't mind that at all. Hasn't eaten since breakfast.

We elbow our way out of the arcade, past a floor of scaffolding with a sign announcing the opening of a new Battletech Centre, head down into Coventry Street. Jez opens the door into McD's, immediately peels off to one side.

'I'll have a happy meal, £2.98.' He wanders off to find a table in the family section. Not on the top floor where the youth go. Not with me in tow.

We sit and eat in silence for a while.

'Did you know,' I say at last, 'that this part of London is known as the Meat-Rack?'

'Nah,' replies Jez, nodding at the mess of waxed paper and mayonnaise on the table in front of me, his face flushed with that smile. 'Mind if I finish your fries?'

ONE THURSDAY
A lover's eyes

England hasn't changed much. The Common might be a little greener than I left it. The butcher's shop has closed down, Block-buster Video gone up in its place. There are a few nominal additions to the graffiti on the walls outside my flat. As from Tuesday next the tube train drivers will be on strike. A bomb has exploded in Earls Court, no one hurt. Otherwise England is as England always was, an isolated little piece of island washed up on its own dank shore.

I have changed, though. At least, America has changed me. I've bought an Apple Mac with the remainder of my savings, and it's beautiful. A mysterious grey sarcophagus with magic innards.

I've also got a modem and a subscription to the WELL. England and England's concerns matter less. I can now be in the same place as my fantasies. America. A few clicks of the keyboard, a tumble of lights, an instant's wait, and the new frontier comes rushing in toward me.

No one here appears interested in my impending conquest of the digital frontier. After some dark muttering about anoraks and computers the subject is waved away. Meanwhile, my life is becoming very altered. Friends are beginning not to bother to call, knowing that I'll either be online, or be wanting to talk about being online. They think *I'm vacant, pretty vac-ant*. But *I don't care*.

Also, I've met someone. Not face to face, but as good as. It began a few days ago in an idle moment. This is how it happened. I posted a short provocation on the WELL – a small uncommitted riff about the media being our chief source of shared values, and he, this someone I'm talking about, replied with a long treatise, the gist of which was that the situation wasn't so bad because it at least implied that there *was* a shared set of values. And so it went on. We e-mailed back and forth exchanging our armchair philosophies and cod theories. A strange textual flirtation started up but the stranger thing is, I don't know anything about him, except that his handle is Macadamia. He's my souvenir of San Francisco, my memento. And yet, it's as though I've taken the first step in a series of irrevocable steps towards another life, as you do the moment you first meet a lover's eyes.

Last night, I e-mailed Nancy.
>**I'm very taken with a nut,** I said.
And she e-mailed back
>**It's a newbie phase, sweetie. Bob was just the same.**
I found a small part of myself hating her for that, but I woke up this morning with the usual pangs, missing America and wishing we were walking through Muir Woods together.

Observation: Why is it that technology designed to be used by women is white, while technology designed to be used by men is black? The washing machine vs the VCR. The tumble dryer vs the remote control. Computers, on the other hand, are grey, which must be one of the reasons they're so intriguing.

SATURDAY

I appear to have given up on the real world. At least, I am spending less and less time in it and as a result I find that it has transformed into a drab waystation for the satisfaction of what Mac calls 'meat needs'. Food, a bed, a shower.

The most valued part of my day begins around six in the evening, which is morning in California, of course. And also, conveniently enough, when telephone charges fall. It ends at dawn. In between Mac and I compose our e-mail, argue through the finer points of this and that, draw our secret conclusions. We don't talk about our lives, what we eat for breakfast. We don't have lives as such to talk about right now, we only have survival tactics: sleep, drink, eat, shit. We don't go in for revelation. We're already far too intimate. We chew over the things that matter. The issues.

For example, is the real world binary or analogue? According to Mac, the binary world of 1s and 0s that the computer under-stands isn't necessarily a description of real reality because real reality deals more in degrees of grey than in black and white. But then light grey is not-dark grey just as much as black is not-white. Which makes it binary. We considered this conundrum at our respective screens six thousand miles apart and came to the con-clusion that we'd got ourselves into a loop. So I called it a day, which it was actually becoming, and fell asleep with sunlight beginning to warm my eyelids.

SUNDAY

I mention binary vs analogue to Nancy. She mails back:
>I'd check that off your list of concerns. It's one of those typically recursive analytical things that nerdy types get all steamed up over.

That 'been there done that' edge to all her messages pips my wick. Plus, Macadamia is *not* 'a nerdy type.'

The real world seems more lonely than before. Sitting here at my screen in England, I feel like a one-woman species.

MONDAY

Discovery! I am not a one-woman species. A home-grown electronic scene has been going on quite nicely without me all this time.

iD magazine runs a piece about a seventeen-year-old electronic musician, techno's latest wunderkind. Eyes skulk out from the page in imitation menace. Puffa jacket expands the frame. I make a note to track him down.

SUNDAY, NEARLY A WEEK LATER

A suburban train trundling west. Daniel the wunderkind meets me at the station, dressed in an outsized hip-hop hooded coat. The same uncertain flicker on the face. The same aura of in-difference.

'Hello Daniel.' I meet his eye.

'Yeah, hahaha,' he roars, refusing to hold my gaze, 'let's go.' And with that, he marches through the station, strides across the road, speeds along a genteel street filled with cheap antiques shops and mock Parisian cafés, and swings into a long residential road, dragging me panting behind him.

We are standing in an Aladdin's cave posing as a kitchen. The room is strangled in stuff: papers, envelopes, posters, pictures, milk bottles, flower pots, tins of floor polish, spare curtains, photos, books, ancient magazines, biscuits, scissors, drainers, pans, packets of crisps, flowers, fruit, memo pads, wine bottles, telephones, pencils on string, children's drawings, hairbrushes, highchairs, napkins, drying cloths, fridge magnets, a bath sponge, the whole finished off by the smell of a warming oven and roasted garlic. Daniel's mother appears, looking far away and harassed.

'Would you like a cup of coffee?'

'That's OK,' I smile, 'I'm sure Daniel can make it.'

'No, actually, I can't.' Daniel contradicts me with an awkward sort of playfulness. 'I broke the cappuccino machine, hahaha.'

'I'll have instant coffee then.' Daniel reaches for the jar, tips it towards me for inspection and adopts a helpless air. 'Uh, haha, Mum uses it to dye fabrics.' The thin black crust clings to the bottom. A young woman walks into the kitchen, takes note of Daniel's lost-boy look, says:

'I'll make the coffee, OK?'

'OK,' says Daniel.

Later, we're sitting at the kitchen table cupping our coffee mugs. I ask:

'Was that the au pair?'

Daniel throws me a strange look, catches my eye fleetingly, and, pretending he thinks the whole thing a joke, blusters: 'Hah-aha, that was my younger sister.' Daniel has four younger sisters and no brothers. I guess that can't be easy.

You wouldn't believe the Daniel household existed unless you'd seen it for yourself. On the ground floor oak chests crammed into every corner, dolls, toys, rocking horses pressed against the windows, paintings, prints, posters on the walls, walls thick with layered paint and images, Turkish kelims fighting for space with knotted Persian rugs, cushions everywhere, never-watered plants clinging on to life, books, magazines from the seventies, goldfish in lime green aquaria. One storey up, angelic-looking toddler twins chasing from room to room followed closely by a six-year-old throwing dolls about, phones ringing, the sound of ascendant violins from the father's study, more oak chests spewing bits of paper and embroidery from their stuffed drawers, a dust crust lying over everything.

We climb to Daniel's bedroom on the third floor. Bed unmade, smell of skin, magazines in piles fanning out from every horizontal surface, posters of Orbital, snowboarding and computer games on the wall, in the centre of the room a home-made horseshoe consisting in keyboard, four-track and Atari computer.

'So,' says Daniel, fitting himself into a chair behind the horse-shoe, 'I suppose you'll be wanting to hear *Bedroom*.'

Bedroom is Daniel's first and recently released album, the thing that got him written up in *iD*. He was sixteen when he made it. In his bedroom. He takes a copy from its jewel box, hands me the CD cover.

'See that?' He points to a red smear on the cover. 'That's my shit robot I had like when I was six, and that bit's a piece of wall, hahaha, you'll probably think it's crap and yeah, so this is the first track, I like this bit where it goes . . .'

A resonant boom fills the bedroom. Daniel reaches down for the track skip button.

'And then this is one, which I think's shit, really, although Morris likes it, hahaha and listen to this track, "Underwater", which has this wicked noise I taped in the toilets at school, and here's . . .' Each track in turn a throb, a series of sound pictures. Nothing you'd call a tune, quite. Daniel races through the tracks, two seconds per track, talking at ten to the dozen. He moves along his CD collection, extracting jewel cases, flinging them in the player. 'So this one's Wagon Christ,' pulling them out again. 'Yeah, listen to this MLO track, it's really cool,' casting them aside and moving onto the next. 'And this bit by the Aphex Twin, wicked, better than some of his other stuff, hahaha, although I like him and this is David Toop who I'm gonna do some work with, but hahaha you'll probably think it's crap . . .'

'Daniel,' I say, looking up from the magazine I'm leafing through. 'Why aren't there any pictures of supermodels in your bedroom?'

'I am *not* gay,' says Daniel emphatically, his face developing a reddish glow which makes me feel as mean as a scalded dog. 'Although I'm not saying it would matter if I was, except to my dad.'

'Who's Morris?' I change tack while Daniel fights off his embarrassment, but at this he looks up momentarily, decides it's a joke and giggles.

'No, really,' I pursue, 'Who *is* Morris?'

Daniel is stunned. Uncomprehending. *Speechless.* I don't know who *Morris* is? *Mixmaster* Morris? Morris of the mixdesk? Morris of the music scene? *DJ* Morris, top bloke Morris? Ambient techno's own Mixmaster?

'Not Morris as in dancing, then?'

Daniel ignores the jibe, or maybe just pretends he hasn't heard it.

'So,' he says, blustery once more, 'you'll probably be wanting to see this really crap Yamaha keyboard, which my parents bought me for my birthday when I was like a kid, hahaha, and then this is the four-track, and this really cool keyboard, which is a Korg Wavestation and . . .'

'Daniel,' I say, 'can we go and have some lunch now?'

Lunch turns out to be a benign chaos of toddler demands and counter-demands, mother organizing, au pair sister rushing about, curly haired six-year-old banging her spoon on the table, oven timer going off, kids wanting gravy, no potatoes, or potatoes and no carrots, more carrots, fewer potatoes, more orange juice, less meat. Daniel and his father sit in the midst of it all, unbowed. Phone ringing again, Daniel answering it, shouting through toddler cries:

'Hahaha, yeah, can I ring you back? Thanks.'

'Daniel doesn't like my cooking,' says the mother.

'Yes I do,' says Daniel.

After lunch Daniel makes a bold attempt to play me a few more selections from his CD collection, but I cut him short. I want to know where he made the money to buy his kit, which leads to a safari through Daniel's magazine collection, featuring articles by . . . Daniel. Aged twelve he pesters his way to a job writing computer games reviews for *Zero* magazine, then moves on to a more serious role compiling a tips column in *GameZone*. At fifteen he's making a mint.

'In fact,' he rallies, 'I designed some games myself. They're crap, but I s'pose you're gonna want to see them, hahaha . . .'

I emerge from Daniel's bedroom about two hours later, battered but unbloodied.

Whatever aching tangle or peaceful blue lagoon exists beyond the bloom in Daniel's eyes he keeps hidden beneath a whirl of talk and action. Nothing of the real Daniel, whatever that may be, is available for public view save for a few minute and unconscious inflexions of his voice and body. Nonetheless, I have a sense that Daniel is about to become an important part of my little project. I request another meeting. 'What?' He exudes an air of puppyish hurt. I shake my head by way of reply, faintly bemused. Some small shutter closes over the chink in Daniel's armoury.

'I'm DJing at the Big Chill in a couple of weeks. If you want to go on the guest list, you'd better speak to my manager and say you're from one of the papers, and thank you very much,' says Daniel, cold as January wind.

I ring the manager and mention I've been round to lunch.

'What a cacophony,' I remark, in what I hope is an indulgent tone. The manager takes it differently.

'Well how d'ya think *I* felt?' he replies, sounding plaintive. 'Sitting down to roast lamb and mint sauce with my client's mum and dad? *I'm a rock'n'roll manager for chrissakes.*'

MONDAY

Early morning, wind hammering on the windows and the cat curling through my legs to remind me I haven't yet got round to feeding it.

Thinking about Daniel, or maybe the electronic scene, I e-mail Mac:

>Hey, Mac, do you think it's possible to make generational statements, or are generations created by the statements made about them?

He mails back:

>What do you have in mind?

I scribble down on a piece of paper all the generational clichés I've ever come across. It's a long list.

>Well, the presumption that 15-25-year-olds have a totally relativist set of morals whereas all us older people are more absolute about things.

You tap out an e-mail message and play it back in your head and Bingo! It becomes the most profound, the most meaningful, the freshest thought you ever had.

>Actually it seems to me that pretty much *everyone* has a relativist set of morals, it's just that *society's* morals have traditionally been absolute.

I suppose it's a silly fantasy of oneness, e-mail. But then again perhaps it's not a fantasy. Perhaps, maybe. I don't know yet.

I sit and think blanks for a while, then finish tapping in my note to Mac.

>Maybe the 15-25-year-olds feel that society's mores have broken down and they're simply less hypocritical than the rest of us. Or maybe it's just that they haven't learnt how to be full-on hypocrites yet.

No, it's not the perfect communication, but it's damned near. An imperfect kind of telepathy.

I leave the screen for a moment and fetch myself a can of root beer. Cat follows at a hopeful trot. Mac's answer is scrolling up on my return.

>I'd go along with that. Younger people are less hypocritical, definitely. Oh wow, it's just started to rain.:-)

I glance towards the window, notice twists of rainwater spiralling down the panes and whitened in the light of the desk lamp. Cat yells.

>Here too.

How weird.

>What else?

>Well, issues. When I was a teenager... I think back and do my best to stifle the memory . . . it was nuclear war and trades unions. These days it's animal rights, anti-racism, ecology and homelessness. We didn't really think about that stuff. Oh I don't know. Things change so *fast* is all.

Animal rights. Cat's begging has become so insistent I'm driven to leaving the screen and pouring him some Go-Cat biscuits. On my return I tap 'A' to send the mail, remember all the points I've forgotten to mention and open another e-mail file.

>The decline in trust - another generational cliché. Can't rely on your education to equip you for a job, there aren't any jobs, can't rely on your parents to stay together because half of them won't, can't rely on care when care means weirdos and sex abuse, can't rely on god and the church ditto, can't even turn to that old teenage staple, sex, on account of AIDS. Or how about this? A generation used to the idea that the only power they've really got is consumer power. Disenchanted with politics, enamoured of product.

I tap in 'A' again and take myself off for a pee. No word from Mac on my return.

>Mac, hello, I'm talking to you!

Electronic silence prevails. I wait a little while, humming over my screen like a wasp circling a honey trap but no word arrives. Mac has taken on such a sudden and unexpected importance in my life and yet I've never met him.

TUESDAY

This is Mac's eventual offering, paraphrased:

Even though the culture is ridden with premillennial tension the great thing about living at the end of the century is that there's at least the theoretical possibility of being able to start out fresh. New beginnings, redemption, the Second Chance. So typically American.

WEDNESDAY

A disconcerting lunchtime revelation. Mac is *not* American. I suppose I should have noticed that he doesn't spell like an American, but I was too busy making assumptions.
>**Why didn't you tell me before?** I typed.
>**The Internet makes national borders irrelevant.** He typed back.
   Somehow all this matters terribly. The beautiful edifice of projections tumbles. Macadamia the California nut is actually Mac a British human being . . . which makes me what? Some lovesick clown dreaming of California on a computer.
   Dawn arrives, but I don't sleep. I drift about in the pale half-life between unconsciousness and dreams.

FRIDAY

A ticket to Daniel's DJ event arrives, along with his World Wide Web address. I spend ten minutes leafing through its two main sections, Boredom and Bedroom. Bedroom is the life story of his ambient techno album, Boredom is everything else that has ever happened to Daniel and is capable of being distilled down into two-sentence sound bytes and graffiti graphics. A lot, in other words.

The moon is made of gorgonzola

Determined not to be entirely ignorant in the face of 'the scene' event tomorrow, I pass much of the day in Ambient Soho, Unity, Tower Records in Piccadilly Circus and with a pile of *NME*s, *Melody Maker*s, *iD*s and *Mixmag*s catching up on being young. Nonetheless, I feel like someone trying to swing. My one comfort is that at least I now know what ambient techno is. It's aural wallpaper, slews of electronic sounds devoid of narrative. Future noyz. Geek pop. Which makes Daniel a geek pop king.

Four hours with the music press has taught me something else too: Geek pop kings make it big on the quiet. They don't appear on the covers of *NME* and *Melody Maker*. Aphex Twin, the Orb, MLO, Muziq, Wagon Christ, Cosmic Baby – a bunch of egghead boys with tiny marble eyes and thin white features bounded by fuzzy hair and street style. Mostly they work alone, up in the teen-boy heaven of circuitry and kit control, remixing, re-modelling, switching names as fast as record labels, in constant drift and flux; sampling, distorting, sequencing, dipping, cruising around the musical ether. Occasionally they collaborate – two tides of repressed testosterone converging in a sound wave.

Geek pop albums – *Lunar 7*, *Electron Pod*, *Weimar Supernova* – are named after bits of Germano-Japanese technology and scifi tropes, presented with sleeve notes quoting from French deconstructionist theory and *The Brady Bunch*. The albums are divided into quadrants and sectors, their tracks given numinously impenetrable titles. 'Phragmal Synthesis Part 3'. 'Nexus Techtronics'. 'Tokyono'. 'Space Warp Exodus'. Albums more like pieces of machinery, heavy with devices, levers, buttons, musical gadgetry, technical gewgaws, bytes and showy displays of novelty. Sometimes a secret track lurks beyond the album's seeming end, causing entire Internet newsgroups to spring up in order to explore more fully the profundities of geek pop secret tracks, the digital generation's equivalent of 'Stairway to Heaven' and 'Sympathy for the Devil' played backwards.

From 'A Thousand Plateaux', a geek pop manifesto, written by two French theoreticians, Gilles Deleuze and Felix Guattari:

> A musical consistence-machine, a SOUNDMACHINE (not for the reproduction of tones) one, that, molecularises the sound material, atomises and ionises and captures the COSMIC energy. If this machine should have another structure than the synthesiser, in that it unites the modules, original elements and working elements, the oscillators, generators and transformers and brings together the micro intervals it makes the sound process and the production of this process itself, audible. In this way it brings us together with more elements that go further than the sound material. It unites the contradicting elements in the material and transfers the parameters from a formula to another. The synthesiser, with its consistence-operation, has, a priori, taken the position of establishing in the synthetic decision: this is a synthesis of molecular and cosmic, of material and energy and no more of form and material, ground and territory. Philosophy no more as a synthetic judgement but as synthesiser of thought, to allow thought to travel, to make it mobile, and make it to an energy of the cosmos as one sends sound off to travel . . .

A reminder, incidentally, of a course in formal logic I took at college:

> It is raining
> It is not raining
> Therefore Paris is in France.

And the moon is made of Gorgonzola.

SUNDAY FOLLOWING

The Big Chill. Daniel's hair is plaited into embryonic dreads and stuffed into a multi-coloured woollen hat with woollen tube extensions running from its centre, giving him the appearance of a sprouted octopus at carnival.

Neo-hippies crash on sweaty mattresses caressed by the velvet pall of ganja smoke and Daniel's ambient techno seepage. *Chillin'*. Overhead a video jock projects computer-generated images across the walls as Daniel mixes the Radio One Top 40 live into his set. The room so dark that, save for Hindu goddesses, mandalas dancing alongside dolphins, the sun rising in reverse, a tribe of faceless mannequins running through a perspectival tunnel, it might be a solitary cell or even a womb.

Across the corridor in another room technopagans flip through the World Wide Web and patrol the alternative spirituality channels in Internet Relay Chat, pondering the Jungian archetypes over leaden carrot cake.

And all this time Daniel is looming over his mixing desk, shaking his tentacles and mixing the Radio One Top 40 live.

Afterwards he says: 'That was the first Radio One Top 40 ever mixed live into a set. Hahaha.'

I doubt anyone noticed Daniel making musical history, but that's the way it goes.

TUESDAY

I phone the editor of *iD* on a whim.

'Daniel, oh yes. After our piece about him appeared, he called wanting to write for us and he didn't stop ringing until I'd given in.'

'Guts.'

'Yeah,' the editor chuckles to herself. 'Daniel is definitely a one-off.'

Memories of my late teendom include a tumble of hopeless crushes, Steppenwolf, *Jaws*, electro-pop, *Saturday Night Fever*, suicide bands. And a permanent rictus of raw and unrequited rage. All the usual teenage apparatus, in other words.

WEDNESDAY

E-mail from Mac, requesting my public key. Whatever that is.

THURSDAY

More discoveries. A public key lets Macadamia send an encrypted message. What message, he won't say. Some time after midnight he forwards software called Pretty Good Privacy, along with a list of instructions which will supposedly enable me to generate some secret codes called keys.

Note: Though we both live in London, we work on California time. Like I said, we're sadsacks.

>The US government has classed pgp as munitions. Exporting it from the USA is illegal, like running guns writes Mac.

I can't imagine what he has to tell me that's so secret. That he's a hitman perhaps? A secret agent? Herpes carrier? Cricket fan?

In order to send or receive a PGP-encrypted message, I have to command the software to generate two keys, a public one which I can give out to Mac and a private one, which I have to keep to myself. The public key can only encode. It can't decode. So the principle is that I send Mac my public key, he encodes his message with it, sends it back to me, and I decrypt it using my private key. If he sends the message via an anonymous mailer, a computer which removes all reference to his name and e-mail address, it's almost untraceable and almost completely secure.

Oh well, however shocking or terrible the message is, I don't care. Mac makes me laugh and I like the way his mind works and we're only friends in any case.

A long paragraph of capital letters and keyboard symbols appears on the screen some time after two. I instruct the programme to decrypt and stand back. The hard disk light topspins on-offs. Symbols flip as fast as numbers on the propaganda boards advertising the savings you make by switching telecom companies. In America. Eventually, four lines of message emerge from the chaos, like Poseidon coming up to quell the sea. Line one: Mac's real-life name. Lines two to four: his address and phone number.

>Mac, your name and number are in the phone book. I just looked them up.

Phone numbers? This isn't the point of virtual life at all. The point of virtual life is to remain apart, distinct, ethereal, untouched by the mess of reality. The point of it is its sheer mystery.

>I won't phone you, Mac, and you won't phone me.

Sometimes people have to be told things they ought to know already.

TUESDAY
Britpop bands

First Tuesday of every month the Electronic Lounge meets at the Institute of Contemporary Arts. The apparent pinnacle of the 'underground' e-scene.

Daniel is a regular, of course. I'm not, but I'm pretending to have checked it out a couple of times in order to avoid – can I say this? – the embarrassment of being uncool. Today Daniel is decidedly down. He left his new T-shirt on the bus. He has scrawled 'I am in a bad mood' in gothic letters on my notepad. I offer him a Camel by way of compensation.

'Don't smoke, don't drink, don't take drugs,' he moans.

The Electronic Lounge is filling up with young people in

extreme outfits. Platform shoes, kipper ties, fat glasses, trousers made of plastic. All part of the underground now. Just about everything is underground. Mainstream life is what happens to the characters in *Neighbours*.

'*Don't drink, don't smoke, what do you do?*' I discover a line from an Adam and the Ants hit on my tongue. Very early eighties. Daniel misses the reference (he would have been five) but his face blooms purple all the same.

'Thanks very much,' he says, avoiding my eye.

Over Coca Cola (Daniel) and Jim Beam (me) Daniel confesses he hasn't had much of a love life for years. This takes me by surprise. Conventional wisdom suggests teens are hard at it from an ever earlier age. If you believed everything you read in the papers, you'd think the entire population under twenty had degenerated into a busy whirl of nymphomaniacs and prepubescent pervs.

'You know what really pisses me off about that T-shirt?' says Daniel, backtracking.

He sees someone he knows over my shoulder, waves at whoever it is.

'No, Daniel, but you're going to tell me.'

'I got it in the sale at Slam City Skates. Reduced from, like, fifty quid.' He begins rooting around in his bag, then pulls out a bar of chocolate and signals to someone else he knows.

'What's the worst thing you can imagine, Daniel?' I ask, as a sort of comforter. 'The *very worst thing*?' Like losing a T-shirt not so bad, blah blah. A look of concentration falls over his face.

'My parents break-dancing.' He tinkers with a follow-up idea.

'Or them having sex,' he says.

Glancing over to the crowd gathering at the bar discussing techno, multi-media applications, the direction of narrative in computer game design. I feel suddenly overcome by the weight of my ignorance. It would be easy to write the whole thing off as trivial, but there's something more enduring about the e-scene than that, which is to say that a tribe of under-agers in thrall to technology might really constitute the future in the making.

'What I think I meant was, what's the *scariest* thing you can imagine?' I continue, attempting to draw Daniel back into some kind of seriousness. He picks up the change in mood.

'My parents dying, I suppose. And growing old too quickly. Hahaha, it seems as though I was seven yesterday hahaha.'

And it seems as though I was seventeen. The screwy truth of the matter is that we speed through the years so fast we can hardly tell we've lived them. Even boys of seventeen worry about how to put the brakes on.

'Do you know what really pisses me off?' asks Daniel, readying himself to leave me in favour of his younger friends.

'Quite a lot at the moment, I'd say.'

'No, but what *really* pisses me off?'

I bite my lip and pretend to consider. Let's see.

'Uh uh, I can't think.'

'What *really* pisses me off is Britpop bands.'

WEDNESDAY

It's been six months since I compiled my first e-mail at Nancy's house in Strawberry Point.

THURSDAY

Apple Mac is in a parental mood and has imposed a curfew, allowing me to switch it on, but refusing to log me onto the Net so that I am effectively grounded.

My first impulse is to contact Mac, but, since the computer has crashed, I can't send e-mail. I take to the manual, get no further than the index. Mac's phone number lies on my mind like aversion therapy. Best sort the thing out myself.

So my next idea is to reach for the help button and tap in 'HELP'. 'This cannot be found,' bleeps the Apple Mac. I do it again. The same message appears. Rationally speaking, I am aware that the computer either recognizes an instruction or it doesn't. I know it can't interpret. But this is a crisis. Why doesn't the damned thing just *do something useful*? If it's supposed to be so clever . . .

I try:

> Internet
> PPP
> comms
> help TCP
> help Internet
> and so on

Eventually I call up the company which sells me my Internet connection.

'Is it a TCP error?'

Shrug.

'We'll send you the software.'

Go and boil your head, in other words.

FRIDAY

A floppy disk containing forty-two programme files arrives. No instructions. Most of the files appear to be compressed, so I have to decompress them before they can be used. But they haven't all been compressed using the same compression software. Some are .hqx files, others .sea files, .sit files, .cpt files. Some of these I know to be self-decompressing while others require separate decompression software, which I don't have. I can download it, but only if I can get online. And I can't get online, because I can't decompress the software files.

Pouring out some more biscuits for the cat, I poke my tongue at the rain outside, return to the computer and in a moment of inspiration type 'help MacTCP'. Bingo. The processor generates a help file.

'Because using the MacTCP control panel is technically complex, you should get assistance from a network administrator or other communications expert for this procedure.'

Boil that head.

MONDAY

The hype has hit! *Wired* launches in the UK.

What an unhappy crossbreed it is, half boisterous American technological boosterism, half apologetic British understatement, a hybrid as contradictory as the issue of a Great Dane and a Dachshund.

> *Internet, Internet, where have you been?*
> *I've been to London to visit the Queen*
> *Internet, Internet, what did you there?*
> *I frightened a little mouse under the stair.*

What I want to know is, why do we Brits feel obliged to ask America's permission before daring to be upbeat about anything?

TUESDAY
Playability

Mac and I are recovering slowly from his phone number. As it turns out, he plays Streetfighter. At least he *has* played Streetfighter. Which makes me wonder if I'm the only living creature who's a decade behind the times?

Noting my interest, and being a fact-oriented person. Mac sends the following e-mail:

>**I read somewhere that in 1991 10% of Japan's trade surplus with the US was due solely to Nintendo, which makes more money than all the Hollywood film studios put together. Computer games is currently a $6bn industry in America.**

I give Nintendo UK a call, but they don't seem eager to want to talk to me. So I ring Sega, and they do. Andy in product development says the popularity of any game's all down to play-ability.

'But what *is* playability?'

'A feeling,' says Andy.

Wondering if Nancy has the answer, I despatch an e-mail to Strawberry Point. She returns mine in her lunch break.

>**Playability is the thrill of anticipation driving a player forward. It's the potent magic of immersion inside the world of the game. Playability is the ability to command the gaming character to act, without the character's actions becoming predictable or pointless. It's the accumulation of power with the goal in sight, but not made easy to reach. It's the learning and rewarding process of continual feedback, the accumulation of an in-depth knowledge of bonuses and hidden dangers and powers and magic. Playability hints at the infinite time-space warp at the heart of the game. It promises mastery and escape; a magical, almost shamanistic power to the player, who by virtue of being (most likely) a young man in the midst of the ethereal, numb, dizzying hyperreality of our culture, senses that in 'the real world' he has none.**

How's that?

My friend Nancy, the 'been there done that' queen. I'm happy for her, really. But I'd still like to be first at *something*, dammit.

WEDNESDAY

Daniel calls.

'Hello,' as if embarrassed by the intimacy of his own name.

'Hello, Dan-i-e-l.' I linger over it.

'I'm playing a set at Rocket tonight.' This is code for 'Do you want to come too?'

'Rocket?'

'You've never heard of it? Hahaha,' says Daniel. This means one of three things:

1. Rocket is a big deal and I am a predictable old cube for failing to recognize it.

2. Daniel merely *supposes* Rocket to be a big deal.

3. Daniel secretly *knows* Rocket is not a big deal, but wishes it were.

'Yeah, well,' he concludes. 'It'll probably be very lame.'

I begin again:

'What was the worst present you ever got?'

'You go.' Daniel perks up.

'I got a goldfish tank for my eighth birthday. And that was it. No bubble-maker, no plastic treasure chest. It didn't even have a goldfish in it.'

'Hahaha,' warbles Daniel happily, convinced he's got me licked. 'Mine was worse. When I was fifteen my parents gave me an office chair. An office chair! I would have got an office chair *anyway*.'

SATURDAY

Trojaning the D-135a

Hacking was bound to feature in my little project before long. In spite of the fact that the hacker myth is as hackneyed as a rabbit in a top hat a certain mystique remains however hard you struggle against it.

Just a couple of weeks ago, some British teenager was discovered to have been dipping in and out of the US Defense Department computer systems for seven months without being detected. He posted minutes of secret meetings between US agents and the North Koreans on the Internet. The US Defense Information Systems Agency admitted that he'd 'affected the Department's military readiness,' but he wasn't traced until he made the mistake of leaving his terminal online to a US Defense Department computer overnight. Now tell me, is that art imitating life, or the other way around?

Anyway, I do wonder how many of the couple of hundred geeks, acid kids, nerds and curios hanging about outside King's College waiting to be let into the first ever UK hackers' conference are actually hackers. The guy behind me in the beige quilted parka and grey shoes? The scattering of teenage boys wearing woollen breeches and farmers' smocks (I know, it's weird)? And what about those two suits with dark glasses who strolled right past the queue and into the building carrying outsized attaché cases?

Kid A standing in front of me leans over to Kid B next to him and says: Did you crack the D-135A? B replies: Nah, there was a packet switching problem at 2100 but I think I can trojan it.

A says: You could always outdial on the T switch.

B replies: Of course, but that doesn't take frequency modulation into account.

No one is going to admit they're not a hacker at a hackers' conference. It would be like saying you're an atheist at your own Last Rites. It would be like confessing to wearing your mum's nighties. It would be like inventing boyfriends and being found out by your best friend.

Inside the lecture theatre the two suits straddle the middle row creating a vacuum around them as big as the parting of the Red Sea. In fact, the suits are the only two people sitting right up against each other. They're also the only two people wearing sunglasses.

'Who do those guys think they're fooling?' asks Linux, sitting a way along the same row as me. Now, I call him Linux because that's what's written on his T-shirt.

'It *is* a bold look,' I reply, sensing Linux knows something I don't.

Early on it's clear that I should not have sat in the same row as Linux because when he isn't bobbing his skinny knees up and down in his seat, he's scribbling billions and billions of tiny circuit boards on the back of an envelope, reciting all the passwords he knows by heart and humming the first line of 'Freebird' in a selection of different keys.

'Shh,' I hiss, in a plausibly indignant tone.

'Pardon *me*,' he replies.

At question time after the first lecture, I raise my hand. Linux notices, leans in.

'I think you'd be better off waving that about,' he says, confidentially.

'*What*?'

Linux shrugs, as though innocent. Starts waving his hand towards the speaker and pointing at me. I can hear the first line of 'Freebird' rumbling along somewhere in his chest. Meanwhile, he has his hands cupped around his mouth and is whispering as loudly as he can.

'Hey, speaker, question here.'

'Piss *off*,' I whisper in return, reeling in my arm. 'I've answered my question myself.'

But, of course, in that exact same moment the speaker notices me.

'You have a question, there?'

I ask my question and Linux takes notes.

Around lunchtime two of the delegates set off the building's alarm system. Sorry, *hack* the alarm system. The suits in sunglasses pull Ginster's cheese and onion pasties from their attaché cases. And just about everyone else heads for the bank of computers in the annexe room where a computer security firm is offering a free something or other to the first hacker who can break their brand new patented anti-hacker software firewall.

The boys in farmers' smocks are eating sandwiches in room 34a, which is down the corridor, up two flights of stairs, along another corridor and through three swing doors. It turns out that they're not hackers at all, but extras on the set of *Sense and Sensibility*, which is being filmed next door.

In the concrete square below room 34a, a circular man sits reading the paper and guarding a row of caged whippets. Assuming I'm a member of the *Sense and Sensibility* crew, he asks me how the ball scene is going and I reply that it's going just fine, and, by the way, what are they planning for the whippets? Whippets? the circular man snarls. If I am referring to the precious parcels in their cages they are eighteenth-century Italian greyhounds and worth £1500 a piece. I can see him wondering whether I'm crew at all. To be so *ignorant*. I shoot him my best smile and shuttle back to the annexe as rapidly as can be done through six corridors, two flights of stairs, three swing doors and a chemistry lab. Back at the annexe everything is as if I'd never left. Banks of hackers still punching away at their keyboards in an attempt to crack the anti-hacker firewall. Banks of others pitching advice. 'Type 2.7,' 'Engage the command control.'

Aside from myself, there are two women at the conference. One is a pretender, like me. We meet in the toilets, and – being pretenders – pretend to exchange hacking tips.

'I'm thinking of trojaning my D-135a,' I say, burying the technical detail in the roar of the hand dryer. (It might actually be Dee-wan 35a or Dionne 35a or something else entirely, come to that.)

'But that doesn't take frequency modulation into account,' replies my fellow pretender, convincingly, scraping the soap from her fingernails.

About halfway through the afternoon, in the middle of a lecture about Satan, the hack-detection software, a film crew bursts in and begins showering the audience in video input. You'd think it was the Valentine's Day massacre. There's a momentary freeze followed by chaos. Two-thirds of the audience dive under their seats, the other third jam their Tolkien T-shirts over their heads and the suits just sit there looking mildly keyed. The film crew is muscled out, and the lecture continues, with everyone glancing over their shoulders at regular intervals and being twitchy.

By the end of the day, I've learned so much it would be impossible to remember it all.

I discover that there's a strict hierarchy in the hacking world, and everyone is trying to fit themselves into the highest slot they can. At the bottom of the hierarchy are the WareZ dOOdz, who cruise the bulletin boards swapping pirated copies of computer games. The ultimate prize for a WareZ dOOd is a perfect pre-release or O-day copy of a new version of Doom. Naturally, everyone at the conference holds the WareZ dOOds in complete contempt, even though you see groups of delegates break off to make wareZ deals every time there's a gap in the lecture schedule.

Living one rung higher are the COdeZ KidZ, who specialize in swapping fraudulent credit card numbers, and break authorization codes to the phone company lines. Carding and auth. code boards exist everywhere, but particularly in Eastern Europe. Most CodeZ KidZ don't seem to be able to screw much more out of their trade than the odd free mail-order item or long-distance phone call. It's a bit of a loser's game, tell the truth.

Both WareZ dOOdz and CodeZ KidZ hang out on sub-lamer boards, local bulletin boards for geek saps. If a kid is ambitious and patient and makes the right connections, he might get taken up by a mentor one rung higher up the hierarchy, who'll give him the number of a bigger, better board. The cooler the hacker board, the higher the proportion of non-local calls it receives, and the more barriers there are to gaining access to it. The really cool boards are intergalactic and no-one knows how to access them.

When WareZ dOOdz and CodeZ KidZ get together to trade codes or wares they must wage ritual warfare with each other first, so that both parties are entirely clear that neither party is a pushover.

>ZUK MI DIK, AZZWYPE.

>SHIT, DOOD, U DON'T NO WAT YOU M*ZZING WITH. 1 WYPE ALLRYTE. 1 WYPE YOUR DRYUZ SO KLEEN U KAN C YOUR BALLZ IN EM. NOT THAT U HAVE N.E. BALLZ, WUSS.

>KIZZ M1 AZZ, MUTHAFUKKA

Top hacker boards are constantly in flux, changing host computer and address, so as to make them more exclusive and less traceable. Most contain philes, strings of passwords to company computers, password dictionaries, authorization codes for phone exchanges. The spelling of 'phile' is important. It's a *homage* to phone phreaking, an early form of hacking in which hackers tapped phone lines in order to gain free telecom time, or sometimes simply in order to become familiar with the whole web of routing and switches and trunks and bridges and outdials that makes up the global telecom system. Blind kids were particularly good at phreaking because they could recall tone sequences with greater accuracy.

What else?

The fact that most hackers do not dream of cracking into the Pentagon and stop-starting nuclear war but of landing themselves a $250,000 job in computer security with a blue-chip company offering generous benefits and a subsidized canteen.

Social engineering. The easiest hack in the book. You persuade a telecom operator to give you a password by pretending to be a telecom engineer. You stroll past security waving a fake business card. You read off someone's security code whilst passing on a message. You cheat, you shoulder surf, you wheedle, you demand and, if you're good, you get what you want. Passwords, data, binaries. Half the hacks in the world turn out to be masterly pieces of social engineering.

Other factoids:

1. Emmanuel Goldstein, Eric Bloodaxe, Bill SF are three of the brighter stars in the hacking firmament, and *I've actually met them*. (So pip that, Fancy-Nancy.)

2. The phone system distinguishes between a data exchange and a voice exchange and tries always to route data exchanges terrestrially. So if you bleep your modem down the line during an international call the system will reroute terrestrially and you'll avoid that weird satellite echo of yourself talking or those embarrassing 'You go,' 'No, you go,' conversations.

3. There's a five-storey structure built underneath the Queen Elizabeth Conference Centre in London *which does not appear on any maps*.

4. Most of the people who go to hackers' conferences are not actual hackers, but wannabe hackers playing parts.

BUT . . .

The most surprising lesson I've learned is that hierarchies of technical arcana can be as beautiful as rainbows, which small epiphany I'd previously imagined reserved for men alone.

> Hic haec hoc
> Bit byte bloc
> *Puella, puellam, puellas*

THURSDAY FOLLOWING

It's the school holidays and the hottest summer on record. The Common looks like the set of *Lawrence of Arabia* with trees.

I'm round at Daniel's house, sitting at the kitchen table while he makes himself a snack. While Daniel cuts the avocado, shaves the red peppers, skins and cubes the chicken, heats the frying pan then tests it out, he is wondering whether I'm going to the Big Chill next week and if I have a ticket for the Tribal Gathering. Strips of sentences and words are falling from him like agitated ropes of sweat.

'So, hahaha, I did this hip-hop remix thing with Jon Tye from MLO and it sort of got more recognition than *Bedroom*, which pisses me off. But it's no big deal really, because, uh, I could do an album a month, if I wanted. Each in different genres. Hip-hop, ambient, trip-hop, jungle, easy listening. You'd probably think they were shit, but, uh . . . Ben and me are doing this weird thing with his guitar.'

'Who's Ben?'

(And what exactly is the weird thing you're doing with the guitar?)

'Uh, you know.'

Think. In my mind a tall dark boy, older-looking than Daniel, but not actually older. Daniel's best mate. The same Ben he's known all his life. Ben the looker. Ben the rake. Ben Speed as in weed. Ben who would be a guitar *phenomenon* if only he'd get off his arse.

Daniel lobs me a quick look, uncertain of the territory. Winkles himself out with 'Did I tell you about Bloggosoft?'

Think blanks, shake my head.

'It was this shit software company I set up with this friend and we programmed a joystick to do, like Etch-a-Sketch, hahaha.' His face is pink from the cooker, and every so often he wipes his forehead like a windscreen wiper on low.

'Uh, can you watch that?' He gestures to the frying pan, and vanishes upstairs. Presumably to take a slash, have a leak, piss, pee, empty his bladder, attend to the call, see a man about a dog.

His notebook lies open on the table. 'This notebook is named Rubic Cube. It was started on 8.1.93.'

Page One. A list of phone numbers, labelled 'Top Phone numbers'. Mixmaster Morris, an A&R guy from Virgin Records, the techno musician Moby.

On other pages lists of sound effects and how to achieve them: Sireny noise, Acidy 808-ey noise, space bleeps, phaseree space bubbles, sea squidge, space lights, industrial steam stuff, bell in space, and then the final one, underwater love.

After that a list of important dates, including:

6 July 1993 M. Morris phones

23 July 1993 My braces are removed

Rubic Cube is the complete distillation of Daniel's ambition. And what ambition! A notebook almost unhinged in its discipline. Two years in existence and not a single doodle, no marginalia, no overstrike or last-minute thoughts, no swell of feelings, copied poetry, scribbled song lyrics. A single qualification appears on the page listing Daniel's most important dates: the addition in pencil of 'ish' to the word important. Other than that tiny betrayal of vulnerability, Rubic Cube gives very little away. It's a catalogue of deeds. I did, I am doing, I will do.

I ask Daniel if he keeps a notebook of his feelings.

'What do you mean?' He adds more sauce to his stir fry.

'Well, presumably you do have feelings, Daniel?'

'When I stub my toe it hurts, yeah.'

Three months on I'm no nearer to understanding Daniel than I am to understanding why the sun comes up.

On our way to the front door, he says:

'Uh, I'm not going to the Tribal Gathering next week', and realizing from the expression on my face that I have no idea what he's talking about, refuses to walk me to the train station, which small rejection hurts more than is strictly necessary, or even appropriate.

FRIDAY

Not only have I discovered what the Tribal Gathering is, I've actually bought tickets and am presently astonishing myself by messing with the idea of asking Mac to accompany me. This is my list of pros and cons:

Cons first:
1. Almost everything I think I know about Mac is actually a projection of some kind viz: he's tall, handsome, mysterious and eggheady in a strictly sensual way.
2. He may well be short, old, and ugly and thus: unsuitable (yes, I am sufficiently superficial for these things to matter but not so superficial as to obviate the desire to excuse myself.)
   cravat wearing
   easy to mistake for someone's garden gnome.
3. We may discover a mutual real-life antipathy, which would jeopardize our virtual friendship.
4. I may fall headlong for him in an embarrassing and swift manner whilst he remains – at best – unmoved and – at worst – utterly repelled (he may be gay).
5. He may find the whole idea of raving an impossible joke.
6. He may be a woman (unlikely).

Pros:
1. Almost everything I think I know about Mac is actually a projection of some kind viz: he's tall, handsome, mysterious and eggheady in a strictly sensual way.
2. My projections may be right.
3. I can't think of anyone else to ask.
4. My most secret self is unsatisfied by the insubstantial nature of our virtual friendship. Ultimately, satisfaction calls out for reality.
5. He may be a woman (unlikely).

Heart thudding in throat I make myself some toast, throw some coffee granules into a mug and boot up. Naturally, Mac is online. Both of us seem to be online almost all the time now, most often to each other.

Mac asks:

>Did you finish *Data Trash*?

His CPU converts the letters to a sequence of 1s and 0s, spurts that sequence into the modem, which in turn converts it to a series of bleeps and tones, which slips into a phone line carrying it momentarily to a mainframe in North London, then around the country, and after that, as if no time has passed, across the Atlantic to a computer at CUNY, which switches it to some CPU in Chicago, then through Indiana and finally into the bank of modems at the water's edge in Sausalito, where its destination is noted, and the 1s and 0s of its constituent parts flown out again across America through the ocean and back to the mainframe in North London from thence to its final rest on my screen. A journey of twelve thousand miles for 'Did you finish *Data Trash*?' And, in a way, that seems perfectly reasonable. The human imperative to communicate is as fierce as war.

>Yeah, last night in fact.

The author of *Data Trash* thinks society is trying to cleanse itself by technological means because we're all so damned scared of the mess of ambiguity, the muddle of our bodies, and we're reaching out towards the purity of the information space as if it were the last piece of driftwood floating on the waters of the Great Flood. He has a point. Think about the dazzling hygiene of 1s and 0s. On and off, us and them, controller and controlled. The look/don't touch life: the telephone sex lines, the electric chair, computer dating, nationalism, gated communities, electronic tagging, computer games, virtual reality.

>And?

Two transatlantic trips and an inter continental crossing later . . .

>And we are two of the saddest sacks the world ever saw, communicating through San Francisco, when we both know that I'm in Clapham and you're in . . . where are you in?

>Hampstead. The San Francisco of North London.

I think everyone is feeling very endish right now and technology is brimful of a sense of beginning and possibility. That's what I tell Mac, anyhow. Then I finish my toast, and take the plate back into the kitchen. The phone rings, but I leave the answer machine to pick up the call. The moment to ask Mac to come to the Tribal Gathering has gone before it ever really arrived. I'm too wary of disillusionment. Besides, how would you go about it? 'Here's my theory of life, now please come to a disco?'

>All this e-mailing. We're becoming more ethereal. Living in our heads.

>You mean you and me?

Well do you? You and me? Yes, all of a sudden, yes. U + ME. You-and-me. Me 'n' you, you and me. It'd be so nice, so sugar 'n' spice. Youandme, youandme and youandme. Yes yes yes.

Mac e-mails

>Did you know that our brains are 9 times larger than is required simply to keep our meat in working order?

>Get away!

Brains again. Mac is very concerned with brains, but – dare I admit this to myself? – being male (which I am sure he is, though it's never been proven) and into computers, Mac assumes that brains are the things which enable you to learn the Greek alphabet and speculate imaginatively about gadgets, but have absolutely no role whatsoever in feelings or remembering your mother's birthday.

What now?

SATURDAY

The papers are saying it's hotter in London than in Athens and certainly it is warm. The pigeons on the Common have taken to holding out their tongues to catch the breeze. Oven air blows up from the underground and falls into the arms of the sun, dogs burn their pads on the tarmac in the park and all over the city people are tossing aside their routine business and turning instead to pleasure. Even the bums (America again) asleep in the shady corners look halfway content. None of us has aircon, of course. For weeks tepid nights have followed languid days, the heat leaking from the buildings keeping us awake. The bars and cafés in the centre of town, even those in the outskirts, are still busy until the early hours of every morning. We've grown to expect the heat. It's unheard of. We're doing all the things Londoners don't do; we're showing off our bodies, we're throwing out our umbrellas, we're speaking to the strangers sitting next to us, we're smiling at the thought of rain.

Every window in the city that can be opened is open, shedding indoor music onto the street. Jazz from cafés and bars. Britpop from the boutiques along Kensington High Street. There are buskers on every corner and you can barely walk anywhere in the West End without catching from some direction the faint tones of a Simon and Garfunkel number sung to an untuned guitar. The birds sing more loudly, people take their boogie boxes to the parks and lidos and the white noise of play all but drowns out the customary bleeps and ticks of taxicabs and pelican crossings and tube trains. London is no longer a city of villages or districts, but a series of musical patterns. Reggae, soca, Hindi, balalaika, hi-life, top-ten, Rai, each rooted to a particular area. A sound map.

Anyone under twenty-five is listening to House – machine music, technology's true song. The tabloids are so full of shocker stories you'd think they'd come across the new rock 'n' roll. Kids Go Raving Mad! Off Their Heads! Ecstasy Rave: Dancing to the Music of Death! The government, meanwhile, in its usual way, sees fit to do nothing more than panic, marching police in riot gear to break up raves, turning back convoys, tapping telephones, as if by making the whole thing harder they might turn teenagers on to the idea of a quiet night in with a cup of cocoa and the cat.

So now we have the Criminal Justice Act, which regulates in law the music 'wholly or predominantly characterized by the emission of a succession of repetitive beats'. Machine music, in other words. No gatherings of six or more vehicles, nor more than one hundred people. A complete teenage lifestyle made not only suspect (teens being already quite used to that) but plain illegal, punishable, imprisonable, criminal, and all enacted by a government no-one under twenty-five ever voted for.

Of course some of the ravers take drugs, many actually, and occasionally, very occasionally, someone dies. And of course, this is waste. But between 1990 and 1995 more than 750 teenagers died at their own hands, several hundred were murdered, killed by drunk drivers, beaten, raped, laid low, cut down and killed inside. Think about it.

Kids Go Raving Mad! Off Their Heads! Ecstasy Rave: Dancing to the Music of Death! Illegal, criminal, punishable, imprisonable.

Mac left uninvited, the Tribal Gathering is to be a lone expedition. My window, one person's view.

I set off at lunchtime in my twelve-year-old Nissan. Traffic piles out of the city, backs up in all the usual places: Scotch Corner, Hangar Lane gyratory system, the Hogarth roundabout. It takes an hour and a half to reach Hammersmith. The water I've brought to last through the day and night is already tasting warm and saline.

At around two thirty I've hit the motorway and half an hour

later I'm rolling through what passes for open countryside in southeast England. By the time the car has clocked up forty miles or so the blacktop looks as though it's on the move, throbbing from the sun and the thump of house spilling out from the jalopies of young and younger people heading west, same as me.

This is another world from the sticky walls of hometown discos, the village halls and mirror balls and top-ten hits that were the songs of my adolescence.

The Nissan runs into heavy traffic again outside Oxford, and by the time we've reached the Headington roundabout a long line of vehicles is stretched before and behind us. More than a thousand vehicles, windows down, musical offerings drifting up into the air with the gasoline fumes. Thousands more young people, anticipation of the night ahead dizzying their heads, and crackling on their tongues. The cloying smells of petrol and sweat and youth. Nothing moves for an hour, only pulses. Now and then a trail of tarry marijuana smoke snakes by.

I leave the car in the jam and walk across to a Shell garage over the other side of the carriageway. They've done good business. No bottled water, no cans of soda. I pick out some chocolate and nuts and ice cream and stand in line with thirty or forty others, eating the ice cream and eavesdropping on the others' gabbing and chattering. Subjects are: the weather forecast and the bizzies, which DJs are expected, how long their sets might be. The dammed boundaries of teenage bodies oozing at the fragile points of eye and mouth and ear and sex. Me beside, still feeling like a swinging aunt. No one else notices, of course, or cares for that matter.

Back in the car I fall on the chocolate, my mind heavy with reminiscences. The razor-like treachery of the girls and the careless surges of the boys. Skipping along to discos full of hope only to find myself hiding in the toilets during the slow numbers, a humiliated and lonely solo. The sad attempts to catch the attention of the boys — pencil skirts so tight you could barely breathe — and the puzzling little *frisson* of revulsion when you succeeded. And also in my mind is that holiday on Venice Beach with Nancy and beach volleyball and Nancy's brother waving goodbye from a field near Santa Barbara, the train ticketing past him like the rush of mercury in boiling water. A sudden flush of envy and regret wells inside me. The more I look out at the easy community of cars and music and young people, ripe from anticipation, the stronger the feeling becomes, until it has grown into such a puzzling, infantile rage I have to bite my lip in order to make the pain more tangible.

The venue first appears from the brow of a hill about a mile away. A dozen or so marquees have been set up in a rough circle, beyond them a Ferris wheel and some smaller structures I can't make out. A large field next to the road is already shiny with vehicles, and it looks as though another is being opened up. On either side of the thick flow of cars the hedgerow is garish with hawthorn blossom and hogweed. Every so often I am overtaken by a group of kids on foot, carrying small daypacks and, occasionally, drums or other instruments. If you call out to them they salute with their fists and smile.

The cops are patrolling the gates beyond the car park, along with a police doctor who confiscates my antihistamine and a bottle of paracetamol before losing interest in my situation which is as well since I *am* carrying. An E – pink, with a bird stamped on it, so a Dove, I suppose – one blotter and a little grass. One of the organizers says they're expecting twenty thousand people. I'd guess two-thirds of us are carrying. What can the police do? Take our antihistamine and pretend not to have noticed the rest.

I sit on the grass next to one of the marquees for a while, sunbathing and watching the venue gradually filling up. Kids born into punk and power cuts, and matured in Thatcher's Britain. White, working-class kids for the most part. Ten, maybe fifteen years younger than me, the boys arriving in mixed couples or male-only packs, the girls in girl groups. There are a few other types, wrinkled swingers, hippies, not many. I don't feel out of place. No one's counting.

As it begins to get dark I wander over to the ferris wheel, and sit beneath it, smoking. A few transitory conversations, amiable enough.

'Hey!'

A smile.

'Having a good time?'

Another smile.

'Respect!'

At about nine my baggie comes out of its hiding place, I break the E and gulp it down with the salty water. It's loose packed, crumbles instantly on the tongue. That burning bitterness, like malaria prophylactics. Find myself on the wheel thirty minutes later, playing with a red sun. A surge of completeness.

By midnight, the dance floors are full, and there are dancers spilling out into the night at the entrances to the marquees, arms outstretched, feet sliding around in the grass, lost to music. Inside others are breathing life into the beats. The boys have taken off their shirts and knotted them to their hips. Auras of fabric and sweat whirl about them, their exposed skin glowing like an alchemical coat pulled taut over the spare frames beneath. Assured-looking boys, abandoned to the haunting auto-erotic romance of adolescence. I find myself moving along, as if involuntarily, towards the centre of the crowd.

For a time I watch the girls dancing, some with wildness in their faces, and I recall with what ease I'd given myself up to my imagination and with what unease to my body at their age. I wonder vaguely if it is the same for them. The fanatic urgency of the things is hard for girls. We're taught against it.

Chewing the remaining half of the tab I take to the dance floor. At the first rush I'm waiting for the acid to reach the E and lift it higher. I'm dancing hard now, or rather, a hard dance tumbles through my body, running along the limbs and leaking out from the fingers. People are belting out the beat, high on everything. At some point I see myself standing on the platform next to the sound system overlooking the writhing of the thousand heads and I hear the thought that in some way I am witnessing the species-consciousness, the human song.

I find new companions outside, and damp from dancing we watch the dawn come up together, smoking spliffs and laughing about nothing. Later we fall into a dream-lapped sleep and wake up stiff as toffee block. For the first time I feel part of something bigger than my life. I feel in on the trick.

MONDAY

I head out to Soho, and buy a pile of techno records and spend the day playing with them. Dulled by the comedown, but contented. Included, finally. In on the trick.

FRIDAY

It's too hot to stay in London over the bank holiday weekend, so I've decided to take a drive through the country.

I pick on Portishead. It seems as good a place as any. Having shoved a few vital fluids into my Nissan (root beer, oil and windscreen water), I pack up a bag and mail Nancy to let her know I'll be back when I'm back. She sends a reply within the hour.

>Have you been to Portishead before? Sweetie, *be careful*. I read an interview in *Rolling Stone* which made it sound like the South Bronx.

I arrive in Portishead at eight, find a B&B, pick up some fish and chips and head down to the waterfront, past the Edwardian town hall, municipal bowling green and tennis courts. Two elderly women walk their fattened pets and a couple gaze out across the slick of muddy sand to Wales. Streetlights have just come on, patching white sails over the town's red-brick houses, flower beds and polite concrete pavements. And although I've never been to the South Bronx I caught a glimpse of it from a round-Manhattan tour boat once and I can't say it looked much like Portishead to me.

SATURDAY

Today the blue beach at Magor in Wales is clearly visible from the seafront and the chimneys of some blackened factory spin bronze smoke up into the air over the Bristol Channel. By mid-afternoon I've been up and down the esplanade four times, viewed the chimneys in early morning haze, in mid-morning clarity, in midday funk and looming mid-afternoon shadow. Now I understand why the band who took the town's name writes such spaced-out doped-down tunes. There is absolutely nothing to do in Portishead but play bowls, walk along the esplanade and smoke enough blow to be able to forget it all.

Early evening I find myself in Mr B's Amusement Arcade in Weston-Super-Mare, feeding the one-armed bandits, nostalgic for last weekend's outing and also in thrall to the surreal graphics, repetitive bleeps and promises of transformation the machines give out. To the west the brown sea stretches behind an outdoor lido surrounded by windbreaks. Beach donkeys plough up and down, there are variety acts in the theatres and curry sauce and whelks in the food stalls and above all, lined up in huts and rooms and back bars all along the seafront, there are ranks and rows of squawking slot machines.

I've always liked one-armed bandits. The heave of the arm and the jangle of coins appeal to the kid in me. First time I went to Las Vegas when I was twenty-one, I won 287 new nickels from one of the nickel slots at Caesar's Palace for an outlay of 10 cents. A $14 profit, an approximate 700 per cent return on investment. The jackpot, two million, eluded me.

At Mr B's on the pier the jackpots are more modest. Twenty pounds or a set of redemption prizes including a potato peeler, curly plastic drinking straws and a mixing bowl. Not Vegas exactly, but popular with kids who've come down for the day with their families and wish to be rid of them. By nightfall every teenager worth the name is down on the pier, working the slots, the UK being one of the few countries in the world where minors can gamble on machines.

I begin to notice some kids hanging over certain slot machines but not playing them. Guarding them, more like, for older co-conspirators. The protector hangs over a machine that hasn't paid out in a while, to stop it being used by someone else, in return for a cut of his patron's eventual winnings. It's all systematized.

By now, having been through Battletech, Streetfighter and a good few more, I know the ropes, but I'm still lacking an education in the finer points. The modern slots continue to defeat me, with their nudge and stop buttons, the hold bars, the digital bank tally. Too technical. I don't get to within five miles of a win.

A pallid boy with long hair plays the machine next to mine, deep in concentration, eyes focused on the magic line of symbols. Each time the line comes to a standstill, he's crouching down and peering into the window. On occasion, he peers into the window, and attempts to shuffle one of the reels round by grabbing the sides of the machine carcass and giving it a shake. Always conscious of the security guard before he does it. After a time this boy notices me watching him, and he shoots a barbed look at me and says:

'What you lookin' at?'

I shrug, feeling vaguely threatened. It strikes me how skinny the boy is. Can't be much older than eighteen.

'I ain't getting off this machine, all right?'

We continue playing our separate slots for a minute or two, then the boy motions me over:

'What you after?'

'Depends,' I reply.

He looks up out of the machine space, checks for security, gestures with his left hand. An instant later, a younger boy appears.

'Look after this one, Spaz.' The younger boy nods his head and adopts the slouched but wakeful habit of a watchdog. 'Back in a blink.'

The older boy and I then wander casually toward the door of Mr B's, out into the twilight, along the pier and down a set of concrete stairs to the beach. It's gone eight in the evening now, and a cold whipping wind is slashing in from the sea. The first brisk air since April. The donkeys have been packed up, and the only other creatures visible on the beach are a couple of locals out walking their dog, heading away from the pier towards the lighthouse. My boy says:

'I'm learning the reels on that machine, but I run out of cash.'

Takes off his shoe by the breakwater and fishes out a little ziplock baggie containing a thimbleful of white powder.

'Whiz. Ten quid.'

This explains the skinniness, the fast-forward look in the eyes. I shake my head. I have no use for amphetamines. Whiz is an insomniac's worst nightmare.

The boy is not pleased. It's possible he thinks the deal was done the moment we left Mr B's together. He says his machine's just about to pay out and he needs a bit more cash to get the payout. He speaks with a Welsh lilt. Stop-start. Difficult not to be won over by him. We swap our prizes by the breakwater and split up at the stairway and he waits for me to climb back up to the pier. I take my stash out in the ladies' toilets on the pier head, smell it, put a grain or two on my tongue, consider what to do with it for a moment, then put it back in my pocket.

Whiz is back at his machine in Mr B's, punching the nudge buttons with his thumbs, I catch his eye and smile, trying to make him understand that I'm looking for something else from him. He smiles back, on automatic. Watches me from the corner of his eye feeding ten-pence pieces into my machine. Can't bear to witness the incompetence. This is how I knew I'd get him.

'You won't get nothing out of that,' he says finally, coals of eyes staring out at something else. 'I just emptied it.' A chuckle and a sweet bad grin. 'Fundamental rules. One. Wait for someone to stack a machine before you play it. Keep an eye open. Two. Learn your reels. Look.' The boy gesticulates towards his magic window, already lost in the flow of his voice. 'The reels on each machine are different, see? Sometimes the cherry will be next to the melon, sometimes it won't. So you have to put in the work, you have to learn the reels, and then you can take advantage of the nudge system to crack the jackpot.'

He puts a twenty into the machine, stamps on the start bar, flaky black eyes locked onto the window. Cherry, bell, plum, cherry.

'Now, see, if I had five nudges stored up, I could get a win out of that. Hold on the cherries and the bell, nudge the plum up five and get a bell. But that's cause I know that reel, see?'

I'm not sure I do, but I nod all the same.

The boy flips his hair back. Wired with adrenaline. Maybe speed, but I don't think so. He is simply bursting with attentiveness.

'So if you know you're not gonna get a win by nudging, then you save up your nudges for next time.' He punches the start bar.

'Trouble is, if security see you know the reels, they're gonna move you on, so you have to be, like, quiet about it.' He looks about the room.

A hold button begins flashing. The boy crouches down to look at the reels.

'Flashing hold after a nudge means you can let the reels spin for an automatic win.'

A flare of silver spews out into the trough at the base of the machine. This truly is knowledge.

'Normally,' says the boy, 'if the machine is paying out, you leave the money in the digital bank.' He points to an LED window displaying winnings at the top of the machine. 'Not until the sequence has stopped. The machines play in sequence. You take money out at the wrong time, see, and you break the sequence.'

Whiz has put his heart into the reels, but I'll bet he hasn't lost it to a human being. Soon, perhaps, but not yet.

'You have to respect a sequence.' The boy looks up, alerted, darts his head about checking for security again, makes the same whirl with his left hand as before and, as before, Spaz materializes from the blur, a beige-haired runt of a thing slightly bowed.

'Watch that one over there,' Whiz instructs his lookout. 'Saw a woman come in, play for ten minutes on it, no payout. I'll be along in a mo.'

What simple beauty the system has. The boy uses his eyes to play, his ears to track the payouts in the room, his hands to cheat, his head to learn the reels. Spaz is the final simple but effective detail, a reservation card.

The boy hits another small jackpot. Nickel suns begin to tumble into the trough below four bells. The boy allows himself a little look, then assumes an impassive air. About a hundred coins, I'd say. He removes a few, pushing them into the coin slots at the top of the machine, bashes the start bar and is on his way again.

'I thought you said a machine's no good once it's paid out,' I protest.

'I always invest a pound to get the sweetener. That's my rule, and I stick to it.'

The boy earns a nudge, holds a jackpot bar and two cherries. Looks up and spots the incomprehension on my face.

'After a jackpot, the machine pays out a sweetener. A mini-jackpot to encourage you to play on. Most people, they think, fantastic, man, they're on a lucky streak. But that's the thing with the machine, see. It *knows*. It don't pay out nothing after the sweetener. Once you've won the sweetener, it's curtains.'

SUNDAY

Late afternoon I wander up to Mr B's, but neither the boy nor his assistant are about. I give myself an hour to get the jackpot by applying my new-found knowledge, and I leave Mr B's that evening without winning a penny. I feel a sudden urge to call Daniel. I'm not sure why. There's some flicker of age about him, a whisper of mortality.

Daniel says, 'I've got this great new idea. Everyone's doing urban techno, so I'm gonna do country techno. A whole album about lounging around on a farm listening to the cows go off.'

'Go off where?'

'*Go off*. You know, like car alarms.'

WEDNESDAY

Daniel calls *me* to say his work is being discussed by Stockhausen on BBC radio. Also, that he's been interviewed on MTV and looked 'completely shit'.

FRIDAY
A dogs' home for motherboards

My day is spent skip-raiding with Heath. At the end of it all we part company at Vauxhall, he empty-handed, me with a stash of stolen circuitry, surprised. I saw a documentary about skip-raiding once, but it was nothing like this.

In the documentary, three or four young hacker types dressed in black overalls crept about the back streets of Austin, Texas, invading industrial lots, clambering over blue-chip company trash bins and fishing out from among the official office excrement technical manuals littered with security passwords and access codes. It was ice cool.

Heath has been skip-raiding in one way or another for years. Says it's his urban hunter-gatherer ritual. You go on your feet, and you take out whatever you can carry away. Back home, you redistribute the booty to whoever needs it. He says it keeps him in touch with his primitive side.

When Heath takes a mouse or a motherboard from a skip, he leaves behind its image chalked up on the metal. All over London there are waste bins decorated with representations of ethernet cards and monitors and mice in a stylized, blocky hand.

Heath is one of the pivots of the electronic underground. He runs an electronic bulletin board for folk with handles like 'Astra None' and 'Force for X'. Knows just about everyone who knows anything about contraband circuitry, techno-anarchism, political hacking, technological subversion techniques. And there are more of them than you might think.

Heath has been around. For a while he lived in Bristol, making stained-glass graffiti, crazily beautiful nuggets of red and blue set into the grimy panes of disused warehouses. Kids would watch him put them up and smash them once he'd gone. He didn't care. One time, the police tried to arrest him halfway up a ladder inserting a gold-leafed cube into the window of a storage building. They assumed he was nicking his own graffito. When they let him go, he fixed a pane of toughened plastic over the cube so that the kids wouldn't smash it. But, of course, they did.

He cleaned up a subway and turned it into a gallery for his murals, but the cops kicked him out. He took over a bank of telephones in King's Cross station and had people call in and chat to strangers waiting on the concourse. Someone put a stop to it. He sent out anti-advertisements on the World Wide Web. The last was for Glaxo, listing all of that company's alleged transgressions and malpractice. Glaxo wasn't thrilled. He worked for British Telecom once, in some technical sales capacity, but they sacked him for swinging on his swivel chair. Leastwise, that's *his* line.

Heath works in an area of central London stretching from Covent Garden in the west to the Tower in the east, and then along a thin strip south of the river, up to and including the South Bank Centre just short of Waterloo Station. That's his manor, his territory. A skip beyond those boundaries is anyone's for the raiding, so far as Heath's concerned, though he's not really bothered if his patch gets encroached upon every now and then. He's reasonable that way.

The first stop on Heath's skip manor is the Civil Aviation Authority on Portsmouth Street, between Covent Garden and Holborn. Actually there are two skips. Heath takes one, I take the other. Mine is smelly with last week's sandwich lunches. I emerge with three technical manuals for radio transmitters, a print-out from the finance department marked PLEASE RECYCLE and a golf-ball typewriter. Heath scans the bounty. 'Crap, out of date, broken,' and tosses the lot back where it came from. At Serle Street, the Department of the Environment's skip – red, rather than the usual yellow – yields nothing. We walk past the Public Records Office and into Fetter Lane. Heath points out a large bin belonging to Routledge publishing company. 'Book manuscripts, computers sometimes, pretty crap though, publishing doesn't make enough money.'

The British Telecom skip in Fleet Lane yields up an ethernet card, a couple of mice and a motherboard. Some security guys look interested, but as they're on coffee break they're not that interested. We put the motherboard back. Heath's got dozens at home, awaiting connections and boxes and so on, and I wouldn't know what to do with one if I had it.

Another British Telecom building in Gresham Street, curtains drawn over every window on the second floor. A sign in odd red lettering outside the main entrance reads PRIVATE PROPERTY NO PARKING. It's a Ministry of Defence listening station, according to Heath. Even the typeface on the parking sign is the same as the MOD's, printed in the same colour. It doesn't belong to BT, anyway. Heath tried marking the pavement opposite with white chalk crosses once. The police turned up in seconds.

'What are you doing?' they asked.

'Chalking marks on the pavement,' said Heath.

'What kind of marks?' said the police.

'It's art,' said Heath.

'We don't care what it is,' the police replied. 'You're not to do it here, all right?'

'Why?' asked Heath in an innocent tone.

'Because,' they said. 'You can take your art marks and put them somewhere else, where people don't have to look at them.'

'It wouldn't be art, then,' said Heath, 'it'd be a private act.'

'You don't expect strangers to view your private acts, do you?'

Heath shrugged.

'Exactly our point, see,' said the police. 'Our point exactly.'

We run into trouble at Merrill Lynch, the merchant bankers in Ropemaker Place. An office Dictaphone, a digital monitor and a modem are languishing in their skip, waiting to become landfill, but they don't want anyone else to have them. The security guard says he'll call the police and have us arrested and we'll both get criminal records and it won't be his fault. Heath explains to the security guard that this is working equipment, and there are some folk Heath knows (doesn't mention the fact they're anarchists) who could make use of it and don't have enough money to buy their own. And the guard says that, yes, he can sympathize, but there's company policy and the law, and they both happen to be leaning in the same direction, which is to say that Merrill Lynch's trash belongs to Merrill Lynch.

We enquire at what point Merrill Lynch's trash *ceases* to belong to Merrill Lynch. On the rubbish truck? En route to the landfill? In the landfill? The guard really doesn't want to chew over the finer points, but he'd just like to make it clear that whatever is Merrill Lynch's now is Merrill Lynch's forever. Does that include you? we ask. The guard knows what we're saying, but a job's a job. We offer to wait until he's off shift before taking the equipment. He has finally run out of excuses for being decent.

'You do realize you're on camera,' he says at last, and with some reluctance. 'We know who you are.'

The sun is shining, and the banks of the river down by Upper Thames Street are beginning to smoke their odours onto the streets above. Heath clambers into the skip at the Midland Bank, emerges empty-handed. Midland claims that its old computers are given away to schools and worthy causes, but Heath says he's watched them dumping computers into the skip. Either way, there is none in the skip today. We climb down a ladder hung under the jetty beyond Upper Thames Street and onto the river bank. A spray of old coins and some plastic tubing lie on the mud by the water, and there is a smell of moist, unwanted things, which reminds me of Henry Mayhew's account of the Thames beach at low tide in the 1860s, when it was pocked with human corpses, part melted by the effluxion of chemical waste, and with sad, drowned litters of kittens and dogs; the time it was populated by a nation of scavengers, picking through the spoils of industrial carnage left by the dead river water at low tide.

The Thames is cleaner today; there are fewer boats, perhaps, since the closure of the docks, but a steady stream busies up and down nonetheless. The beach, on the other hand, is avoided by all but a thread of urban anglers, as though there were still a taint about it. People walk their dogs on the pathways overhead while weary remnants of the sea submit to the suck and pull of dormant mud below. Gulls mill about the stones, and pigeons nest undisturbed in the beams of the jetties. There is an air of abandonment which stills the air on the beach, as it does everywhere it lingers. Heath finds the stem of an old clay pipe and I take up a shiny brown bone from among the litter of shiny brown bones and pretend it's human. 'That is someone's femur,' I say, holding it up to Heath's view. Heath thinks it's from a cow. 'Believe me, Heath,' I add. 'I studied biology.' He sniggers, we both snigger. He lobs the femur back into the river.

We wander over to Tower Bridge, through the Tower gardens lawned with mossy grass and along the walk heavy with tourists. At Shad Thames we tail off into the side streets and end up at a pub on one of the red alleyways just south of Conran's complex of reconstructed Victorian warehouses and receiving sheds and jetties. Inside, two drinkers and the barman are debating what to do with the money from the National Lottery, though none of them will have the slightest impact on where the cash will eventually go. The barman is in favour of huge subsidies to opera. The men in front of the bar think differently. One wants the money put into kidney dialysis machines, the other into football.

'It's a tax on the poor,' says the football fan, concisely.

'Yep,' replies the other.

'And more folk play football than clap out from kidney failure,' concludes the football fan, taking a swig of his pint. His argument is unarguable. We struggle to steer the conversation off in other directions.

'So have you seen that MI6 Building?' asks the kidney man, all round.

Heath and I and the man behind the bar mumble our affirmatives.

'Cost a fortune, that did, see.'

We nod. None of us knows *how* much it cost exactly, but we all know that it was a fortune, more or less.

'Well it's crap,' says the kidney man.

Heath and I smile nervously.

'And I'll tell you *why* it's crap.' The kidney man pulls something from his bag, holds it up for inspection. A snake of telephone cables. 'It's crap because there's no proper access from the roof to the telecom outlets serving the west side of floors six to twelve. Take my word for it.'

'We'll do that,' remarks the barman.

Heath walks me to his favourite spot in the city, at the bottom of Cardinal Cap Alley in Southwark, just west of London Bridge, where there is an ancient wooden door with an iron grate set into it. If you stand on a brick and look through the grate you can see a fat koi carp floating in a pond, and the zigzag edges of a secret garden. The rest of the alley is black and forbidding, reeking of slime and piss. Heath's left his mark there by carving into the green scum growing up the walls.

Further west a couple of teenage skate punks shearing round the Ring fix on Heath and me watching, make as though they haven't seen us, but jump a little higher and turn a little faster all the same. One of them, a boy with thin shoulder-length hair, no shirt, catches up with us at the skip in the car park at Jubilee Gardens. He's been looking at the sheet of plyboard wedged into the side of the skip for a couple of days and reckons it'd make a great jump ramp for him and his board and his mates. So, can we help him lift it out? The boy presses his thick-veined hands on the rim of the skip and vaults onto the muddle of polystyrene and card and plyboard inside. Remarkable body. Skin-wrapped pebbles move under his T-shirt, at the side of the bones a broad shelf of muscle, drawn down from the armpits to the waist, stomach pads fluted like wings, and the line of his shoulders interrupted by bone pips at the brow of the collar. His skin flattered by the sun making shadows of the curves. When he stands straight, as he does to pull the plyboard from its foundation in the garbage, two ramps of muscle bubble up at the pelvic bone. When I was the boy's age I'd look at boys and all I'd see would be skinny, autonomous, scary things, devoid of morality or love.

There is nothing in the skip for us, and we are now beyond Heath's manor, but we carry on westwards for a while, encouraged by the sun. At Ernst and Young, opposite St Thomas' Hospital, we discover the complete first draft audited accounts of Elite Filters Ltd, marked 'private', but private no longer, two circuit boards, transformers and a pile of ethernet cards. Heath has plenty of these right now and leaves them be. I'd like to take a power transistor, but I don't altogether know what it is, or how to use it, so I move on, regretting every step that takes me farther from it. By Lambeth Palace, I'm half resolved to go back and take it once Heath has gone.

I'm keen to discover whether MI6 has a skip, and Heath agrees to walk with me to Vauxhall, mostly because there's another BT skip on the way. Round the back of the spy HQ, Heath points out a large concrete tunnel giving out into the Thames, the outlet for the River Effra which was buried some years ago to allow for the development of Brixton and the Vauxhall intersection. Heath says it's a metaphor for what's going on inside the building, where every tiny trickle of information inflow is instantly housed and contained and re-routed and otherwise hidden underground until it loses its power, at which point it is quietly dispersed into the white noise of daily life, where it mingles with other, mundane data and becomes indistinguishable from it.

We look about, closely followed by a bank of cameras and the eyes of two security guards, but MI6 does not appear to have a skip. Up close, the MI6 building looks like a concrete block onto which someone has hurriedly pasted a failed DIY experiment and forgotten to take it down. There's something suspect and silly about the whole edifice. Perhaps it's the cameras zigzagging about in a frenzy of frustrated surveillance every time you stand behind a pillar, or the inadequate rows of conifers supposedly concealing the listening devices and photographic equipment beneath. Whatever it is, it's hard to take the place seriously.

On the other hand just imagine what we might have found in their skip! Closed circuit TVs, bugs, spy equipment, and discarded copies of reports on, say, the nuclear capability of Tajikistan or the government's latest plan to swap drugs for arms in Panama.

Heath asks a woman emerging with a briefcase if she's a spy. '*No I am not!*' she says, irritated. 'She'll never make it to the top,' says Heath.

So I now have an armful of rescued circuitry littering my flat and not much idea what most of it is, or how it works. At some point, I suppose, I'll have to take it all over to Heath's flat, which really is a dogs' home for motherboards.

MONDAY

Daniel calls. Says he's had a new idea for promoting cutting edge rural art: sheep graffiti. It goes like this: you spray your tag on a sheep. And then when the sheep's time is up, you market the skin as a piece of shag-pile graffiti art. Very now, thinks Daniel. And by the way, Stockhausen thought that Daniel's *Bedroom* album sounded like an ice-cream van stuck in a loop.

THE NEXT DAY

Three e-mails. The first from Nancy. She's come across some research which claims that you can put four ten-year-olds in a room with four TV screens showing, simultaneously, *Bugs Bunny*, *Baywatch*, *Gladiators* and *Roseanne* and they'll be able to follow every turn in every show. What's more, they'll *know* that none of it is true. Dave brought his TV round, and he and Nancy set up three TVs in the same room and tried the experiment themselves, but *Baywatch* kicked off in a slightly different way from usual so they got distracted and missed the end of *Roseanne*. They tried again, and failed again. And now Nancy wants to know whether efficient multi-screening is the gift of under-fifteens in general or only of *American* under-fifteens, since they watch more TV than their European and Asian counterparts.

The second e-mail is from Mac. Something pretty unreadable about his theory of liquid systems and the principle of anti-chaos, followed by a mention (backing up the anti-chaos theory) of . . . the Tribal Gathering! So *Mac* was at the Tribal Gathering after all.

But which one was he? Mind toggles back to everyone male and roughly my age. There weren't many. Beery bloke with a red neckerchief, tanned bloke with thinning hair, tall guy, somewhat beaky, wearing a baseball hat which might have read Trix or Trixy, a couple of long-haired dropped-out types, a guy in a suit (why?) . . . oh – wait – what about the incredibly attractive man with blue eyes and dark hair who asked me for the time while we were waiting in line for the big wheel. Yup, that's got to be him! That is Mac!

Damn! Now I'm trying to recall whether he was on his own. Perhaps he was in a group of five or six. I only remember the face of the blue-eyed dark-haired one though. Or do I? For instance, was it really blue eyes or were they actually hazel? Damn again! If I'd only asked him to come with me that day I'd know by now. I'd have proof, something to go on. Except, of course, that he might have said no. Humpf. I feel like a thwarted fifteen-year-old with an impossible crush. How ridiculous!

Then, suddenly, I'm on the phone, dialling Mac's number, *one banana two banana three banana four.* An engaged tone pips its way along the phone cable. Mac's online. I think about messaging him, but decide against it. It's as if he's suddenly grown a body, and only phoning will give me access to it. Press redial. Engaged again. My pulse is banging away like a drill. I know him so well it hurts, but the *nerves.* Who'd have thought it? A sudden panic.

What do I say? Rehearse a few lines. Press redial. What if I clam up? What if he clams up? I glue the phone to my ear, then lose track of myself in the bleat of the busy tone. I plug in the number once more, in case I've got it wrong, *one banana two banana*, and I'm thinking about the man with the dark hair (how dark was it?) when a voice on the line says:

'Hello?' A man's voice, soft as coconut milk.

'Mac?' My own voice replies, as if from a cloud up in the atmosphere somewhere. Very distant.

'Bloody Hell!' says Mac. He knows it's me. I guessed he would. He sounds squeaky all of a sudden. It makes me titter, involuntarily, and only to myself.

'Mac, I was there,' I begin, my rehearsal out the window. 'I was at the Tribal Gathering!' I sound totally zapped and absurd, but since the sound is emanating from a cloud, there's not a lot I can do about it.

A long, long pause follows. An uncanny pause. Then Mac says:

'I'm surprised. I wouldn't have thought it would be, like, your cup of tea.' The squeak is alternating with the coconut milk. *Tralala, tralala, one banana two banana.* A small panic sets in somewhere at the base of my brain, where the stomach controls are, then spreads into an orange blob behind my eyes. For chrissake stop counting bananas and *think*.

'What do you mean, not my cup of tea?' I say, though by now the sound emanating from the clouds is nothing like the one I've pictured in my head. It resembles someone talking into water and it's all slowed down, like a weird bit in a horror movie. I have a sudden urge to take the words back, so I add: 'Were you the one with the blue eyes and the dark hair at the big wheel?'

'Eh?' slips down the phone line. This is not so much an expression as a honk.

'Then what do you mean, not my cup of tea?' My voice appears to be ululating while attempting at the same time to sound calm. Like someone staring at a fish tank and talking into a helium balloon. On the other hand Mac appears to have found his stride. The coconut milk is back.

'Oh you know,' he says, smooth as sun, then with a tricky little tone. '"When I was a teenager, it was nuclear war . . . these days it's all animal rights and anti-racism and raving."' Oh no. He's quoting my words back to me! And misquoting at that! And making me sound like some awful retired brigadier. The humiliation! My throat begins to clot up and I have to grip both hands together to remind myself I'm still sitting in my room talking down the phone. Else I'd be thinking I was having some kind of bad dream. Somehow, I manage to gather my senses. A clear, calm vista opens up.

'Why the hell didn't you tell me you were . . .' I scan about for the word '. . . younger?'

'The Internet makes age, like, irrelevant,' replies Mac, the smug bastard.

The voice from the clouds has touched down in my throat, bringing with it a sour taste. He knew. He *knew*. And he had me for a greenie, a sap.

'How old are you anyway?'

The squeak returns. Mac says 'Nineteen.'

Shit.

'"My Generation",' adds Mac in what he supposes to be a teasing sort of voice, "*Saturday Night Fever*".

Right, that's it. Fuck him. Just fuck him.

'*Fuck you*.' Thwomp. Ping. The phone lands on the floor with a thump. I feel my eyes filling, but blink the stuff back in defiance and set my jaw against the world.

And then I log on. Breeze around in the Web for a while. Feel a little better. Check my mail to see if he's got round to apologizing yet, but he hasn't. Instead, another message from Nancy appears on the screen.

>Want to talk to you about something, sweetheart. Please phone.

I find myself irritated and gratified at the same time. I *always* pay for our transatlantic calls. This one turns out to be brief. I don't mention Mac. Nancy says a huge anti-Internet backlash is raging (raging is the word she uses) across America like bushfire. And more importantly, she's having a backlash all of her own. What are the chances of my coming to stay?

THAT WEEKEND

Spend a day weighing up my options, this time with a small and somewhat surprising twinge of regret at the idea of leaving England. Nancy is offering to pay half my fare. She says I don't have the full story. What a let down. I was just beginning to feel I had discovered it.

Still, when Daniel rings and I mention I'm heading back to America, the word feels as warm as ever. Free, wide, loveable America. So I guess I must have decided.

'Tops,' says Daniel, 'You can get me a T-shirt while you're there.'

'OK, but only if I remember.'

'With long sleeves and a patch pocket.'

'Right.' I make a mental note.

'In cool colours. Not, like, in school-uniform colours.'

I nod, disengaged, my mind set on America.

'Made by Fuct, Pervert or Alien Workshop.'

A thought interrupts the train. What are school-uniform colours anyway?

'Or X-Large,' adds Daniel.

'Daniel,' I blurt out, sounding like the brigadier again. 'What *is* it with you?'

'I guess I'm just a sad, fucked-up fashion victim,' says Daniel.

intermission

WIREDWORLD

Hey! This is a literary newsgroup! Were you all asleep at the back of the class when your teachers went through passive vs active, reflexive nouns, clauses and subclauses, subject and object? Did you fast forward through elementary spelling? Were you pitching baseballs when you should have been learning your tenses? C'mon, for chrissakes, Neal Stephenson is a great author, so if we're going to discuss him like the sensible, mature wireheads we are, then we can at least get our spelling right, OK? And, by the way, it's *Stephenson*, not Stevenson.

Bluesky

'...For I am nothing if not bard; and, not bard, I am nothing in truth...' PATRICIA KENNEALY 'The Hawk's Gray Feather'

>>>>>>>>>>>>>>>>>>>>>>>

Hi, Bluesky, I just read your posting on alt.fan.Stephenson. It rocks!! The newsgroup needs people like you to counteract all those dorky thirty-something deckjock types. Well, OK, so I'm a bit of a deckjock myself, but I do other things as well, like listen to cool bands and code cool stuff and I am *way* younger than 30.
Snow Crash rules!!
Kurt S. Westerburg

'Independence is the only gauge of human virtue and value. What a man is and makes of himself - not what he has or hasn't done for others.' AYN RAND

>>>>>>>>>>>>>>>>>>>>>

I'm not finished up with *Snow Crash* yet. But I like what I've read so far, actually. It's this whole amazing world!

Hey, thanks for e-mailing! :-)

Bluesky

'Life is worth living; life is beautiful. The crux of it is to realize the fulfillment of your personality.' ALFRED LEVITT

PS So, you're a coder, huh? Don't do much of that myself anymore, but I'll be taking a pascal course in senior year.

>>>>>>>>>>>>>>>>>>>>>

So where did you get to in *Snow Crash*? Wow, I've read that book so many times, I could recite it!

Kurt S. Westerburg

'Condense fact from the vapour of nuance.' NEAL STEPHENSON

>>>>>>>>>>>>>>>>>>>>>

I've got to the part where Hiro Protagonist is heading towards the Raft to rescue YT and Juanita. DON'T tell me how it ends up :-) Although, I've got a hunch that Hiro's gonna be OK, actually :-)

I'm signing off now. My mom says my modem keeps my kid sister awake. Oh, don't worry, I'm saving up for a stealthy one and then I'll be up all night on the boardz and my mom will *really* phreak out. :-)

Bluesky (aka Susan J. Durrant)

>>>>>>>>>>>>>>>>>>>>>

Here's how *Snow Crash* ends up ... Hiro gets YT out, but only just, because she's about to be consumed totally by this flesh-eating viral structure and when Hiro rescues her, she's

already lost her right arm and part of her lower leg. ONLY
JOKING :-)

My mom is totally against the time I spend online, but my dad
says it's OK, because I'm learning stuff for future use plus
my computer (486 Compaq, not Pentium, sob sob,
unfortunately) is in my bedroom, which is cool. By the way,
where have your sigs gone? They rocked!!!

Kurt S. Westerburg

'Condense fact from the vapour of nuance.' NEAL STEPHENSON

>>>>>>>>>>>>>>>>>>>>>>

Kurt. Sorry not to have e-mailed for some while. I had a crisis
with my boyfriend, actually. I mean, not to go into it, he's
gonna graduate this year (his name is Kevin in fact) and go to
Harvard or something, and he's getting 'this relationship is a big
deal' all over me. And I'm like, noooo way!! I'm not even
seventeen yet. So I guess he's my ex-boyfriend, which feels
weird.

Any case, I've been on the sexuality forum on MindVox and the
WELL and talked it through with some of my online friends,
how I don't believe in monogamy and all, which is good,
actually, because I think there's a consensus growing.

I just got Nine Inch Nails blasting out on my earphones, so my
mom doesn't complain, which she usually does. Totally cool.

Bluesky

>>>>>>>>>>>>>>>>>>>>>>

Nine Inch Nails!!! Don't get me started!!!:-) Pretty Hate
Machine is the best album in the universe right now.

Sorry about your ex. People can be sooo shitty.

Hey, I just realized, I live in a Burbclave!!! Like YT in *Snow
Crash*!! (Well, it's a suburb of Boston actually.)

Kurt Westerburg
'Call me Kurt.'

>>>>>>>>>>>>>>>>>>>>>>

For your information, I live in the West Village, NYC, in my
mom's place. I've lived there all my life, which is 17 years on
Monday two weeks away. My stepfather works for IBM, so he
brings home lots of cool stuff like beta testing chips and
software and my mom's a writer, and she doesn't know shit
about computers. I had to teach her how to use the Windows
environment! And she's going 'why can't I just stick with DOS'!
My father does some work for *Wired*, but mostly he's known
for his science fiction. My father and me are very alike. Which
is why I read Kennealy and Heinlein and even Stephenson,
actually. I love that stuff.

Bluesky

PS I guess I'm a little confused over all that nam-shub stuff
in *Snow Crash*. I just don't get it. OK, so call me a twinkie.

>>>>>>>>>>>>>>>>>>>>>>

The nam-shub is this original Babel thing, right? Like, before
the nam-shub, everyone in Sumer and the outlying lands spoke
one language. But this priest or god or whatever, Enki,
invented this nam-shub, which was like this Sumerian poem
about languages. The nam-shub was spread around by
Asherah, the original meme, and it made people unable to
understand each other's languages. Just like different
programming languages. Because language is just information,
like code, right?

So everyone understood each other, until the nam-shub came
along. Which was OK, except that there wasn't any momentum
for change. Everything was the same, so it was all static. The
nam-shub turned everything around, because it made people
unable to understand one another. People began to have

different words for things and that introduced differences between things, so the society wasn't static anymore.

And the original language was like machine code, which Stephenson equivalates (is that a word?) to the language of creation. 0s and 1s fracture the original static state of chaos or paradise or whatever and provide the algorithms that make civilization possible. Like laws and rules.

The Deuteronomists were the first heroes. They rationalized Judaism, by writing down its rules and regulations. It's as if they took all these programming languages and wrote operational manuals for them so that everyone could get hold of the manual for a particular programming language if they needed it. And their priests were the people who could see beyond the programming languages into the deep language, the language of creation. Machine code, 1s and 0s.

And so the priests, the people who really understood deep structure, like the deepest neurolinguistic paths, they were like ... hackers!

Kurt

>>>>>>>>>>>>>>>>>>>>>>>

Awesome!!!!

My ex finally decided not to stay friends, so now we avoid each other in the cafeteria at Hunter College. It's dumb.

I've got this job during the vacation, maybe, working at the Internet Café in the East Village showing people how to navigate round the Net. So I *should* be able to buy a 14.4 baud modem by the beginning of the fall! Which is good, cuz my mom's mad at me about the 'phone bills. I keep telling her, this is my *life*. This is part of who I *am*. I'm, like, hello? the Age of Information is upon us, Mom. She's just a typical old-time writer type, I guess.

I told my friend Greg about you. He's a totally nerdie but cool wirehead techie type who's really into Ayn Rand (whom I don't know yet, as such, but who I'm looking forward to reading about) and this weird industrial-type music stuff from Belgium. Apparently. So anyway, Greg says keep on hackin'!

Greg gave me a tape of the Prodigy and they totally rock.

Bluesky

>>>>>>>>>>>>>>>>>>>>>>

This is spooky! I bought The Prodigy last week. I don't believe in coincidentalists or e.s.p. or any of that bullshit 'cuz I'm an Objectivist, so it must be that we have two halves of the same brain or something! :-)

I was thinking about you last night, and wondering what you looked like, but I guess that's the point of the Net. I can like you just from what you say, even though I don't know what you look like.

Kurt

'Truth is the recognition of reality.' AYN RAND

>>>>>>>>>>>>>>>>>>>>>>

Smiles and Grins. Bluesky inflates own ego.

Bluesky

'To be able to defy a culture which states that "Thou shalt not touch this", and to defy that with one's own creative powers is ... the essence.' STEVEN LEVY

PS An Objectivist is someone who believes in Ayn Rand's philosophy, right?

>>>>>>>>>>>>>>>>>>>>>>

If your interested in Objectivism check out my web pages at http://www.utcp.edu~/westerburg

Hugs

Kurt

'A is A' AYN RAND

>>>>>>>>>>>>>>>>>>>>>

Neato!!! Tell me more!

Susan

PS Uh, maybe it was just a blooper, but you put 'your' instead of 'you're' a coupla times. Just pointin' it out!!

>>>>>>>>>>>>>>>>>>>>>

Yeah, so spelling ... what the heck?

Anyone who's into computers has to be into Ayn Rand because she's so logical. Complex sometimes, but always logical and rational.

1. Reality is objective. Denying it or trying to escape it (like so many lame people do, particularly collectivists and hippies) is hopeless. A is A.
2. Man's tool for survival is reason. It's his only way of perceiving reality, and his only guide for action.
3. Every man is an end in himself. In other words, you're (note spelling:-)) on your own in everything, and your life's main goal should be to achieve happiness for yourself.
4. The only rational and ideal economic system is capitalism.
5. Man is a hero. Altruism and collectivism tramples individuality.
You should read *The Fountainhead*, about this guy who doesn't give a shit. I guess he's an individualist, like Hiro Protagonist in *Snow Crash*, actually.

Hugs

Kurt

'The word "We" is as lime poured over men, which sets and

hardens to stone, and crushes all beneath it, and that which is white and that which is black are lost equally in the grey of it. It is the word by which the depraved steal the virtue of the good, by which the weak steal the might of the strong, by which the fools steal the wisdom of the sages.' AYN RAND'S *Anthem*

>>>>>>>>>>>>>>>>>>>>>

Kurtie - I'm so glad we met.

Hugs

Susan

>>>>>>>>>>>>>>>>>>>>>

Me too.

Smiles :-) :-) :-)

Hey! This weird thing happened to me. I was hanging out on MicroMUSE (which is an activity I haven't done for a long time, actually, and it's still as lame as when I last went there, except ...) and I got talking to this character who turned out to be your bud from Hunter, Greg. And he's into Nine Inch Nails!!! Why didn't ya tell me! :-)

At the risk of sounding a dweeb, I'm getting into classical music. There's this symphony called *The Planets*, which has like one node for every planet in the Solar System? Mars is the god of war so the music's kind of punky, and Uranus is eerie, like being in someone else's time warp or something. I guess when they find some more planets further out, the record company will have to put out a longer version. Or, like if there turned out to be aliens on the planets (which rationally there won't be).

Whoa!

Did you see that the Feds or whatever are trying to re-instate affirmative action? Jeez, that makes me mad. I mean it's so goddammed stupid, obviously!

All respect to the individual!

Greg is cool!

Kurt

>>>>>>>>>>>>>>>>>>>>>

Affirmative action sucks! We've gotta fight for our right to privacy and freedom of speech and so forth so that we don't live in a totalitarian regime like communism, blah, blah, etc. No, I believe it, really!!

Greg and I set up this club thing at school, and we're putting out this newsletter about freedom. It's only in dead tree format presently, but Greg wants it up on the Net too.

It's weird that we agree on so much and still we know so little about each other. Like, I was thinking, do you have any brothers and sisters? I have a younger brother, 11, who's a pain in the ass, actually, but I try to put up with him! What are your folks like? Is your dad a famous scientist? Most important, who have you got pinned up on the walls of your room?

Bluesky

>>>>>>>>>>>>>>>>>>>>>

My room is kinda neat, brag brag. At the centre is my Compaq 486. Well, it's not actually at the centre, it's in the left-hand corner as you walk in the door, but it's probably the most important thing in my life right now. (Apart from you, of course!!!:-)) I painted the walls black but my mom made me paint 'em blue again. My dad was cool about the black 'cuz he's an Objectivist too, but my mom is more kinda conventional about most things. He's not what you might call famous, my dad, but he's pretty famous round here, by the way.

I have the following poster art above the computer: Rocket Science poster advertisement for Loadstar: The Legend of Tully Bodine (way cool with this baby-alien humanoid thing that's got like a space station in its eyes)
Kurt Cobain ('cuz he's my namesake, tho' his music and values suck)
Cover of *Wired* issue 2.10, with Neal Stephenson on the front
Above my bed are:
Various supermodels blah
No Gray Areas: A is A poster from RIC Trading (Objectivist products etc)
PGP poster (encryption rules!!)
And some postcards from cool parts of the world, like Alaska and Moscow, from online pals.

Uh, that's probably about it for now. I'm trying to get a Bladerunner poster, with the Darryl Hannah replicant on, but it hasn't come yet.

I have an older sister who lives in Wisconsin, and a dog called Spike, who sleeps on my bed sometimes and, like, drools on the carpet. He's gross, barf!!!! Oh, I've got some technical stuff, like an old fax machine and a stack of old circuit boards, but I guess you don't wanna know about them!!!

Hugs

Kurt

PS Album Collection includes:
King Crimson
Soundtrack from Bladerunner
Pink Floyd
Kraftwerk
They Might be Giants
Soundtrack from Streetfighter (a lame film, but cool music)
Beastie Boys
Hole
Etc etc blah

>>>>>>>>>>>>>>>>>>>>>>>

My stepdad gave me a USRobotics 14.4 baud V.42 bis
faxmodem!!

Bladerunner is sooo cool.

We got our 'zine out! It looks great. Greg wrote a long article
about how the government is going to keep tabs on everyone
and maybe sell the information to megacorporations for
advertising (which wouldn't be so bad). I've got a couple of
pieces in about important concerns. Like what's gonna happen
when videophones come in and the whole thing about chips
being more valuable now than gold, pound for pound.

Anyway we're gonna try and burn our own CD-ROM e-zine next.
Greg knows this guy who's got mastering equipment, actually.

Your album collection is awesome. Except King Crimson, which
totally sucks. I don't have so many albums 'cuz music's only
been a recent influence on my life.

Truth is, I'm pretty pissed right now. My ex is, like, giving me
some hard time or other at school and I think my mom is going
nuts or similar. Well, she's like 'What are you doing, where are
you going, you're grounded,' all the time, and I'm like, 'Fuck you,
mom.' Latest thing: she's scared about me using the New York
subway in the middle of the day, even, but, it's like, mom, am I
a kid or what? Wakey wakey, OK?

I guess you never come to New York normally, Kurtie?

Love

Susan

PS I just noticed that I wrote your for you're, so I guess it's
easy to do when you feel like nothing matters. Not that that's
why you did it, necessarily :-)

>>>>>>>>>>>>>>>>>>>>>>

Susan - I just picked up a ticket for the bus from South Station,

Boston arriving at Penn Station, NYC at 2.45 p.m. approx on Saturday. It's OK if you don't wanna see me, but I think you might need my support right now.

Love

Kurt

>>>>>>>>>>>>>>>>>>>>>

A WEEK PASSES . . .

Kurt, you're overreacting, OK?

Susan

>>>>>>>>>>>>>>>>>>>>>

AND ANOTHER WEEK . . .

Kurt - I'm sorry but, you know, like I said before, as long as you're honest with someone that's enough, right? I mean, I just think you're overreacting.

Bluesky

>>>>>>>>>>>>>>>>>>>>>

I am NOT overreacting

Kurt S. Westerburg

>>>>>>>>>>>>>>>>>>>>>

OK, OK, so you're not overreacting. I just happened to think we valued the same things, OK? Simple error, OK? In any case, you and Trabbi were gettin' along just fine when Greg and I left. And, OK, so we were stoned, which didn't help actually, but, you know, we *had* this conversation already in e-mail. Exclusivity sucks, right? You have to create your own values!

~~Remember what Wynand says in *The Fountainhead*~~ 'Notice how they'll accept anything except a man who stands alone.

The independent man kills them because they don't exist within him and that's the only form of existence they know.' Or something like that.

You're so much better than that shitty frat-boy 'my date is my possession' stuff. C'mon Kurtie, I mean!

If you and Trab had, you know, got it together or whatever, I'd have been goddammed pleased for ya.

So are we buds now?

Bluesky

>>>>>>>>>>>>>>>>>>>>>>

OK, I guess I *was* being dweeby. Anyway, I had fun visiting with you guys, even if Greg did go and steal my dream date from under my nose (OK, OK, it's a JOKE!!!:-)).

I'm gonna be in Redwood, WA for a coupla weeks from tomorrow, staying with this hacker friend, whose phone line's being bugged by the Feds. He's, like, on his way to cracking some heavy code, so I won't be able to e-mail you, or even speak to you, actually. I'll try and tell you what it's all about when I get back. I probably shouldn't even have told ya that I'm gonna be in Redwood, on account of the security factor, but I trust you, so that's OK.

Kurt S. Westerburg

>>>>>>>>>>>>>>>>>>>>>

Kurt. I know you're away on this major deal, or whatever, but I'm writing so you'll get this when you get back.

Trabbi told me what you said about me.

Susan

>>>>>>>>>>>>>>>>>>>>>

I just came back and picked up your e-mail. I have no idea what this is all about. :-(

Kurt S. Westerburg

>>>>>>>>>>>>>>>>>>>>>

Kurt, I can't *believe* you. I mean, this is ridiculous, actually!
You invite yourself down to stay, which is OK, and so we get
on together and we both agree to be friends and it's no big
deal, and you don't even *know* what's going on with me
and Greg and you tell Trabbi all sorts of things.

Susan

>>>>>>>>>>>>>>>>>>>>>

Whatever Trabbi said is her responsibility. I believe in that
from my Objectivist principles, OK?

Kurt

>>>>>>>>>>>>>>>>>>>>>

What really got me, Kurt, was you told Trab I didn't know shit
about *Snow Crash* and I'd got all the Sumerian stuff mixed up,
and how it was embarrassing. Greg says THAT'S EMOTIONAL
ABUSE.
Plus you *still* mix up 'your' and 'you're' which is profoundly
lame.

And I don't even care that you're (sp.=correct) not answering
my e-mail, 'cuz I've put your e-mail address on my kill file,
so even if you try to send mail it won't get through.

Susan J. Durrant

'They'll accept anything except a man who stands alone.' AYN
RAND, *The Fountainhead*

PS So don't even think about replying. **EVER** OK?

iii: LOST IN SPACE

There she is again, hands on hips, her mid-blue dress hitched under her fingers, staring into the arrivals board. Her hair has the summer in it, and the eyes are far-off. She hasn't seen me.

I stand and wave. She turns my way and her face sheds all its anxiousness and shines out, smile blaring. How easy it is to forget a friendship until a small but familiar expression on the face of the friend reminds you of it. I stand there just beyond the customs hall with my bags slung about, smiling. Nancy grins back and for a long moment we remain fixed to our spots fifty feet apart, two rediscovered friends, stung with affection and wariness.

Sitting in the car as it bowls along 19th Avenue, I tell Nance that I really do feel like a new person. She wants to know if that's a good or a bad thing. You tell me, I say. She has the decency to laugh. I try to get her to talk about her backlash, but she won't. Wait till you're over the jetlag, she says.

We flap along the Golden Gate Bridge in silence again, stoked with happiness. At the Sausalito exit we swing off the freeway and pick up some fancy food and a bottle of white wine in Molly Stone's. It being August, the California hills are honey brown.

She has moved the bed in the spare room without disturbing the cobwebs. Some of her old books have gone, others have taken their place. Thoreau, I see, which is strange. You couldn't really call Nancy a transcendentalist.

I sleep for three hours, and then, in typical contradictory style, Nancy insists on dragging my lifeless jet-lagged body to a backlash cocktail party in Sausalito. Assorted high-tech types with spritzers discuss the true beauty of real life versus the quintessential futility of the chip. I drink too much, which is to say, I drink some and before long I'm so honked from flying and snatched sleep, I can barely stand. The only detail of the evening I remember was someone insisting the world's best computer programmers come from Iceland.

WEDNESDAY
Beelzebub's bandwidth

The *San Francisco Chronicle* reports on the opening of the new Center for Online Addiction (e-mail only). The day before a couple of the papers ran a piece on computer embezzlement and another on the proliferation of Nazi groups on the Net. The digital revolution which was God's Own Gift to America only a few months ago is now nothing less than the Bandwidth of Beelzebub. Nancy has a boxful of backlash clippings in her garage. Consider these horrifying possibilities: A lonely gun freak living with his mother lets loose a computer virus to prove to the world that Elvis is alive. A crazed Iranian crashes the world banking system and demands retribution for two thousand years of Western imperialism. Russian Mafiosi buy up all the bandwidth and use it to negotiate a deal for the entire nuclear arsenal of the Ukraine. The Feds, under the control of un-American forces, convert the infobahn into a giant surveillance system and start arresting any American citizen sending or receiving an e-mail containing the word 'freedom'. Nintendo turns out to be a plot to convert America's youth into a tribe of voiceless epsilons leaving Japan free to take over the world. Computers attain consciousness and decide to rebel. The maths behind UPC bar codes actually does spell 666 like the Christian fundamentalists say . . .

This is the Accelerated Age. Even America's dreams, the foundations of its nationhood, are icicles in summer now.

*   *   *

Nancy has taken the morning off work so we drive down to Strawberry Village for breakfast. I'm not sure how much of the backlash she believes, but it troubles her. Her eyes are preoccupied and distant, there is no longer a carefree swing in her step. 'When you were here before,' she says, turning the car into the bend around Strawberry Point, 'I said that the great thing about technology was that no one really knew how it would develop. I used to think that was fun. But now I don't. You know, computers are being put into every one of Canada's schools because the government thinks they raise educational standards, but at the same time the *Japanese* government has banned the use of computers for third graders and below because *Japanese* research shows kids who use computers very young don't develop language skills. I mean, what is going on? These are people's lives.' We park up by the deli and sit outside with coffee and some cream cheese and lox bagels.

Not much has changed in this abundant patch of Northern California since I was last here. The spring flowers have been replaced by brown bunch grass, the taqueria has abandoned its high-tech burrito special and a few more smart houses have gone up at Belvedere Point. And there's been a backlash. Of course. A backlash. But the air still smells of Marin, which is to say, gasoline and eucalyptus. And the deli still stocks cream cheese and lox and the people still go about their daily business.

'Infotech is worth too many dead presidents for the backlash to bite.' I say in answer to my friend and anxious not to submit to the general cynicism. 'Before we know it, it'll have given way to some new kind of affirmation . . . everyone really does want to believe we're on to something big and life-affirming. I know *I* do.'

Nancy finishes chewing a mouthful of bagel dough.

'I guess what's really changed is me.' She throws me an awkward look, as though confessing to a shameful secret. 'For all that hype about dispersion of power, and shifting identities and electronic anarchy, I've never quite been able to stop myself from thinking it's all just 1s and 0s. The same old binary stuff of haves and have-nots, blacks and whites, us and them, men and women. You know — and this is going to sound totally cornball — I sometimes wonder whether this weird fixation on the power of computers is some kind of attempt by the patriarchy to reimpose rationalism on a feminizing, arational world? A masculine response to the *fin-de-siècle* mood.'

We both giggle into our napkins. Nancy flips a piece of salmon gristle into the car park.

'How often have you thought about, you know, *kids* over the last few months?'

'Having them, you mean?'

She nods her head and gazes out into the middle distance. In truth, I've thought about kids a great deal but I haven't spent much time wondering about having any. Nancy's face betrays a flicker of disappointment, as though she'd anticipated one of those telepathic conversations women have together.

'The thing is,' says Nancy finally, '*I* don't really want a kid, my hormones do. What a bummer.'

Each catches the other's glance. We are suddenly stranded in deep water. That same haunted pain I recognized on Nancy's face a few months ago has drawn around her again. I struggle to change the subject.

'Oh my god,' I say, 'What if the digital revolution is just a re-run of *The Stepford Wives*?' We both adopt daytime TV grins.

'Computers,' continues Nancy, picking up the theme in a whipped cream voice, 'are really best left to boys, along with wood chopping and high finance.'

She pulls herself free of her introspective gloom. 'No, really, though. Suppose computers are just a way of making traditional female skills like communication and networking appear technical and masculine so men can assert their dominance over them.'

I'm reminded of my beautiful grey Apple Mac back home. A small bubble of homesickness makes its way across my stomach.

'I'm beginning to think it'll all turn out to be about money after all. Don't you? Money and hype.'

I have no answer to this.

'Well whatever happens they can't take baking and periods from us.'

Mac e-mails in the evening, late morning his time, to tell me it's raining in England. He says he's missing me even though we've never met. I don't reply.

THURSDAY

Late morning I turn east over Richmond Bridge and make my way through the poor industrial town of Richmond, close and regretted neighbour of Marin and the city of San Francisco, to Berkeley, liberal capital of the universe.

Nancy's friend Clare meets me as planned at an Italian place on University Avenue. We both order minestrone soup. Till last year Clare was a student at Berkeley High School, which was one of the first public schools in the country to use computers in the classroom, on account of its position in high-tech liberalsville. Clare now teaches a multimedia course at the school while she decides what to do with the rest of her life. Clare is eighteen and given to random assertions like most teenagers who are uncertain of the adult world but determined to stake their place in it. Clare will say, 'You can't possibly eat minestrone soup without parmesan,' sounding like a flustered fifties housewife and then she'll contradict herself. 'But what the hell do I know?'

'We had this teacher who made everyone sit on cushions.' She makes vengeful digs at her soup. 'He said there was no point learning about the National Debt and the Federal Reserve. He said the movie *Wall Street* covered everything you needed to know.' She waves a strand of frizzy hair from her face and sets her pallid features against the world. 'So he got us inventing utopias instead. It was viciously lame.' She stabs a pea in her soup bowl. 'He said utopia was Buddhist Economics. But when I asked him about Buddhist fascism he just got mad. *There's no such thing as Buddhist fascism.* I thought he was gonna cry.'

We stroll along Martin Luther King Boulevard towards the school. Most of the kids are back in class after the lunch break, but here and there a few drifters hang about.

'Those are the skateboarders' steps,' Clare points to where the drifters are slouching, 'that's where the cheerleaders hang out, and these are the black steps we're on now . . .' She leads me into the building through a corridor of graffiti, past kicked-in lockers, along walls strewn with teen art.

'It looks kind of downbeat,' I whisper.

Clare is genuinely amazed. 'Berkeley? On the scale of public schools, Berkeley High is, like, Bel Air.'

We reach the computer room just as her class is due to begin. A thin blonde girl is seated at a terminal in one corner of the room. In another corner, a wide-eyed boy is playing Doom. 'In this class,' declares Clare, sweeping in, 'the girls sit at the computers and do stuff and the guys talk about how much more they could do if they had better computers.'

'Right,' says the boy, looking up from his game, 'because we're white male pigs commanding the best machines and oppressing third world minorities.'

Clare raises her eyes to the ceiling. 'David is kinda oddball.'

David, delighted by his new-found menace, logs out of Doom and brings a 3-D graphic onto the screen.

'I'm doing this multimedia project thing,' he shouts, not caring to wait for introductions, 'where there's this community of tele-pathic mushrooms, and each mushroom only has one thought, and they're in telepathic communication with each other. And anyway, every time the mushrooms communicate new ideas spring out in colourful abundance in the form of mushroom spores. And then new thoughts develop into mushrooms. And it's this metaphor for the brain as this symbiotic fungus with mushrooms coming from outer space and our ancestors eating them and evolving.'

A low groan emanates from the opposing corner of the room.

'See,' continues David, oblivious to everything but the thrill of being himself, 'we got used to thinking each of our neurones think their independent thoughts, but they're actually probably just part of this huge mind thing. Every time you have a thought it's like new universes are created and there's an infinite number of universes bifurcating and it's a Tesla . . . tessellation and even a minuscule point in the universe is a thought and . . .'

'That's completely illogical.' Clare lifts her eyes from the UC Santa Cruz application form she's begun filling in.

'Well, perhaps it's not a tessellation, maybe it's a shape with an infinite number of angles which are all forty-two,' continues David, fiery-eyed.

'Maybe you shouldn't put so much trust in Douglas Adams,' adds Clare, returning to her application. 'You know most people worry about their place in society,' mentions Clare, as though adding to the general stock of wisdom. 'Whereas David just worries about his place in the food chain.'

I lean in to David's screen.

'How long d'it take you to do those mushroom thingies?'

'Oh god, don't ask.' David senses an opportunity to offload another little piece of his personality. 'But I don't care. I *love* my computer and I like to spend *time* with my computer and next to my computer I love my carnivorous plants and next to them I love my family.' Encouraged, he returns to his mushrooms and to some impenetrable half-cock theory about fungal fenestration which leaves me wondering why it is that all teen boys feel obliged to go through a fenestration phase, generally after a garrotting phase and before trepanning.

After a few minutes of David looning and no one listening he's bored.

'What do you know about psychology?' he turns to me for amusement.

'Very little, really,' I say.

'Because in my psychology class I discovered I'm this extroverted intuitive type and in the future only people like me who are on the intuitive side will be able to shift context fast and keep up.'

Oh God. This is all sounding so *now* and at the same time so eternally fifteen.

'I crave not to experience loss and therefore I crave permanence,' David begins again. 'I get happy when I make anything permanent, and I get scared and depressed when I realize that it's eventually going to be gone.' He sighs and returns to the glare of his telepathic mushrooms: '. . . like the mayflies, all these endless, endless days of school to prepare us for a job, and what's a job for? We're just empty vehicles of evolution which has no purpose other than to keep us alive so that we can be empty vehicles of evolution which has no purpose and the universe is an empty void but it isn't even a void because we can't picture it . . .' His voice begins to quaver with histrionic self-importance, '. . . because it's an emptiness too empty to even think of, yet our minds exist in it and project onto it the illusion of reality and . . .' he gropes towards his grand finale: '. . . and Kurt Cobain is *dead*. All he ever wanted to accomplish in life is gone. He's nowhere, the cognitive void. And I could have told him. I could have said: Hell is not a torture or a flame. Hell is an absence of thoughts.'

'Or an afternoon with David,' says Clare.

Not so long ago in the scope of human history, maybe four hundred years, fifteen-year-olds like David would have been leading armies of men into battle. That must be the explanation for all the fenestration and trepanning that went on back then.

Later, Nancy says: You see how pointless the whole thing is? It takes them four weeks to model a mushroom they could have painted in four seconds.

I say: But they're in love with the computer.

Nancy says: That's precisely why it's so scary.

SATURDAY

Nancy thinks there's no point in going to Muir Woods today because it'll be too crowded.

SUNDAY

The *Los Angeles Times* and *San Francisco Chronicle* are stuffed with features on cyberlove, cybersex, cyberfashion, cyberfun, cyberscare, cyberwork, cyberplay, cyberscene. *Onebananatwobananathreebananafour.* Nancy comes to the conclusion that the Information Age is nothing more than a media invention.

> *Oh no it isn't*
> *Oh yes it is*
> *Isn't*
> *Is*
> *Isn't*
> *Is too, is too, is too*

In the evening, we lounge along the sofa watching Aerosmith's first live Internet chat session on MTV.

Me (eating potato crisps): What would you do if your kid turned out to be a heavy metal fan?

Nancy (picking her toenail): Gee, that's a toughie.

Me (eating): Imagine. The clothes, the hairstyle, the lyrics.

Nancy (staring into space): I guess you'd put up with it for a while. I mean, it would be your kid, so you'd love it. But after a while I guess you'd have to sell it to an orphanage.

Me (picking my toenail): You can't sell kids, Nance.

Nancy (doing nothing in particular): Sweetheart, that's just where you're wrong.

Me (eating): OK, but you can't sell heavy metal fans, then. Who'd buy them?

Nancy (doing nothing): Good point.

Me (eating): On the other hand, there are some sick people out there.

Nancy (eating): Right.

The new gold rush

Nancy and I pick Clare up in Berkeley and head down to a meeting of the Northern California Multimedia Developers' Association. Within seconds of arriving, 'Guess who' appears to have forgotten her backlash and is busy folding into the crowd as sweet as sugar in meringue mix.

Clare and I make for the finger buffet.

'The thing about interactive multimedia,' says Clare, looking around at the demo disks of Myst and Peter Gabriel Interactive, 'is that it's viciously lame. All you ever do is pick one of two things, go down one of three roads.'

'You're right,' I add, plucking a chocolate-covered strawberry from its tray. 'I hadn't thought about that before.'

'Interactivity should mean, like, being able to contribute to the thing.' She inspects the canapés, spots a link.

'Like here with all this food. I can have a chocolate strawberry or a piece of pizza or, like, this viciously nasty-looking cheese-whiz thing here, but I can't go, oh, there aren't any hot dogs, let's make some.'

'Whereas on the World Wide Web, for example, you can put up anything, and make your own links.'

'Uh huh.'

'But then you have to compete for attention on the Web because it's so huge.'

'That doesn't bother my generation. We're used to competing for attention.' Clare stops to think. 'Then again . . .' she shrugs, '. . . what the hell do I know?'

We stand and chew cud until a man in a sports blazer wanders up to me with a predatory smile on his face.

'So what's your involvement in multimedia?' He draws a business card from his wallet. I inspect my shoes. Clare pops a strawberry.

'You're not with any company?' asks Blazer, looking confused. The business card disappears as fast as a fly on a frog's tongue.

I shake my head. 'You?' I return, but he's already gone.

'We are not worthy,' adds Clare from the sidelines.

The big question on everyone's mind is what's going to be the next big thing, the new money-spinner, tomorrow's motherlode. At the table, among the coats, in the women's toilets. 'So what's the next big thing?' There's a rush for reservations on the bandwagon, but no one wants to have to build it first.

Nancy drives us home, and we sit about with a bowl of chile chips watching *Letterman*. Nancy is in one of her strange, prickly moods again. 'It's *disgusting* the way the multimedia industry behaves as if it doesn't have a backstory,' she screams (a propos of nothing.) 'Disgusting and flaky.' Sensing a tortured tidal wave about to hit, Clare and I keep our eyes firmly on the TV but the wave hits all the same.

'Those people just don't want to take responsibility for the fact that they're machining the culture. The moment there's any criticism, it's like, "Well don't look at us, all we're doing is shipping plastic boxes with circuit boards inside." I'm sick of it.' And I suddenly find myself in the odd position of defending the very thing my friend once championed to me.

After *Letterman*, Nancy begins to sound more like her usual self. 'Oh, I just remembered,' she says, 'rumours are that the next president of Sony is going to be an Icelander. It's too weird.' We get to imagining how things will be when everyone's life is sponsored by corporations:

Hi, my name's Susan, and I'm brought to you by Cheerios.

Nice to meet you, Susan. Chuck here, but first a message from my sponsor.

Nancy reckons she'll be able to cut sponsorship deals with Häagen Dazs and DKNY, whereas I suppose I'll be stuck with

McDonald's and A&R frosty mug root beer. I must try to become more upmarket in my consumer orientation.

WEDNESDAY A.M.

Another message from Mac. I don't answer it. I'll let him sweat a little.

WEDNESDAY P.M.

On the other hand, what the hell?
>Hi Mac. San Francisco says hello.
    Can't quite bring myself to use the personal pronoun, though.

THURSDAY

I pick out an article from the clippings box about a young man called Adrian T who lost his memory in a car crash when he was sixteen. His dad invented a pager to remind Adrian what he should be doing and when. I make a note of his name in my notebook. Plans take root in my brain.

The backlash is back again. *Time* runs a cover story on cyber-porn, saying the Net is overrun with the stuff. There's the usual follow-up hullabaloo about paedophiles in the conservative broadsheets, while everyone on the WELL nervously defends the right to free speech and questions the research on which the *Time* article is based.

The way I see it, people don't mind kicking up a fuss about paedophiles so long as they belong to someone else. The moment it comes to being vigilant in their own families and among their own kind, the eyes close, the backs start to turn, the denials begin. Circuit boards make no real difference in the end.

FRIDAY

Nancy and I spend the evening formulating a constructive critique of *Wired* magazine, the mouthpiece of the electronic entrepreneur. It sucks says Nancy. It stinks. It's so smug its asshole smiles. Nancy's most pressing gripe is that the magazine does its best to make pan-global techno-capitalism and its unpleasant consequences look like some morally imperative crusade bravely undertaken by a bunch of hip dads and oversized boys on shiny motor-bikes . . .

Burn up the Infobahn, Kill the Competition, Do or Die, America or Asia: it's your choice. You wanna become just another piece of Roadkill out there on the Information Superhighway? You wanna?

The exercise sparks a rant from Nancy:

'Work more, be freer! Ha! Why do people swallow that crap? Behind all that nineties dreck about teamwork and office campuses and free exchange of information is the familiar bullshit routine of working your butt off for someone else's bottom line. The only really new thing is that no one has any job security any more.'

But what choice do we have?

Nancy doesn't know, and neither do I.

I tracked down Adrian T. Running through my mind was the possibility that computers might one day replace human memory altogether. I'd found another article in Nancy's clippings box about the Extropians, who believe they can become immortal simply by downloading the contents of their brains onto a computer. It made me think. Can computers ever actually capture the human memory? And what about human identity too? I wondered whether Adrian T, his memory banks full to sixteen and virtually empty thereafter, would be forever condemned to adolescence, hanging static and unchanged by experience.

The father, Larry T, gave me his son's phone number. I rang Adrian. He was on his way out so we arranged a time for me to call back but when I did he'd gone out again. I rang once more and he didn't seem to know who I was.

So I called the father back. I asked him about Adrian T's pager. He said it wasn't perfect but it was the first memory aid his son had actually been able to use. According to Larry T, people who've sustained brain injuries are so easily distracted they tend to lose themselves in the workings of their memory aids and forget what it was the memory aid was there to remind them to do. Since Adrian was dependent on taking his drugs at regular intervals, it was imperative that he not be allowed to forget. Shortly after his accident, he'd tried carrying a notebook about, but kept forgetting to look at it. Then he'd been given access to a computer messaging system, but lost himself in the maze of the keyboard. He'd been followed about by nurses, but found the dependence on other people depressing. What he needed, his father decided, was a prosthetic memory, a piece of technology so simple and unobtrusive that it would not distract him, yet so insistent he could not ignore it either.

Larry T invented the pager himself. It simply bleeps at pre-programmed intervals and leaves an alphanumeric message telling Adrian where to go next and how to get there, or when to take his medication. If Adrian doesn't ring in to let the control computer know he's understood the message, the pager bleeps him again. If he still doesn't ring in, the computer sends an alarm message to Adrian's nursing help.

The point about the pager, Larry said, was that Adrian trusted himself to respond to it, he trusted it more than he trusted his own damaged memory, and as a result of that, he had come to trust himself to rely upon it. What had been so difficult for him was not so much that he forgot things, but that he was unpredictable and couldn't rely on himself. Unlike the rest of us, who can and do simply block out the sense of our own inner chaos by picking and choosing from our remembrances of things, Adrian T was never able to escape his own white noise. What Adrian T could do was turn to his pager, not as a substitute for memory, but as a still voice in the scrambled energy of his mind.

SATURDAY

A whole day spent cataloguing Nancy's technological grievances:

1. The WELL is no better than Battletech – banality lurking beneath a series of complicated-sounding rules devised for the sole purpose of deceiving people into thinking they have a community.
2. Far from being a medium for equality, the Internet merely allows a certain sort of type-A white male to get away with reasserting his economic and cultural dominance.
3. Virtual communities are actually nothing more than self-serving common interest groups (see also 1 above).
4. Everyone is equal on the Net, but some are more equal than others. There are as many undeserving celebrities online as there are in real life.
5. Internet culture has become a parody of itself, an excuse for aspirational consumption. Icon Byte, bleah! Cyberpunk, bleah! Hacking, bleah!

Ho hum.

SUNDAY

Tramping from Muir Woods up onto the plateau, where the tourists don't go, we hit a patch of low-lying cloud and, a little further on, burst out into the clear air above. On a good day Drake Beach, where Francis Drake landed the *Golden Hind*, is visible to the north, but today is not a good day. Our notch on the cross-section of the redwood tree marking the beginnings of the Digital Age has been worn away by busy hands and rain.

Nancy pounces on this as though it were some kind of symbol for the futility of technology in the face of nature.

'Nothing is as bad as you're painting it,' I moan, in an effort to comfort her. (Frankly, I'm beginning to find her pronouncements pretty hard to take.) 'We're simply living in very uncertain times. Mac says . . .'

'Oh,' replies Nancy, as though suddenly enlightened, 'Well, if *Mac* says . . .'

I ignore the jibe.

'Mac says insecurity is part of the post-human condition.'

'What's so damned post-human about that?' asks Nancy. She has a point.

Back home we are out on the deck watching the city disappear into the night when Nancy announces that she finds my continued optimism about the Internet an offence to reality (her words). Not to be outdone I accuse her of exaggeration and drama queening (my words), she hits the roof and wishes I'd never come, at which I let *her* know the feeling is quite mutual, thank you, whereupon she launches into a tirade about my crass attachment to America as a symbol of hope, and to technology as a symbol of America.

'*And* you only seem interested in kids for what you think they say about the future,' she continues, twisting the knife. 'It's so self-serving.'

TUESDAY
Anti-matter Berkeley

Nancy and I have called a fragile sort of truce by renouncing all verbal violence and patching everything together with some wheedling good humour. Aside from one difficult moment over breakfast, when Nancy demanded we 'talk everything through', and I clammed up like a barnacle, we are managing to rumble along in a friendly manner.

We are walking across the parking lot at Paly High School, or the Geek Pod, as Nancy refers to her alma mater, taking in the smell of Cyprus resin and wondering if there are any natural odours that have not yet been incorporated into a product. Nancy suggests cut grass, I suggest horse manure. Nancy: ice. Me: cat's piss. Nancy: burning peat. Me: rotting corpses.

Nancy has taken the day off work to have lunch with her mother, who is recovering from a minor operation of some sort, and she's suggested I visit the computer labs at Paly High, one of the most fertile breeding grounds for Silicon Valley on the planet.

Reaching Palo Alto earlier than Nancy expected, we drive along University Boulevard past strip malls set with frozen gourmet yoghurt stores and kooky-decor mocha java joints, past chintzy boutiques, past palaces of electronic appetizers and silicon snacks, past the columnar offices of patrician physicians, past the lean-looking stripes of infotech HQ lawns, past sago palms and planted flagpoles mulched in cedar chips, past menus du jour typed in *monotype corsiva*, past children's nurseries, shrinks and gourmet pet-food stores. Nancy's parents were something big in technology in the early days, and she spent much of her childhood in Palo Alto, home of Stanford University, Hewlett Packard, Xerox, IBM. She has it that the average Palo Altan is white, fit, owns at least one car, works at the university, or in high tech, has above average IQ and buses in a Latino maid. According to Nancy, if anyone has pulled off the American dream, it's the Palo Altans.

We leave the car in the lot, cross over the street and find a café at the Town and Country Mall, where we sip tea beside two women practising their French.

'*Je voudrais aller à Paris avec Ken le printemps prochaine.*'

'*Ooo, bon. Comment il va, Ken? Judy, que tu pense – ce bagel-ci, c'est un peu ancien, n'est-ce pas? Il faut prendre un autre, je crois.*'

Outside again the air smells of whatever it is they use to flavour the crust on doughnuts, and gourmet coffee.

'Palo Alto,' declares my friend, 'Is a sort of anti-matter Berkeley.'

The computer lab at Paly High is divided off at one end of the engineering workshop with partitions. Two rows of identical CPUs run in a line down to two naked walls, with office-style workstation separators and identical workstation swivel chairs. Pinned up over some of the separators are a series of technical drawings and computer-aided industrial designs. Way overhead run the air-conditioning tubes and vents for the workshop next door, and a stifling corporate fug clings to the slabby walls.

Four boys are working through their lunch break. We make the necessary introductions, which is to say, I ask if it's OK to sit in and watch, and receive four shrugs by way of response.

The following conversation takes place:

Rob (to Marc): 'Have you transferred the video?'

Marc: 'Uh huh, to AVI flc format.'

Rob: 'Run Photomorph to windows.'

Marc: 'I think I got it going.'

Rob: 'What d'you capture?'

Louis: 'Is this LST OK?'

Marc: 'I left C3K here.'

Rob: 'Did you do the full spread or just part?'

Louis: 'Off the TV?'

Marc: 'Yeah, but I haven't checked it yet.'

Rob: 'Open her up, then.'

Marc clicks on a file icon and a crudely pixellated video grab recorded from the TV appears. An advertisement for sanitary towels. Louis screams:

'MOVE TO ORCHID VIDEOLA, *NOW*. GO, GO, GO, *RIGHT NOW*. JUST KILL IT.' He lunges for the keyboard and jabs at the escape key.

'Shit,' says Rob, 'We crashed.'

I suggest the manual.

'We don't use manuals,' says Marc.

'Let me at it.' This from Louis in commanding tone. 'I'll play with it, figure it out, and then I'll play with it a bit more, and then I'll get bored.'

'Cool,' replies Marc with new-found deference.

Marc is the student head of the lab as it turns out. 'It looks good on college applications.' He is currently applying to Berkeley to major in computer science. The way he sees it, 'You can be a really good student, get amazing grades, a good SAT score, make yourself look good by doing lots of extracurricular activities and still not get into college. Listen, I'm not looking to be a millionaire, but with all the competition in this area these days, I don't wanna end up a bum. People who graduate from Berkeley have a higher starting salary. It's a statistic.'

The mood on the journey back to San Francisco is bleak. I make a few attempts to lighten it. Nancy doesn't respond. Eventually, I grow bored with the sound of my own voice and we continue on in silence. Just before San Carlos we hit some late rush-hour traffic and the freeway seizes up. Four lanes of vehicles, the light from a thousand headlamps seeping into the blacktop and draining out of the sky. Nancy reaches for the radio, tunes into a country and western station. We bump forward, one pedal's worth of accelerator, one pedal of brake, Nancy's blue-lined ballet pumps creasing on the rise and fall.

I'm calculating the amount of money represented by the Silicon Valley executives stuck in traffic. Nancy pulls the car off at an exit and draws up outside a drive-thru McDonald's.

'Apple pie?' she says.

'I think I can eat two.'

'Times four then,' she says in a conciliatory tone, while what remains of the tension between us drifts off unwanted into the dark.

WEDNESDAY

Cyberporn stories fill the newspapers again. Swarming paedophiles put kiddies in peril! Hard-core porn proliferates! Electronic Frontier Foundation evokes First Amendment for filth! Mom – is your son a computer crotch potato?

You actually have to seek out porn on the Web. It doesn't drop into your modem by accident. On the other hand, it isn't exactly what you'd call hard to find. Less than five minutes after booting up Nancy's machine today, for example, I'm already logging on to Romad's 'Nudes of the Week' and from there to Italian *Playboy*. A picture uploads while I take a pee and brew myself some coffee and return to discover half a nipple on the screen. I click on reload and the web browser software hangs and logs me out.

I log back in again, find myself a link to Hotsex: the Pictures. A message hits the screen. 'Your client does not have permission to get the URL from this server.' So instead I select a link to a site called the World Wide Wank. A wait of thirty seconds, followed by the message: "Sorry, there are too many anonymous ftp users on this machine right now." Back to the list of links. The Sportsmen's Lounge offers me a picture of Sarah in JPEG or GIF versions. Click on JPEG. Sarah takes twelve minutes to download, and turns out to be a cowgirl in frilly pink gingham lounging across a pink bed. So I return to the Sportsmen's Lounge page, which asks me if I'm ready for some live action video. I move the mouse over to the yes bar, click twice. The page reloads with the message: 'You must have your mastercard/visa number ready to subscribe. Your number may be accessible to others.' Ha! Curious I *am*, but *insane* no.

And so it goes on. I click back to the World Wide Wank, get the busy message again, click ahead to Apocalypse Twat Shots and the legend 'Due to the excessive amount of request and the burden it has been putting on the server, this page has been discontinued. University of Michigan Computer-Aided Engineering Network.' Click on and on. Fetch up at Bizarre Jap Links, click on to graphic of a Japanese woman dressed as a French maid, along with three choice bars: Party Girl, Ancient Japan and Secretary, each of which leads back to the same invisible portrait. After twenty minutes of this listless titillation, my breath has levelled into shallow gulps and I'm flipping through the Web like a possessed thing, clicking from picture to picture, site to site, country to country, promise to promise, hardly waiting to download. Undaunted and excited, clicking on regardless.

A link to the University of Bordeaux pulls up a picture of a woman in a zipped-down bell-bottomed catsuit and priestly dog-collar, and a line of text in gothic letters reading: 'Maybe she is searching for God through mortification', with a link to further pictures. Catholics. Click. On I move, one half completed image leading onto another, aroused by nothing so much as the restless sampling of the Web itself, miniature excitement built upon miniature excitement in a stream of anticipation, each click a grain of expectation in a sandstorm of promises.

In nearly an hour I've seen nothing even remotely shocking, and am drawn to the comforting conclusion that the cyberporn scandal is just another piece of hype.

On the other hand, it takes Nancy precisely ten minutes to locate two text files on the theme of 'child's play' and a Japanese picture of a woman bound up with a dog.

'It's all there, but you have to know where to look,' she says, eyes betraying that new-found cynicism. I'd like to ask her how she discovered the places to go, but I'm too afraid of what the answer might be.

For the first time I begin to find myself looking forward to leaving California.

THE LAST WEEKEND
Bright lights in the distance and the Projects up close

I parked the car in the lot at Santa Monica Beach, walked down to the shore and scanned the bay to where I imagined Catalina Island lay. When I was seventeen and Nancy was nineteen we took a boat trip out there. Someone on the boat caught a fish, and left it to flap itself into oblivion on the deck. I watched it writhing about, gulping at the air, its mouth contorted into a desperate trumpet shape. I tried not to look, but it was morbidly fascinating. I saw myself submerged in a tank of water, knocking madly on the glass to try to attract attention, a beam of panic illuminating the eyes so that they glowed like colonies of phosphorescent plankton. I really wanted to relieve the fish of its death throes once and for all or sling it back into the sea, but I didn't have the courage. Instead I watched it die, listening for the clicking of the lips and the peel of slime when the trumpet mouth gaped open, begging for water. It took a long time to give up its struggle. Once it was exhausted from the flapping, it lay still, popping its mouth and heaving the silver cover which protected its gills. Every so often, it would jerk as if electrocuted. Eventually, the trumpet grew smaller, and the lips ceased to move, but the thing was still alive, and merely biding its time until the last impulse along the nerves, the ultimate breath and who knows, maybe the final thought. (Fish might have them – why not?) When the fisherman picked it up from the deck at the end of the trip, its tail moved once as if in protest at the man's intrusion in the process of its extinction, then it lapsed and fell limp in his hand.

After that, I gave up meat for a while, and although I took it up again more recently, I've never been able to solve the equation: one whole life = one night's supper to anything approaching my own satisfaction.

The sea was livid blue on Friday and very still, rumpling only where it pushed up onto the sand. In spite of its being midsummer, a coolish breeze rustled along, and the beach was nearly deserted. A team of rollerbladers zoomed by the concrete walkway a little further up near to Ocean Boulevard, and someone's dog shook itself free of sea water. A few couples tagged along, hand in hand. Some lights went on along the pier.

Later, I drove up the tiny asphalt capillaries linking the villas in the hills above Bel Air, found myself a viewing point and parked the car. Los Angeles lay below, a huge circuit board of blinking lights turning blue from smog and the disappearing sun. It being a Friday, the twelve-lane freeways were clogged with vehicles filled with people leaving the city for the weekend. I thought about those friends of Nancy's I met at Venice Beach on my first trip out to California. How beautiful they seemed – tall, tanned, lean, and with a sort of casual languor in their bodies brought about in part by the superfluity of money and in part by the lusciousness of the climate. They made me feel so dwarfed and lumpy. My skin was blotchy, theirs luminescent with tan; in contrast to their long and sheeny skeins, my hair was short and scraggy. Their college work was undemanding, their parents uncensoring, their lifestyle careless. They had cars, money, leisure, sex, promise. They played in packs and they always had a date. They seemed so adult it embarrassed me to realize how tied up in childhood I remained. They fitted in, somehow, and they were never on their own.

To me at seventeen and often enough thereafter, California and Californians stood for the two things Britain lost a hundred years ago. Modernity and abundance.

I wanted to believe all sorts of things. That LA was home to surfing and movies and everything fun; that the grey mist was really coastal cloud; that tuna salad was an aid to slimming; that palm trees and backyard swimming pools were indigenous and everybody had them. I thought that any city with so much sun and bougainvillaea and barbecues must be benign and happy. I thought that the sunsets were beautiful enough to live for and that anyone in the city of Los Angeles who wanted something really badly could get it.

Over the years I was forced to make minor adjustments to my views. I accepted that the grey mist really was smog, and that the bus service was as poor as the people who were forced to use it. I realized that the gates surrounding suburban villas were there not to keep the owner's pets in, but to keep other people out. I learned that certain districts, roads, blocks, freeways were considered no-go zones, that not everyone had a yard pool and that tuna salad was full of fatty mayonnaise. The suburbs were dull (though writhing underneath) and you could get bored of the movies pretty quickly. I began to wise up to the bland, listless, uncommitted conformity of much of white Southern Californian culture.

But the point was – *is* – this: I don't always care about the reality. Nancy is right. I *do* love America as a set of symbols, symbols to which I'm so welded that a white-hot blowtorch wouldn't prise me from them. And yes, I know the whole truth, but I'm only in thrall to a part of it. The rest I have chosen to put aside. So what if the suburbs are bland, there are suburbs everywhere, and they are worse. Bland, relentless, intolerable, impoverished. Try Paris beyond the *périphérique*, try Prague outside the tourist zone, try Moscow, try Budapest. So what if the smog is bad; go to Mexico City, Rio de Janeiro, Rome, you'll come back thinking LA smells of roses. Sure, Lalaland is superficial. Ever been to Monte Carlo? Neurotic. How about Beijing? The freeways clogged. Try London on a Friday afternoon. There are riots on the streets; Liberia, Rwanda, Northern Ireland are more deadly. Drugs? Try Bogota, Hong Kong or Glasgow. Homelessness? Visit Sao Paolo. Racism? Everywhere. And what if it *is* true that the West is an imagining and Los Angeles only that imagining's burned out city-soul? What if?

> The owl and the pussycat went to sea
> In a beautiful pea green boat,
> They took some money and plenty of honey
> Wrapped up in a five-pound note

A breeze ran through Bel-Air and began to shake the car aerial, then ceased as suddenly as it had arrived. Maybe, I thought, the grass is always greener, even in the desert.

For some reason, standing at that spot above Los Angeles, I felt the need to defend myself both from my own cynicism and from Nancy's. The doubt was stifling. It wrestled with my fantasies, but it didn't defeat them. I still wanted my dreams to remain intact. They serve me, but they don't cloud my view. I know the truth. But is loving a symbol so bad? Why run from what is resonant? When I first arrived in California I was in freefall, not yet landed on adult ground. Seventeen. Everything still seemed epic and big with meaning. And if California came to symbolize all that was sunny and hopeful and promising to me, then it also gave me the courage as I tumbled out of childhood not to fear what lay below. Here in California I lost that dread fear of growing up and growing old.

Technology is ridden through with fantasies and projections too. Take the fantasy world of vast, benign agri-business, of commuter jet pods, silver suits, perfect, instantaneous communication and ballooning leisure, and take the actual lived world of technologized warfare, of mad cow disease and gene-spliced tomatoes, of machine-generated downsizing, redundancy and unemployment. Looking out over Los Angeles, is it clear to me now what's at stake. Here I am, teetering on the blade's edge between dreams and the world. Between the bright lights in the distance and the Project towers close-up.

That was what was on my mind on Friday.

Saturday, I woke early and called Isaac, who runs the kids conference on the WELL. His mother gave me directions to Orange County, and by mid-morning I found myself driving along by the ocean and up into the suburban streets of Long Beach.

Isaac is fourteen. He has his own phone line with call-waiting, a pager, an up-to-date computer and a high-speed modem. His family are not wealthy. They are middle-class, middle-income Californians.

His mother Dee fixed me an iced tea and told me how Isaac came to be. She'd found herself pregnant while still a student, and faced with the prospect of an abortion or single motherhood, chose the latter. Her decision was in part determined by an advertisement she saw inviting pregnant women to come to live on the Farm, a hippie community resident in southern Tennessee. You could have your baby at the Farm, it would be looked after by the collective, and in return you would be asked to do a share of farm work. So Dee had Isaac on the Farm. Many years later, an old friend from the Farm days introduced her to the WELL, and she joined up hoping to regain something of the spirit of her former community. She waited a year and then signed Isaac on. 'He's real clever but age-appropriate too.'

Within a few months of being on the WELL, Isaac had already made a name for himself, and was invited to set up an on-going electronic conference for kids. He's now one of the WELL's personalities, not quite a fully-formed WELL god, but a kind of trainee god nonetheless.

But Isaac was keen on computers long before the WELL. He first got into the local bulletin-board scene at eleven, phoning into a computer owned by a guy called French who lived in LA county.

'It was just a bunch of teenagers getting together and forming their little cliques and having their little holy wars against each other.' He was sitting at his desk, fingering his keyboard. I was sitting on his bed. Like Daniel, he was small for his age. The computer made him appear bigger. At least, it seemed that way to me.

'A lot of kids at my school are just getting involved with bulletin boards and they think they're hot stuff but they're doing things I did two years ago. The dynamic of power is pretty pathetic. You make friends with some guy called something like Acid Hacker, who gives you the number of a pirate board and then you have to rack up as many pirated games files as you can so you get more points with other people, who'll maybe give you numbers for other bulletin boards. It's mostly kids taking advantage of new people by saying they'll be their friend if they do something. One of my friends called Egypt twice a week to pick up pirate files for his pals. It's pathetic.'

The phone rang, Isaac checked the number on the caller ID screen.

'I'll let the machine pick that up.' He considers his position in the world. 'A lot of people my age are pretty shallow when it comes down to it, and I like to feel that I operate on somewhat different level. But on the other hand, I'm a popular person, not the socially outcast person a stereotypical computer wizard might be.'

Something occurred to him. He opened a drawer in his desk and took out a pile of cards.

'My business card. I had five hundred made at Kinko's.'

I took five. He said I could pass them on to anyone else I might meet. The card gave Isaac's full name, phone, fax and pager numbers, a PO box, and a couple of e-mail addresses.

'At the point I had them printed, my Web site sucked, so I don't have my Web address on there.' He took one of the cards back, wrote down a Web address in red felt pen. I said I'd put the cards in my purse for safekeeping, but he didn't want that. He wanted them passed on.

The pager bleeped. Isaac checked the alphanumeric message, made a mental note to call back later, checked on his notional list of points, retrieved one and output it thus:

'I took the Washington pre-college test which is the SAT equivalent for early admission to Cal State University in LA. You had to score 1000, and I scored 1150. But I decided not to go. The Cal State campus is quite a downer. With my score I could do a similar programme in any college I wanted, but I've decided to go to high school instead.

'Meantime, I've set up a consultancy for businesses wanting to advertise themselves or their products on the Web.

'I always say to the businesses I've helped to get on the Internet, you should make some area of your Web site that's devoid of business. An archive, something that gives back to the community.

That's what I advise my clients, but you can't make them take note, can you?'

'I don't know, Isaac,' I replied more sourly than I ought. 'I don't have any clients.'

The phone rang again. Isaac closed his eyes, waited for the answerphone to pick up the call. The moment he recognized the voice on the line, he allowed himself to relax, and started off on a series of projections about his future as a Web consultant, computer lawyer, software entrepreneur, electronic freedom lobbyist. His thoughts on freedom of speech on the Internet, some arguments about the degree of commercialization the Internet community should tolerate, a couple of pointers on teaching kids electronic responsibility. It suddenly seemed perfectly natural for a fourteen-year old boy to make the round trip from LA to San Francisco on a last-minute business matter. But that didn't make it any more comfortable, not a bit.

Driving back up from Long Beach along the Ocean to Santa Monica, it occurred to me that the success of the technological revolution may well be measured by the number of Isaacs it produces, and the moment the thought entered my mind I heard myself give an involuntary sigh.

MONDAY

The WELL is hacked! Arch hacker Kevin Mitnick cracked the WELL's security and supposedly, allegedly, conceivably, stole some files. Nancy returns from work via the WELL's offices on the waterfront in Sausalito replete with rumour, counter-rumour, speculation. Press photographers and journalists are queuing up outside, she says, and the phone lines are permanently engaged.

The break-in makes the late afternoon *and* prime-time news bulletins. Mitnick is nowhere to be found, having gone into hiding after his last major hack. Wanted by the FBI. A special team is set up to hunt him down across the wires. Meanwhile, a sense of outrage prevails at the WELL. Some members resolve to set up a volunteer Emergency Response Team. Important postings pass to and fro. Vital announcements are made. WELL gods are wheeled out to spout. All the signs are that it'll be a front-page story in the *New York Times* tomorrow.

Nancy and I spend most of the evening fielding calls from fellow WELL members and cancelling her credit cards. Aside from the folk making the vital announcements, no one seems really to know what is going on. There are rumours of stolen credit card numbers and breaches of confidential information.

Nancy is absolutely in her element. She loves the episode's excitement, she's enchanted by the gossip, the attention. She's thrilled to be part of something deemed worth hacking.

And I am left trying to stave off the cynical thought that there's nothing so good as a disaster to hold a backlash at bay.

TUESDAY

The story does make it to the front page of *The New York Times*.

Late in the day, it emerges that Mitnick didn't take anything much worth having at the WELL, so Nancy and I pass what is to be my final evening in California trying to persuade the banks, stores, mail-order firms and credit companies to reinstate her credit cards.

BOSTON, MASSACHUSETTS, WEDNESDAY (JUST OVER A WEEK LATER)

The Anxiety Closet

A smell of burnt metal rises from the tracks as the train pulls into Boston South Station. I've drawn a thousand doodles since the train left New York. Hundreds of black triangles enclosed by squares within circles, the spaces between densely packed with knots and whorls of highlighter pen. A circle dominates the top right corner, leaving the remainder of the page blank. Elsewhere doodles fall off the edges of the paper while the centre is left untouched.

At school I always flunked those parts of IQ and other tests which demanded neat sequential thinking. I don't think it was because I couldn't do them though that might actually have been the case. I think it was just that I found them profoundly pointless.

$$\triangle, \square, \bigcirc, \text{ therefore} \ldots$$
$$12, 34, 67, \text{ therefore} \ldots$$

Therefore . . . what? Therefore . . . so what? Therefore, therefore, therefore. Therefore the process of a process. Dot, dot, dot. Therefore *onebananatwobananathreebananafour*.

It's rush hour on the subway in Boston. I'm forty-five minutes late and in a lather by the time I arrive at Mary Chung's Chinese Restaurant on Massachusetts Avenue. A place is found for me at the end of the table. Chinese food is a tradition among Massachusetts Institute of Technology computer science majors stretching back to the fifties. Steven Levy devotes whole sections of his geek history, *Hackers*, to the early outings of MIT wireheads in Chinese restaurants. Forty years on, Chinese food is still the comp-sci cuisine of choice.

All but one of those seated at the comp-sci table are young, male, and fully representative of the spectrum of geek aesthetics, which is to say they are either stick thin or fabulously obese, squat or tall as totem poles, butt-bald or covered in under-developed furze. Rudimentary introductions are made. I make an attempt at a conversational opener with a woman sitting next to me but she merely looks into her plate and giggles. The man sitting next to her, who has been introduced to me as Andri, leans over and adds his piece to the failed conversation: 'Well, if you're so hungry, why don't you go ahead and order?' So I flag down a waitress and ask for a menu and Andri leans over past the woman eating chilli pork again and says:

'Sippies don't call it the menu, we call it the operational protocol.'

I just say: 'Ha, well, I'm not a Sippie!'

Sippie is the phonetic tag of convenience for SIPB, the Student Information Processing Board, the core of MIT geeks and wireheads, and the Chinese meal is a prologue to SIPB's monthly meeting. Andri explains in most careful terms that, in general, Sippies order in pairs, but hold certain dishes, such as rice and fortune cookies, in common. I order hot and sour soup and a plate of egg-fried rice.

'I, for example', declares Andri, 'am eating half this plate of beef and straw mushrooms before swapping it with Rob sitting opposite for half a plate of Shanghai Chicken.'

'Admirable,' I say, 'but I don't have a partner. So I'm stuck. I'm the odd man out.'

'That would seem to be the case,' adds Rob, pouring me some jasmine tea. And in that moment, the figures around the table make an unconscious species decision to pretend I'm no longer there. A pearl closes around the irritant.

Someone distant says:

'Of course, we could put a power conditioner on the UPS power switch.'

'Did you test the UPS source?' This is from Ken, occupant of the Jesus position on the long table at Mary Chung's.

'We can't simulate that.' Some younger man's voice, a face I can't see.

Ken takes a long lug of tap water to ward off the heat, crushes the ice between his molars.

'Simple. You put a surge protector between the UPS and the wall and a power conditioner on the output.'

'Hey, guys.' Andri changes the subject, 'I have a proposition.'

The table quiets itself in anxious anticipation.

'We have ninety public access terminals at MIT. Through these slave terminals the whole of MIT talks to itself and to the outside world. So, this is my proposition: they should be named.'

This appears to cause quite a stir. The Sippies mumble, speculate, cogitate, consider, confer.

'In clusters,' interjects the woman next to me excitedly.

'Certainly in sequence,' says another.

'Grouped both vertically and on the horizontal.'

'Clearly,' adds Rob, 'from a rational point of view they should be assigned serial numbers, but that would be unmemorable, perhaps even unworkable in practice.'

Andri helps himself to some tea. 'From a resonant point of view,' he lifts a slim, long-nailed finger, 'would it not make more sense to assign serial *names*, organized *thematically*.'

'Exactly. The horizontal and the vertical.'

'That could be done,' says Rob, fingering the facial hair, 'in the place where most of the nodes meet.'

'My point was that where two or three machines were clustered, their names should be clustered also,' adds the woman.

'By departments,' says Andri tentatively.

'So, in fact, the physics cluster could be named after physicists, there'd be an astro-cluster and so forth.'

'A 38 cluster, hell, a 2 cluster, why not?'

'So people could be immortalized by being like a node in the public cluster.'

I continue to shovel hot-and-sour soup from bowl to bowel.

'But we should probably stay away from current faculty at MIT. And, in any case, you'd have a hierarchy problem. I mean, you'd have to have a pattern of naming that follows the rules of the human resource hierarchy.'

It occurs to me momentarily that the entire conversation may well be a parody of itself, but when I look up at the faces around the table, I find that it is not.

'Why don't you name them by countries?' I suggest.

'What countries? And how about countries that aren't recognized by the UN, or by the US, for that matter?' asks Andri, in a weirdly fascinated, rhetorical tone.

'A good point,' adds Rob.

'Hey,' adds Andri, curling his skinny shoulders over his skinny chest so that his T-shirt hangs in pre-Raphaelite folds. 'Jeff Schiller would get to legitimate countries.' Andri begins to snort at his joke. 'Like, he'd name this terminal Bosnia-Herzegovina and he'd get the President of Bosnia ringing up going OK, man, thanks for the accreditation.'

Rob's off now, shoulders shaking with mirth, jellyish lips bobbing up and down over his half-plate of beef and straw mushrooms and hawking little pieces of ground-up food over the surrounding table.

I write 'help' in my notebook. It makes me feel mildly comforted.

'Hey,' shouts Andri, voice vibrato from snorting and giggling, '*she's writing this stuff down.*' He appears overjoyed. 'Man, let's give her something *totally* obscure to chew on.'

'No,' I say, 'no, it's OK, really.'

'Did you see that IRS report about taxing aliens?' Andri's eyes begin to sparkle.

I put down my notepad and pick up my soup spoon. The hot-and-sour has a skin on it, but underneath it's warm and aromatic.

'I'm *serious*,' says Andri, darkening.

'Aliens from outer space,' remarks the guy sitting next to Rob, who really does have little breasts, and a fuzzy cotton candy beard to boot.

'That depends on how you define inner and outer space. Would there be tax brackets for each?'

'I think it's pretty clear that outer space implies the cosmos beyond the solar system.'

Rob looks up from his tea, creases his brow to resemble a pink-skinned serpent and gives out a look of complete astonishment: '*Huh?*'

'That *is* a totally two-dimensional definition,' adds Andri.

'Huh?' says Rob again.

'Aliens, yes,' replies the guy with the beard, staring off into outer or inner space, or most likely, both at the same time, 'I'd like to run some simulations on it anyway.'

'Well Sussman has the equipment,' adds Andri testily, 'so what's stopping you?'

'I'm aware of that, but my question would be: can Sussman

deal with Mercury's relativistic orbit? Only ten people in the *world* really understand that.'

The bill arrives, Ken pulls out a Tandy pocket calculator, punches in the figures. Hang on, it's not coming out quite right. Six fried rice and seven steamed rice. Rob scribbles some calculus onto a napkin.

'Seventeen dollars apiece,' says Ken, finally. Dollar bills are thrown into the centre of the table, where they form a flaky mound between the platters of sweet-and-sour.

Ken counts up, announces there's more than enough to cover the cheque and invites propositions for the redistribution of the surplus. A number of alternatives are mooted and after appropriate discussion the group agrees on a local optimum and leaves an extra fifteen dollars as a tip. Mike offers me a lift to the MIT campus.

We pass by the fountain, talking about the weather. We snake along the side of the Student Building and wind up in the Elevators of the West 20 block, heading for the 'Zone'. 'As in Barry Levine's *The Watchmaker*, of course,' says Mike helpfully.

Having come from where the technological future is being built, I'm finally at the place where the technological future is being imagined. The source.

The corridors are quiet up on the third floor. Set in a herringbone pattern along part of the Zone's corridor is a series of teak doors with locks, and past these into the dark recess of the Zone is a small glassed room. In the communal sitting area two young men with beards and a woman in black Levi's and a school hoodie skim through the *Boston Globe* and a copy of *MacUser*. At the very end of the corridor an airforce blue door marked with the letters DCNS leads into an invisible chamber at the end of the building. The whole corridor has an air of dead, static placelessness, as though the Zone were an anteroom to some other dimension.

Mike leads us into the glass room, where about thirty young men and three young women are popping Dr Pepper's, haw-hawing, nibbling buffalo wings from an economy-sized Safeway

packet and geeking out on one of six or seven VAXes, the dozen
or so Pentium PCs. Condensation bubbles up the walls despite
the air conditioning. Away from the buffalo wings, the air smells
of foot cheese and cooking human fat. A couple of kids look up
from their screens and wave hi to Mike, who waves back in an
exaggerated fashion, the way that puppet characters wave to each
other on Saturday morning kids' TV shows.

Looking about, my eye falls on Bryan Hughes' 6th grade 5.25"
disk pinned on the SIPB noticeboard – presumably as part of
some obscure geek joke – alongside a DCNS advisory, marked
IMPORTANT in red ink.

DCNS advisory:

How to choose a good password

Change it every 3–6 months

Use both upper and lower letters

Use 2 or more words together

Use misspelled words

Create simple mnemonics or compounds that are easily
remembered, yet hard to decipher e.g. 'Iwada Sn, at
Cwt2bmP, btc't' for 'It was a dark and stormy night, and
the crackers were trying to break my password, but they
couldn't.'

'What *is* a DCNS, Mike?' I ask.

'Distributed Computing Network System.' The words tumble
from Mike's tongue with such ease he might have sucked them
up with his mother's milk.

'Phew it's hot in here,' he adds.

He's right. The combined heat of geek flesh and circuitry rises
towards the ceiling.

'You could stick your head in the freezer, Mike,' quips someone at the front of the room. 'Or you could leave it in there a
while and that would be even better.'

Rumbling breath passes along the room, overlaid by the crack of laughter that doesn't yet know how to pitch itself and the crisp whisper of facial hair.

Aside from the password hints and Bryan Hughes' computer disk, the noticeboard carries some notes about PERL, which may or may not be jokes; an announcement of the UMOC or Ugliest Manifestation on Campus competition (generally won by a CS major, or so says the announcement); and a list of codes to help users to configure NEARnet, whatever that might be.

Mike has drifted off to another corner of the room and is securely attached to a screen by a mouse umbilical.

Every computer in SIPB has a name. Mike's is called the 'Anxiety Closet' and the one next to it is 'Bedfellow'. Geeks know how sad they are, but they don't care. Being sad is a badge of geek strength and endurance. The transformation of computer buffs from lonely bedroom moles to triumphant geeks is one of the late twentieth century's existential glories.

Someone suddenly pipes up

'Scourges of the Internet?' and at this signal the Sippies drop everything they're doing and shout back:

'AOL.' America On Line, a large service provider geeks regard as hopelessly mainstream.

'More scourges of the Internet?'

'WWW.'

Just at that moment a blond boy strides through the door, takes in the scene with a scowl on his face and shouts:

'VFS maintainer. And *cut* the noise level in here.'

'That's Greg,' whispers Mike. 'Sippie president. God.' Mike is joking. I think.

'The YFAS was nominated, Greg,' Mike answers God with some wistfulness, tapping in his code.

'W needs to be updated from Granola.'

A mean-looking boy sitting at a computer called the Quiche types in

trap(.) at-trap=0x190.

'*Damn.*'

A tide of geeks washes up at his feet.

'Shit, man. Is there something bogus in that piece of code?'

Ignoring the coding crisis, Greg strides over to the internal phone and asks to speak to the maintenance people to complain about the air conditioning, which is distributing smells of feet around the room, and a group duly gathers around to make suggestions to the maintenance people about what might be wrong with the air-conditioning system, by shouting in the direction of the phone receiver 'Water leakage', 'electricity surge', 'power failure', until Greg holds up his hand to inform everyone that in the opinion of the maintenance department the air-conditioning system just pooped. Whereupon:

'Air conditioners . . .'

'SUCK!' roars the chorus of geek-guys and geek-gals.

'Streets without air conditioners . . .'

'SUCK!'

'Summer . . .'

'SUCKS!'

'Computers . . .'

'SUCK!'

'Shit,' exclaims a beak-nosed boy at Bedfellow. An instant silence.

The Quiche replies 'I *told* you I was going to reboot Zephyr.'

'OK, OK' whines Beaky Bedfellow, peevishly.

'Yes I *did*. I *did*. I *did*.'

Mike looks up, catches my eye and suggests we visit the DCNS machine room and the public cluster.

'OK. I'd like that.'

So Mike and I head off through the blue door at the end of the Zone corridor and through another door marked MACHINE ROOM 11 ADMINISTRATOR JEFFREY SCHILLER. Mike enters a security code and we're in. Rows of grey terminals, mostly static or blank, are stacked in a shelving unit, on the tables around screens blink and spew out text into the eyeless room. Machine Room 11 contains part of the AFS, or Andrew File System, which stores all the files of all the people working on the public terminals at MIT and allows them access to those files from any other terminal. One third of the Athena server machines, which run MIT's internal network, are also stored in the room along with stacks of disk units, each of 5 gigabytes, containing the working files, the theses, the working papers, the CVs and the love letters of the three thousand odd students at Massachusetts Institute of Technology. The AFS is one of the largest data storage systems in the world.

Mike says he left MIT's computer science undergraduate programme after freshman year when he ran out of money, and got a job working for the DCNS administering the system.

A series of lights begins to shiver over in the corner of the room, opposite the AFL stack, silently shaking hands with the spinning disk inside.

'Those modems are running off the Usenet FAQ server which SIPB operates as a service to the Net newbies.'

We watch for a while. Mike has a faraway look on his face, but I'm wondering who's skimming the Usenet Frequently Asked Questions archive, and in what country, which time zone, on what continent.

'I'm dropped out right now,' says Mike.

'Yeah, you told me.'

Back inside the SIPB room, Mike waves me over to the crash couch, which is where Sippies sleep if they're coding and can't be bothered to make the trip back home to bed. A frail-looking girl is balanced on the armrest at one end of the couch, between two older boys, who are lost in admiration.

'I heard someone's been complaining 'bout me hangin' here and borrowing the books,' the girl is saying. The boys are shrugging and shaking their heads.

Mike moves closer and whispers into my ear, 'She's an urchin. Still at high school, but likes to hang around here. We get heaps of 'em.'

'You know,' continues the girl, 'at school its like FORTRAN, Noble, Lynx. Like who cares? It's like, when was Byron born? Who cares?'

'Phew,' says one of the boys, edging towards her.

'Which is why I learned C++ and got into tunnel-hacking . . .'

'That's so cool,' groans the boy. The girl flicks at her hair and smoothes a hand over willowy legs. Boy-oh-Boy. Being a codegirl at an SIPB meeting must feel like being a jar of marshmallows in a kindergarten.

'I went on this outreach Harvard thing and it sucked, like, how to bullshit around stuff, object-oriented dynamic linked list with code in C++. Like, *sure*, being able to create variables in four loops.' The girl skips on, smoothing those legs.

'Technically, you can do that in C, actually,' says one of the boys, forgetting for a moment that he is in the presence of a goddess.

'Well, I couldn't, so I guess I'm *just* a *loser*,' spits the girl. 'Everyone here's so like oh, I made the Commodore 64 out of toothpicks, and you wouldn't believe how bitchy the CPU was. I'm like, all I've been doing is programming C++.'

'Oh, man, no, C++ is cool, really.'

'So, do you think they like me here, well, do you? Well? Well?'

Back at Anxiety Closet:

'Yesterday was Eric's birthday, and I found out today that one of the major Windows TCP/IP packages comes with help files that suggest people send help mail to me.'

When the laughter has subsided someone calls out:

'Greg, is there gonna be some post-meeting heat-stroke tonight?'

'Of *course*,' says Greg.

Admission: whatever I may think I've discovered about geek minds and geek thoughts, geek hearts will for ever remain a mystery to me.

THURSDAY

Today I came across a story written in the visitor's book at the Boston Computer Museum by a girl named Lisa Tang:

> Long long time ago, there is a girl called Lisa and a computer called Jim. Actually, I am Lisa. I know how to use the computer well. However, I did not know if the computer know me well. One day, I typed into the computer if he knew me well and the computer answers me he has been knowing me for years. However, he cannot understand my world because his world is only filled with letters. He told me that he would like some computer engineer to make him smarter.

NEW YORK, NEW YORK, TUESDAY

A transitional phase

The @ Internet Café in St Mark's Place is full of multimedia yuppies air kissing, swapping Web addresses and bragging about their kit. 'Is telnetting from this terminal as simple as it is from my own SPARC station and my 8100 PowerMac?' The sole rationale for renting machines at @ apparently being to invite unfavourable comparisons with the kit you already own at home. It was a mistake to come, I realize. This is not the kind of place to be in if you're struggling to fend off a creeping scepticism about the power of technology to change human relations for the better. It *is* the kind of place to encourage feelings of monumental hipster-dom, should you have any, what with everyone wearing black and drinking stratified lattes and holding conversations in such keywords as dollars, deal and dividend and moaning about the café's pitiable hardware. 'Oh my, these machines are soo slooow. At home, with my brand new T1 high-speed fibre connection, I'd have circumnavigated the globe, scoped out the Web competition and checked into the Dow, the Nikkei and the Footsie already.' It's all just a bit too much. Like the eighties plus Internet.

New York City. Whenever I'm here I feel it's because someone has abandoned me.

A message from Mac is waiting for me in my mailbox at the WELL.
>See you back in London soon.

See me? Well, that's something new. The possibility of Mac and I meeting flesh to flesh. But why not? A twinge of yearning disrupts my glum mood. This is the first time I've allowed myself to miss Mac's proximity since I left England. It's rather liberating. For whatever the global village boosters may say about the Internet, geography *does* make a difference. All the same, Mac will not be seeing me in London all that soon because I have other plans. A strange thought pops up. Back in England everything under the Internet sky will still be sunny. The backlash won't have happened there. Not yet.

I pick up a Shaving Ken in FAO Schwartz as a present for Nancy. When you leave him in the dark he grows a beard, which you can then remove with his special Shaving Ken kit, thereby giving yourself all the pleasure of having a realistic man about the house with none of the inconvenience.

FAO Schwartz is packed with toys which, being a toyshop, probably isn't so surprising. I read somewhere that a child plays in order to explore her psychological landscape. She will play with a doll as a way of working out some unfamiliar feeling without psychological risk to herself. She'll beat the doll about a bit, throw her against the wall, dress her up, and feel a sense of resolution. No matter whether or not her resolution makes sense to those of us in the adult world, to the child, it is perfectly satisfactory.

Half the toys in FAO Schwartz didn't exist when I was a kid. The world of merchandized product – spin-offs from TV programmes and movies and videos and computer games – is more or less new to me. Perhaps that's why I'm suspicious of it. I can't help thinking there's something totalitarian about spin-offs.

Surrounded by the colossal authority of a highly advertised pre-fabrication, a whole invented world of dolls and weapons and costumes and computer games and colouring books and videos and school totes and lunch boxes, what little corner remains for the child? What small space is left for her personality?

The new toys seem so sad. Given the technical possibilities, you'd think that toy designers would have come up with something more inspiring than Telephone Tammy, who answers her phone with the messages: 'I'm hungry' and 'I love to go shopping'. Or TV Teddy ($54.99) who comes with his own Small Talk box transmitter to plug into a VHS loaded with one of the special TV Teddy-ready videos ($12.99 each) to enable TV Teddy to 'join in' the lyrics of songs on the screen or the *Home Alone* Talkboy, which plays thirty minutes of dialogue from *Home Alone 2* for a child to learn and recite back?

Nancy calls to say she's made a positive decision to scale down her personal backlash.

'I think I was overreacting, but only a little.'

'I just sent you a Shaving Ken in the mail, Nance.'

'Oh Sweetheart, you *didn't*.'

The sound of liquid being strawed up, followed by Nancy's voice:

'I can't *wait* for Depilatory Barbie.' Giggles on both sides of the continent.

'I miss you.' My voice is quivering. 'So what did you have for dinner?'

The liquid rush again.

'Uh, let's see. Half a bag of corn chips, some salsa I scraped out of the refrigerator, two spoonfuls of lemon mayonnaise and about twelve handfuls of granola.'

I let out an involuntary moan. Feel my stomach lurch.

'Hey, I'm going through a transitional phase, OK?'

She's right again. You do eat the most punishing load of junk when you're troubled.

★   ★   ★

Observation: I read an article in a magazine which said that the majority of young adults in Japan would rather buy their snacks and clothes and CDs from vending machines than from human beings. Is that bad or good? I don't know. What's more, I have a feeling no one's really going to know until it's too late.

WEDNESDAY

The hacker cliché: lone geek gets caught breaking and entering in the Pentagon's most secret files, is arrested and charged but gets off in court on the grounds that he's addicted and needs psychiatric help. The antidote to the cliché: hacker decides to quit his hacking habit before the addiction leads him to break and enter the Pentagon.

The antidote's name is Thor, and I'm hanging around Grand Central Station waiting for him.

I love Grand Central. There's a robust sort of stateliness about it, and between the morning rush hour and the afternoon dash home it's as peaceful as a seashell. You can stay and contemplate the broad arched windows and the pixillated ceiling for hours without having to buy or consume anything and the concourse has a way of swallowing up the whoops of meeting friends, the slack belches of winos, the crunching of shoppers' bags and sneaker squeaks, remaining quiet and soulful in spite of it all. The big things happen at Grand Central. Important meetings, love affairs, declarations, epiphanies, lies, decisions.

Thor is already an hour late. Thirty-five members of an obscure Korean spiritualist cult are currently strobing around the station concourse like searchlights looking for vulnerables to spiritualize.

Suddenly:

'Shall we crack Grand Central?'

I turn towards the voice. Thor is not as he described himself. For a start he's taller, and more business-like, very young but with a certain aged, waxy pallor. His hair is done in a military style.

'Let's go,' I say, anticipating adventure.

We skip up the stairs at the front of the building, through the cafeteria to a small door at the back, Thor talking so fast all the while that I can't catch what he's saying. The door gives onto a dank service area. We are about to crack Grand Central.

'I've been doing this since I was twelve or thirteen,' Thor says. That's seven years by my calculation. Thor and I exchange glances. We're both keyed up.

With knees bent to keep the noise of our shoes low on the linoleum, we scuttle off along a maintenance corridor in a south-ward direction, past three green-painted doors and towards the huge arched windows at the 42nd Street end of the station. A sign reads PROHIBITED TO UNAUTHORIZED PERSONNEL in red lettering. There is silence and a smell of must. Along the walls the station's innards are strung like giant spiders' silks linking the banks of lightbulbs and rows of padlocked levers. Thor puts his finger to his lips, tenses slightly, listening out for maintenance workers. A muted breeze rushes in from the street pulling the buzz of the street behind it. We press on until we reach the base of the giant windows illuminating the side halls, then follow a stairwell to the right and emerge several flights up onto a platform overlooking the main concourse. The Korean spiritualists are silhouetted against the floor tiles below. We stand and gaze a moment, see a woman and a man meeting and taking each other's hands, three kids carrying skateboards running for a train, an old man slumped against the wall. 'What a rush!' I whisper. 'Like being on top of Mount Olympus.' Thor grins assent.

Before us lies the great prize: the corridor leading through the centre of the vast arched windows to the east and west of Grand Central Station, a slender vein of concrete and linoleum set in an acre of glass, from which, so Thor says, you can see out over most of 42nd street and Vanderbilt Avenue. We fall on our knees, backs up against the door. Thor fumbles for a set of picks and Allen keys from his pocket, checks that the door is locked, then crouching down to look into the keyhole, he selects a pick from his bunch and teases it into the lock. The air feels suddenly damp and weighty. I watch the flare of Thor's nostrils as he needles his way through the cogs and levers of the lock with his pick. Surrounding us now are the smells of metal and electricity. Thor slides his pick to the right, manipulates it from side to side between his right index finger and thumb, then replaces it with another and begins the same procedure over again.

'Damn,' he says softly, after a minute or two. 'It's a double mortise. I can't crack it. I don't have the right pick with me.'

'That's OK,' I shrug, feeling the bubble of adrenaline burst. 'We can go back.' Thor throws me a look as if to say thanks for being easy but I feel hard done by all the same. A hundred feet up, a window overlooking Grand Central Station would have been a one-off.

We find ourselves in a storeroom lined with fuses the size of bricks.

'We could pull the plug on Grand Central Station,' says Thor, then, changing his mood all of a sudden, 'What do you know about the Mole people?'

'You mean the folk who live in the tunnels underneath the subway.'

Thor nods.

'Nothing. I mean, I know they exist. And that there are thousands of 'em, right?'

Thor catches my expression: 'You want to go see?'

However rapidly he speaks, every *t* is pronounced, every syllable enunciated. The effect is strangely archaic, like listening to the voice of a poet on an old wax record.

'Have you *been* down there?'

'Twice. The second time a man chased me with an axe shouting "*I'm doing this for your own good*".'

We spill out into the cafeteria and find a table distant from the door. Thor orders a cup of coffee, I ask for a root beer.

'I think I've had enough adventure.'

'Okeydoke.' We babble on, Thor filling me in on timetabling changes to the Westchester to Grand Central line. I get the feeling

I'm being set up for a night of adolescent confidences but far from feeling put upon, my head is light at the thought of what such a night might bring. Thor, sensing some new and keener mood, takes one sip of his coffee, thinks better of it, turns to me and cries:

'I have to ask you. Do you like *The Great Gatsby*?'

The question produces an enthusiastic nod from me.

'How does it go?' Thor tinkers with his memory. ' "Gatsby believed in the green light, the orgastic future that year by year recedes before us. It eluded us then, but that's no matter – tomorrow we will run faster, stretch out our arms further . . . And one fine morning – So we beat on, boats against the current, borne back ceaselessly into the past.' From the careless fluency of his recollection, it is clear he has recited these words many times. Yet the smooth unlined skin of his face is blank and the deep brown marble of his eye is empty. I wonder what he could be thinking about.

'That's the dilemma with my computer obsession,' he says, lost in introspection. 'You see, I want to give it up, but I'm afraid that the minute you pick something you're not obsessive about is the minute you're running your life backwards. The process doesn't interest you any more. Only the goal, and because you picked the goal out some time in the past, you're always looking back towards the moment when you picked it.'

Thor is still deep inside himself. He has no idea that his words describe my own story. Why should he? It is only this minute becoming clear to me, clear that my own goal was set the moment I chose to believe in a symbol and make it real. Set, in other words, on Venice Beach, and reiterated at Nancy's desk with a Buddha for an avatar. This is the vanishing point I can neither shake nor discard, caught as I am in my own trembling fear of spoiling the dream, destroying the obsession and running my life forever backwards to the girl who was in Wonderland. Backwards on to Venice Beach.

We wander through the streets and fetch up at the apartment I've borrowed from a friend. A sweep of blue light from a film shoot blasts through the glass and it is beginning – just beginning – to rain.

'Tell me about your life, Thor.'

'With the computers?' Thor's voice falters a little. He scrambles over the syllables.

'With everything.'

There is a pause, a short punctuation to allow Thor's multitudinous thoughts to be transmitted in electrical pulses to his mouth.

'My parents' favourite story about me is that I learned to walk in one day. They tried to get me to walk, six months past when I was supposed to be walking, but I refused, until one day, I just stood up and started walking around. I never took any stinking baby steps. I *walked*.'

The voice drifts away, while the brown eyes follow a path over some magazines lying on the coffee table.

'When I was eight my parents bought me a computer, a Commodore 64. Right away, I seemed to have an innate ability for making it do what I wanted. I got good at it. I got obsessive about it. The computer was a way of impressing people into acting like my friends. I ended up with this cult of geekish friends who looked up to me because I could do stuff they couldn't . . .'

I open a window out onto the soft evening rain and the marine blue of the movie lights slices stripes across my hands.

'Then I got a modem. I was nine or ten. I started playing around on bulletin boards. First it was a way to download more games, and then I discovered pornography, text-based pornography. My parents kept telling me not to stay up all night, doing, they didn't really know what, with the computer.'

The evening won't end until Thor has told me everything he has to tell, because he needs to tell it to me and because I need to hear it. It may be that the lock-jocking episode in Grand Central Station may have been a test so Thor might judge to what extent I trusted him, how far I'd go on his say-so. I make us another cup of tea and Thor continues with his story.

'Dad was working at Columbia University and fixed up for me to become an intern there. The guy I was assigned to was working on one of the first massively parallel computers. I learned a lot. I got inured to the culture. Hacker culture glorifies the obsessive and that was a good thing for me at the time. I was eleven years old and I could act as ridiculously and obsessively about computers as any thirteen-year-old, even if I didn't understand them quite as well. The guy died though. Cancer.'

For a moment Thor is abandoned in some past feeling. He sits with the tea balanced on his lap, gazing out of the window at the blue light, and looks suddenly calm. Resignation, relief, or perhaps only nostalgia.

'At this point I'm not doing any work at school. I'm spending all my time playing with the computers at Columbia. There were all these people at Columbia, ten or fifteen years older than me, and my life wasn't like theirs. I wasn't even allowed to ride the subway at night and I hated that.'

The apartment is drenched in blue light now. Down on Greene Street Demi Moore is opening the door of an automobile many times and stepping in, also many times.

'My parents sent me to Choate . . .' Thor catches my look of incomprehension. 'It's a private high school, one of the best private high schools. But the only reason I wanted to go was that Choate had the exact same kind of VAX computer system as the one at Columbia. It turned out that someone who worked for my father was on the board of Trustees. So I got in. My IQ scores were phenomenal 170, 180, higher than that sometimes – but my grades were terrible. I was a wildcard.

'Anyway, that summer vacation I went to work for Digital. I was fourteen. I'd built up this ridiculous Nietzschean man-of-steel persona for myself. We are all of us, at fourteen, so insecure that we make ourselves believe in that stuff. Everyone was afraid to talk to me. And they resented me for being so young and thinking I was so good at what I was doing.

'I started going out in the evenings with these people who did a lot of drugs and booze and meaningless sex and I got a job writing software from someone I knew who'd gone to Choate. Some people can bring creativity to software programming, but

I can't. I find it mechanistic and dull, but I found I could write a lot of it if I got drunk. So I got drunk and got more drunk, got drunk to the point where I couldn't walk but I could still type. The computer was right next to the bed and I'd make sure that the chair was somewhere from where I could get to the bed and the computer without having to walk. When I was drunk I could write a thousand lines of code a night. It was the perfect excuse to drink without having to socialize with people. I like to have control.'

I light a Camel, offer the packet to Thor, who disregards it. I'm thinking about my own adolescence now, full of the same ache of loneliness, the same engulfing expectation, the same sly hints of disillusionment that are the bitter gall in the belly of every adolescent.

'The last year of high school,' says Thor, 'I was a wreck. Drunk, doing drugs. Eventually I got thrown out of school for complaining about a teacher who read my e-mail. And then I got a job at Panix, the Internet provider, doing really menial stuff. One day I told the guy who runs the place that a lot of the stuff I was doing was pointless because I could design software to make it unnecessary. So I designed the software and it worked great.'

The sudden noise of metal falling into the street distracts us momentarily. I light another Camel from the ashes of the first. Thor picks up his tale.

'I was beginning to get into computer security, and I knew a lot about e-mail systems. I knew a lot about the mails. I mean a *lot*. But for some reason I ended up at NYU art school studying photography. It was a lot of no work. I didn't want that. I wanted to make money.

'Then, when I was just eighteen, I went to my first conference on computer security and I caught a technical mistake in the presenter's presentation. Now this guy, the presenter, had been doing theoretical security work for the NSA and the military for many, many years and I'm standing up in front of all these people, at eighteen – *eighteen* – explaining *his* technical mistake.'

Thor shakes his head and smiles at the remembrance.

'One of the guys who'd been at that presentation offered me a security job recently: $90K and benefits worth another $15K. I'm nineteen, and I could be earning a hundred five thousand bucks. And I'm cynical and paranoid enough to be very good at computer security. I love it, I'm obsessed with it, but security work makes me paranoid and suspicious. From early on I'd find myself monitoring people's personal e-mail, reading their love letters and whatnot. And one time when I found myself doing it I just thought, no more, this is reprehensible. It's turning me into someone I really detest. But . . .'

'But what?'

'But when I go home this evening I'll be on the computer for hours and hours. I know I will. All night. And I'm realizing that if the only way I can have it in my life is to let it control me to that extent, I don't want it.'

'What will you do?'

'I'll make enough money to move somewhere so far away that even my SkyTel pager won't work and I'll do photography and vanish into the void.'

'No computer.'

'Uh uh.' Thor shakes his head. He takes a leather file out of his bag and hands it to me. A small portfolio of photographs of trains and train stations. Grand Central is there, along with prints of retired trains, the Westchester line, disused track and broken up signalling houses. All the detritus of America's ruined railways.

Outside, the film crew have long since packed up and gone home. Thor and I have been together for a whole afternoon and evening and into the night, but it seems only minutes since we were standing in front of the locked door at Grand Central Station, and only a matter of seconds since Demi Moore was stepping into the auto on Greene Street, drenched in blue light.

'I know people who've kicked heroin,' Thor says, taking back the photos. 'It can't be any harder than that. I understand how it works now. I understand that there are a whole bunch of sixteen-year-old geeks out there learning as much as they can as fast as they can, just as I did, and I know that as soon as enough of them catch up, I won't be able to make that much money any more because these kids will be working for pennies, just to get the experience. And when that happens one of my biggest positive reinforcements for carrying on with computers will have gone. I won't be able to make the money.' He gazes at the white around his knuckles. 'It rips my guts out to know that's what's going to happen, but I want it to happen. I have to let it happen, because willpower isn't enough on its own. This is the only way out.'

THURSDAY

I wake up feeling flatlined and take breakfast at @ in order to pick up my e-mail. Nancy has mailed me news of the resignation of the Icelandic president, Vigdis Finnbogadottir, the first demo-cratically elected woman head of state, who has decided to quit the presidency and spend more time designing multimedia.
>**Good luck in Reykjavik!** writes Nancy, signing off.

iv: BONJOUR TRISTESSE, or THE UNFORGIVEN

Viking interest

The woman sitting next to me on the plane wants to know if my guide book includes a detailed plan of the shopping complex at Keflavík airport. We check the index. Geysers, glaciers, fjords, northern lights, Arctic circle, fishing, hiking, mountaineering . . .

'Nope, sorry, no section specifically on the airport.' I hand over the guide so that she can look for herself.

'What a *shame*.' She turns to the man in the aisle seat, lifts her face to his ear. 'No plan of the airport, hon,' she says, very loudly. 'My husband', she smiles, addressing herself to me again, 'was a brilliant man once. But he's' – this in a raw whisper – 'got Alzheimer's.'

'Oh dear, tsk.' Uh-oh.

'They don't know it, you know.'

'Dear me.'

'We got a postcard from Ronald Reagan once. Before he succumbed. Something to hand down to the grandchildren. He wrote on it himself.' The husband and his toupee nod in approximately simultaneous response and the plane begins to swoop through pillowy Arctic clouds. His wife cups her hand over the side of her mouth closest to her husband. 'They're *completely* oblivious to it.' She lifts her eyebrows as if to suggest the fickleness of the fates, then starts up again. 'We're only changing planes, of course, but I heard that Icelanders eat sheep's parts.'

I look out at the clouds, trying to distract myself from the suck of the plane's steep descent, taking me back to the afternoons of my childhood spent sliding out of control down the grassy slope at the bottom of the garden.

'They pickle them.' The woman strains against her seat belt and leans towards me. '*Male* parts.'

According to the guidebook, Iceland currently has two major exports, fish and Björk.

Overheard on the airport bus from Keflavík into the capital:

'You can go up to the fishermen these days and ask if the fish is fresh and they don't understand what you're talking about. It's just a fish, they say. But you know very well that they buy it off the Russians and all sorts, so there's no way of telling how long it's been lying around. Now, when I was growing up . . .'

Also overheard:

'Of course, we all know Björk. She used to sing the traditional Icelandic songs when she was a little girl, but now she's abandoned us for over there and there's no saying . . .'

A poster of the singer hangs in the airport, beetle-black hair tumbling about her face, her alien eyes the hue of hawthorn bark.

The road to Reykjavík swoops along a plain of lava and blue-grey moss. Crows and gulls hold themselves fast in the rush of wind. It feels like the last place on earth. NASA brought astronauts here for moonwalk training. Through all time no more than a million people have ever lived in Iceland. One quarter of those are alive today.

I call Thor from a pay phone outside the guesthouse. A woman answers the phone sounding sleepy and asks me to wait. The plane from New York landed at around six in the morning, and it's now nearly eleven. A couple of minutes later Thor is on the line.

'Hi.' I make an effort to sound cheerful, in spite of jetlag. 'Can we meet?'

Silence. Thor is collecting himself, trying to recall my voice.

'It's funny,' I add, sensing the awkwardness and trying to fill the gap. 'I just met a Thor in New York.'

Another pause.

'What time is it?'

'About eleven.'

'Aah gott,' cries Thor, disgusted. 'You'll have to call me back at two.' The line disconnects. I forget, pop stars don't have mornings.

Three hours to kill. I pack a sweater in my bag and head out down Skólavörðustígur to Bankastræti, the main street in Reykjavík, where I'm instantly struck by the number of prams. Prams all over. Prams being pushed along the pavement, prams parked outside shops and along the side streets, prams in cafés, prams stationed by the tables in restaurants, prams piling out of the supermarket, prams waiting in line at the cinema. Fancy prams, solid prams, prams with canopies, so many prams sharing one characteristic: they're all pushed by teenagers dressed as though they're on their way to dance clubs.

Iceland's the only place I've ever been where the cold has a smell. I've no explanation for it. A wide, feral smell, overtaken here and there by bursts of sulphurous vapour carried from the rocks to the air by the wind.

Feeling tired and in need of something to eat, I stop off at one of the cafés on Laugavegur and order a cup of coffee. The waitress brings a menu and says she'll return. From her lips the English language sounds newly beautiful, its hard edges rubbed away and replaced by guttural *aachs* and *ths* and there is a lilt to it which reminds me of Welsh. Icelandic is harder and more Germanic-sounding, with long, softly open vowels breaking up strange chords of consonants. I read somewhere, it must have been in the guide book, that Icelandic is most closely related not to Danish or English or Gaelic or Norwegian, but to old Norse, the language of the sagas.

Someone has left a copy of the *Herald Tribune* and a magazine on the table next to mine. The *Trib* is two weeks old, and the magazine appears to be written almost exclusively in Icelandic. I put it aside for a moment and take to staring out onto the street, by now a perambulator stream. A thought comes to mind that

Icelanders must be pretty inbred, there having been only a million of them throughout time. A few years ago a bored anthropologist started a rumour that the famously unsullied Icelandic Viking blood had received an injection of new genes in the form of Irish slaves captured by the Vikings, but Icelanders themselves, drawn together by blood, were quick to quash the idea. In any case, inbred or not, Iceland has produced more grand master chess players per capita than any other nation, plus two Miss Worlds and, most recently, one of the highest concentrations of computer whiz kids on the planet, among whom can now be classed the country's ex-president herself.

Flipping idly through the Icelandic magazine, I stumble on some English words, the lyrics to a song by local singer Leoncie and my first real encounter with Icelandic culture:

> *My Icelandic man, a real gentleman*
> *You light up my fire*
> *What makes you tick, is it your big Icelandic stick?*
> *I am filled with desire.*
>
> *Grab me, take me, fill me darlin', please don't sweat,*
> *I don't need no lubrication, I am wet . . .*
>
> *My Icelandic lover from a land filled up with lava,*
> *You're volcanic like the country*
> *Your muscles make me shiver, I'm burning with desire.*

There are two types on the streets. The first is beige. Beige hair, ochre complexions, muddy blue eyes. The second, by contrast, is inky and squat, like Björk. The young have the most silken, flawless skin I've ever seen, so radiant that it lends them an ethereal air. Their elders, on the other hand, are as warped and leathery as winter haws, giving them the look of wind-torn storytellers.

At ten past two I call Thor again, who tells me to meet him at four in a bar called something unpronounceable. I ask him to repeat the name, but it doesn't sound any clearer. Can you spell it. He repeats the name again. It's in Klapparstígur. Eh? Clap-arstig-urrr, he says wearily, as though he's done this all many many times before.

The odd thing is, I've really no idea what I'm doing here.

Back out on the street, the pram rush-hour is beginning. I follow the main road down to the offices of *Morganbladid*, the island's main newspaper, turn right and wander down to the shore-line. From this vantage the whole of the capital is spread. You could walk from one extreme edge to the other in thirty minutes. Like the town itself, Reykjavík's architecture is small and boxy, made up of imported concrete cubes with corrugated iron roofs painted in terracotta red and khaki and built straight onto the street. Some boast tiny lava gardens covered in ragged moss and baskets of blue lobelia. Here and there a hawthorn tree bursts from the soil, but there are no living things of any great size. A sharp wind breezes unceasingly between the buildings. The town's modern feel somehow emphasizes its tenuous position as the most northerly capital on the planet. It's as though urban civilization only turned to Iceland after it had visited everywhere else.

The road dips downhill past a couple of dozen prams towards the sea and the sky is cloudless now, exposing the raw light of the bare sun. I stop off at a bakery and buy myself a shrimp sandwich. The assistant tries Icelandic on me, then, noting my vacant smile, repeats what she's just said in English.

'Isn't it *hot*?'

I look down at my leggings, jacket and woollen sweater.

'If it stays like this, they'll let everyone out of the offices on sunshine holiday. We don't get much sun in Reykjavík.'

She giggles and hands me a few kroner in change.

Outside, I cannot help but notice that everyone other than me is wearing a T-shirt. A few of the pram pushers are even in bikini tops.

A twin-prop plane appears in my line of sight and dumps its shadow over a collection of petroleum tanks and an array of fishing trawlers heading out along the western coast. Down on the docks are giant crates of fish, sorted by species, sitting in unmelting ice and waiting to be processed. Whiting, cod, plaice or something like them, a run of silvery herrings, more flatfish, halibut, a second stack of whiting, prawns, a grey roundfish I don't recognize, further stacks of prawns, and in the corner eels. At the market just up from the quay they are selling whale meat, rotten red stuff, the colour of old scabs and menstruum, and boxes of cheap electronic goods. I wander back up the hill towards the café, the sun from the west over my back and the cold wind contradicting it and I imagine the dark blue sea around the island cupping the fishing boats and drawing the fishermen away towards continental Europe two hundred miles to the east.

An Internet café called Siberia has just opened up in Reykjavík. The place is empty save for two men sitting chain-smoking at computer screens, and a huddle of teenage boys clustered around another screen at the opposite corner.

'The English woman,' remarks one of the men, noticing me come in.

Thor, as it turns out, is a type-one Icelander, which is to say beige. And a mad patriot. He once put out a compilation album of Icelandic bands, called it *World Domination or Death*, and didn't consider the title a joke. Made a heap of money from the Sugar-cubes, *Skykurmolarnir* in Icelandic. Five years on he has another band, a record label called Bad Taste and a multimedia outfit. He's become very active on the Internet, makes his own computer animations and is one of the island's more famous converts to info tech. Which is how I know of him.

We sit at the Kaffibarrin each held fast in the other's gaze. A young woman with a pink cockscomb for a hairdo sits between us, smiling. We are all drinking strange-tasting beer.

'So what have you been doing since waking me up this morning?' Thor already sounds bored. How fragile is the illusion of equality provided by e-mail. Only a week ago we were bantering back and forth across the phone lines and now his tone is that of pop star to zealous teenage groupie. Swallowing back a clump of pride, I adopt a cooler tone.

'Wandering about,' I say.

'Well that doesn't take long in Reykjavík.' I ignore the bitterness.

'I went on a pram safari.'

'Oh that.' Thor waves the joke away. 'We have long winters so the teenage women make babies and the teenage men make computer programs. And everyone is in a band.' He smiles a wide, froggy smile. The women sitting next to him begins to giggle. I feel I have just passed some invisible test.

'Obsession with youth culture is a necessary part of Iceland's becoming a modern country. Somewhere deep in our sad little skateboard brains we feel isolated and abandoned,' says Thor.

'Well do *you* feel isolated?'

Thor holds up a beige hand: 'Aah gott, that question's so boring, so tedious.' He lights a smoke.

I throw him a cruel cold stare. The man I'm looking at is different from the e-mail version, all charm and mild-mannered cheeriness. A tiny flicker trembles about his eyes as though he's waiting for me to crack. But the moment passes, he gathers himself and tips me a strange wink.

'What can we do?' he moans. 'We Icelanders are simply struggling to make our miserable Viking lives worthwhile.'

'Well, why don't you just leave if it's all so bad?'

Thor looks at the woman at his side, and she returns his glance, wide-eyed. They both begin to giggle. Obviously I have missed a joke.

'Because I'm planning the next attempt at Icelandic world domination, of course.' He looks about him. 'By the way, try to find Torfi while you're here. When I look at a screen, I still see a computer. But Torfi doesn't. He's young.'

I'm about to ask for Torfi's e-mail address when one of the men from Siberia appears at the door, smiles at more or less everyone in the café and makes his way towards our table.

'I need a drink,' he says, in English. 'Where's Torfi?'

Thor shrugs.

The man turns to me. 'So I see you've discovered the place where all the anarchists are.' He orders a double Campari and soda and another round of beers. 'Björk comes here when she's in Iceland. We . . .' he is pointing to himself and Thor now '. . . used to be in an internationally famous pop group with Björk.'

'Yes, I know.' I struggle to place him. He notices me groping for recognition.

'I just hate people sometimes.' He takes a long draught of Campari and lights up.

'Where the fuck is Torfi? He's supposed to be putting up the Siberia website.'

'No one knows, Einar,' says the woman with the cockscomb.

I'm beginning to notice that there is something really very strange about the beer. It may be vodka.

Einar turns briefly to me. 'Come by Siberia tomorrow.' Drains both the Campari and the beer and wanders out.

A picture of Björk is tacked up in the corridor leading to the toilets, a cranky-looking expression on the black seal eyes. *Karlar* or *konur* signs hang on the toilet door. I make my way back down the corridor and into the main bar, intending to ask Thor whether I'm *karlar* or *konur*, but both he and the woman with the cockscomb have disappeared. I only realize quite how drunk I am when I lose the contents of my stomach to a lava sculpture in the front garden of the guesthouse.

I wake up sometime the next morning, with a clunky head and breath as foul as bat guano, feeling hung over and drunk at the same time. Fifteen minutes past one. The guesthouse appears to be deserted, the breakfast cleared away, and the remaining guests headed out for the day. Outside the sky is a deep dead blue and it's much colder. I wander down Pram Boulevard to the Café Sólon for a cup of coffee, make my way through the crown towards the bar. One thirty, the lunchtime crush. I take my cup and find an empty chair between two young women.

'You're the English person,' says the frail blonde woman with shaky eyes.

'Thor said we should look out for you if you came in here. He said to tell you he had to go.'

'Listen,' I say addressing myself to the two women. 'Do you two have babies?' I'm struck by what a weird question this is.

'Of *course*,' cry the women in unison, screwing their brows in stupefaction.

'Hahaha,' I reply, 'Hahaha, of *course*.' The woman on my right with the shaky eyes stares at me. She says, 'I think you're drunk.'

I look about. Everyone around looks pretty tanked up too but I decide to keep this observation to myself.

Just then I notice a blue roundel imprinted on the frail woman's shoulder.

'Nice tattoo.' I'm absorbed by the system of linked rectangles hidden within the circle, shaped round the warm white curve of the skin.

'Yeah,' she replies, brushing it with her fingers. 'It's a Viking symbol. It used to be burned into wood and held under the Vikings' arms when they were travelling. Wherever the bearer went they would never be lost. Liefur Eiríksson carried one in his underarm when he discovered America.' I notice that the woman's hand is quaking, and the skin on it leathery and worn out, thought she cannot be above thirty years old.

'I used to drink a lot,' she says, answering my eyes. Then returning to the tattoo: 'Björk and I had matching ones done.'

The coffee seems to be taking effect. The world at the end of the telescope I inhabited just an hour ago has been replaced by a more realistic-looking three-dimensional type world. Only my voice belongs somewhere else.

'I'm not very good with drink,' I say, 'it always makes me depressed.' My eyes begin to fill, and then to sting with salt.

'Icelanders usually beat each other up first, which makes them very happy, and then they get depressed,' says the woman.

'It's the weather,' I say.

'No, it's not the weather. It's as a consequence of being colonized.'

I'm in the midst of considering this when a sudden realization hits me.

'It's the night-time, isn't it?'

The women exchange quizzical, knowing glances.

'Of *course*. It doesn't get dark in Iceland in mid-summer.'

'Do you know,' I'm feeling sorry for myself now, 'I've no idea what the hell I'm doing on this frozen bloody island in the middle of bloody nowhere in the middle of the bloody night.'

'Same as us then,' says the woman with the tattoo.

'And by the way,' adds the other woman, 'Iceland's not frozen. That's Greenland you're thinking of.'

An envelope containing a cassette tape is waiting for me in the morning with a note from Thor. I manage to shake off the previous bright-night's hangover in a column of soft, sulphuric, geothermal shower water.

Blue lupins have appeared in every garden overnight and the sky is thin with morning air. I've resisted checking the state of the lava sculpture in the guesthouse garden and I'm down on Laugavegur again, admiring the disco dollies with their pram accessories. On my way, I pass Reykjavík's main supermarket, two designer clothes stores, a pram shop, a thermal underwear store and a purveyor of orthopaedic corsetry, before fetching up at the town's main bookshop, where my attention is caught by a picture of one of the women I met the night before. Beneath her image is a display of books. I make a mental note to stop by later in the day and have a look inside.

But for now, I'm driven by Einar's invitation to visit Siberia. Inside the café the same group of teenage boys is hunched round a screen and Einar is stooped above them, explaining something or other in animated tones. Seeing me come in, he leaves the boys and strides over.

'Fucking kids. Think they know everything when they know shit.' He emphasizes the final *t*. 'Shit-*t*. 'All they ever want on the Internet is hash, tits and UFOs. I caught some of them trying to get nude pictures of Björk once. Tsk.' Shakes his head in anger.

I suppress a small giggle.

'OK,' said Einar. 'Fuck off. Fuck off.' He waves his hands at me in dismissal.

'Sorry.'

'Listen, when *I* was seventeen I had *ideals*. I was angry, I cared about everything. No one cares about anything anymore. Everyone can just fuck off.'

'Oh dear,' I reply, cautiously.

'My trouble is I care too much. I *hate* myself for caring too much. And I have a vision, so take me out and shoot me, put me in an institution, save me from my plight.' I do a mental calculation which puts Einar at about thirty-three, and come to the conclusion my new friend's biggest problem is that he's an unrepentant punk left stranded in a rock pool of bitter bile by the indifferent swell of the times.

'Uh, look Einar,' I try to sound conciliatory, 'you said to come round . . .'

'I remember when the first VCR came to Iceland, I remember when Icelandic TV went on air, when it went colour, I remember when people didn't have fax machines or car phones. Technology can be Big Brother in the wrong hands, if people don't use it. I've trained fifteen hundred people to use the Internet here in three months, I lose money doing it. They all come in here thinking they can learn everything in ten minutes . . . and even when they do learn everything, all they want is UFOs and nudie Björk.'

He looks me directly in the eyes, a disconcerting national habit.

'Which is why I hate people. Want a beer?'

'No thanks.'

Einar pours two beers from the tap behind the bar, inserts a CD into the player.

'We call it the *grýla*,' he says. A tinny break beat starts up.

'*What*?' This has by now become somewhat of a generic question, along with 'why?' and 'how the hell?'

'The Internet,' Einar raises his eyes to the ceiling in sheer despair at my lack of elementary understanding. That same long *t* again. Internet-t. He carries the beer to a table, and motions me over to sit. '*Grýla* means bogeyman. You see, Icelanders think they understand info tech, but they haven't got a clue. It's all bravado.'

He reaches for his cigarettes, lights two and hands one over to me.

'A couple of days ago the Prime Minister rang me up and said, "Einar, we're expecting great things of you. You've put yourself at the edge of Iceland's future by developing the Internet here." But a couple of days before that I'm in the airport, coming back from London and the customs point to me and say, "Einar, you're coming with us", and they start accusing me of smuggling Ecstasy into Iceland over the Internet and I have to waste three hours of my time explaining to them that the Internet is a telephone line. And then Torfi goes missing. So fuck them and fuck Torfi and fuck everyone.' And with that he gets up and walks out of the door, leaving only the scent of rage trailing nostalgically behind.

I wander down to the bookstore and pick up a copy of the tattooed woman's book. Her name is Ditta and the book is a collection of modern sagas, according to the bookstore assistant.

'What are they about exactly?' I ask. The assistant takes up the volume, begins to scroll down the pages of Icelandic text.

'Let's see.' She pauses on a couple of pages, looks up with a sweet smile on her face and says in an utterly impassive tone:

'Fisting, incest and anal sex. We shelve it under Viking interest.'

Walking back up the main street I pass four familiar faces and sixteen familiar prams. Twelve people smile at me in recognition, two more wave and I'm invited to inspect three babies. A woman leans out of her car to ask if I'm new in town.

Thor is sitting at the Kaffibarrin. A Dalmatian shivers on a lead outside, surrounded by a crowd of curious onlookers.

'What's up with the dog?' I ask. Really, this country is too much.

The barman explains: 'Up till last week the government banned dogs from Reykjavík on the grounds that they weren't appropriate to the cosmopolitan lifestyle here, along with non-Vikings, trains and depressives, so no one's seen a real dog before. The policy worked, though. All the surveys show that 95 per cent of the Icelandic population are happy, car-driving Vikings.'

Einar arrives smelling faintly of anger and carrots.

'Where the *fuck* is Torfi?'

Thor, the barman and everyone else in the café shrugs.

'He's supposed to be shooting the UnUn video,' says Thor, 'but he may have emigrated instead.'

UnUn's first US single, 'Super Shiny Dreams' is about to hit the streets under Thor's Bad Taste label. The group is hoping to put some lip-synched video grabs up onto the Net as part of their publicity effort. The technology is a gift to remote economies. If ever the island's fish reserves dry up, Iceland will still have a chance at economic survival.

Torfi makes an entrance about an hour later. The rest of us are already drunk.

'I need a drink,' he says. Another round of beers is fetched, admonishments made and Thor agrees to round up the members of the band and meet for the promo shoot at eleven. Torfi sits himself at my table, downs a beer.

'You're in trouble,' I begin.

Torfi smiles a thin smile. 'I had some deals to do, and then I had to go and see my kid.'

'How old are you?'

'Nineteen. Everyone has kids.'

We sit in a nervous sort of silence for a few moments, while I doodle logos on my beer glass and Torfi fidgets with the unearthly white skin on his skinny wrists and bobs his legs up and down under the table.

'I had a collection to make. Well, download.'

So that's what Torfi's deals are all about. Cracked wares.

'An animation package, probably worth around $10K in the legitimate market. I make the excuse that I'm not making enough money to buy the stuff legit. The market's so small here software piracy is a national pastime.'

He leans into his beer and it's then I notice the tattoo on his arm. In Iceland, tattoos are like signatures.

'Torfi, the no good *afbrotaunglingur*,' says Torfi.

'What's that mean?'

'Juvenile delinquent. It's a made-up word. A committee makes up new words for things like that.'

Torfi smiles that thin smile again.

'Like what?'

'The word for computer, *tölva*, comes from the Nordic god of wisdom and foresight, I think. The word for TV is *sjonvarp*, which is a combination of the words for seeing and casting out, like a fishing line. Phone, *simi*, comes from the word for a thread.'

How long before technology breaks the island nation bound by blood, I wonder? Kith and kin killed off by kit.

'A lot of people here say Iceland is a prison and you can't get very far but it's not true. It's just people using Iceland as a scapegoat for their own inability. In some ways it's *easier* here. I mean, it'd be harder for some nineteen-year-old kid to be shooting videos, having access to huge computers and all of that in London, wouldn't it?'

'Yeah, I guess it would.' Torfi's generation are such pragmatists.

'And what's the point of going to school when you can watch a video of one of Truffaut's films?'

Today is the longest day. The sun will officially set for a matter of a few minutes over the western coast of Iceland, but there will be no darkness.

Einar and I meet again in Siberia. Aside from ourselves and Gulli, the system administrator, the café is empty. Einar is ranting again.

'I've done enough pioneering work in this country. Fuck it. If people don't want the Internet to be accessible to every person, if people don't want to be their own programmers, to make whatever they want, then fuck it.' As he's running with the words, he's scribbling something on a napkin which turns out to be a map of Iceland. On the left side are written the words 'new world', on the right side the words 'old world'. In between the two is a line Einar has labelled cantat 3, the transatlantic fibre optic cable which carries a billion phone calls, data packets and pictures from Europe to North America. Another thin line joins cantat 3 to Iceland. That one cable – cantat 3 – represents a whole new trade route, an electronic passage for the exchange of billions and billions of bits of data from Europe to the Americas and back again. It's as vital to the world's economy now as the old spice, tea and slave routes were five hundred years ago. Einar allows me to study the map for a moment, then pulls it back and next to the thin line joining cantat 3 to Iceland scrawls: 'Leaky.'

'One day,' he says, 'Iceland will be the most wired nation in the world. And it'll be different here, better, because we're so small, a nation of intimates.'

I'm not at all sure that Einar believes in his own anger. I certainly don't.

Thor, Heiða, and I have drunk a good few strange beers before we stumble into Bar 22. It's eleven-thirty. Thor and his band are already twenty minutes late for the video shoot.

'Ah gott,' says Thor, wrinkling up his nose, 'we'll get round to it.'

Bar 22 is Reykjavík's only gay haunt. We're here so Thor can prove he's not homophobic. Only the bar is virtually empty.

'How humiliating, we're showing this woman from England the only gay bar in Iceland and there aren't any gays.'

'They're all upstairs, like I said before,' adds the barman, in English.

'Oh hang on.' Thor points to the door. 'There's one.'

The three of us set our gaze on a middle-aged man standing just inside the entrance to the bar. Thor waves him in, shouting:

'Thossi, come here. This woman wants to meet Icelandic gays.'

'No I don't,' I counter. 'I mean, I don't mind. Yes, fine.'

'Here's proof.' The middle-aged man hands me a plastic-backed card reading: "This is to certify that — is an Honorary Member of the Youth Association of Gay Men and Lesbians of Iceland." I was too old to be a full member,' he adds, sadly.

'See?' says Thor, belching.

We stagger back to the bar with Thossi and order some more beers. Heiða points to the clock on the wall. Twelve-twenty.

'Don't you think we ought to check to see if Torfi's waiting for us?'

'Ach, Gott, no,' mumbles Thor.

'I've always wondered what it's like making a pop video.' This from me in a slurred and strangely distant voice. 'Isn't the lip-synching kind of *embarrassing*?'

'Ach, no. It's a cinch. You stand there and when the director says "go" you open your mouth like a fish and writhe around in agony with the guitar.'

'By the way,' I add — I've only just noticed that the bar is going in and out in a funny way, as though shrugging itself into life — 'I listened to your tape. I thought it was pretty good. Pretty bloody good.'

'Fuck off,' says Thor. 'Ach look, there's another one.' A man in a cravat climbs the stairs towards the bar, waves at Thor and Heiða, who wave and smile back.

'*Stop* it.' We all begin to giggle.

'Listen, about the music,' says Thor. 'Don't ever say that again. Don't *ever* say pretty bloody good again.'

'Piss off, Thor,' I reply. 'Stop being so proud.'

'No, *you* piss off.'

'No, *you*.'

'Piss off *everyone*,' says Thossi.

The rest of the evening is conducted in Icelandic. Leastwise, that's how I remember it.

At three I spill out onto the pavement and make my way tentatively back along the sunlit streets of Reykjavík past the prams in the direction of the guesthouse, wondering vaguely what day it is and whether I should already be at the airport to catch the afternoon flight to London.

LONDON, ENGLAND, THURSDAY

Sex on the wires

Peeping out from the half-life of a three-day hangover, I dimly register that I'm back in England before collapsing in a lump onto the sofa. At some point in the past few days I have noticed another block of graffiti on the wall of my flat; the IRA has declared a cease-fire, the backlash has not yet hit here. I was sick at the airport and sick on the plane. I am sick at heart; full of drink and dull in its wake. I have no conscious thoughts, only a stream of ideas and images and an awareness of my tiny immediate needs. Sleep and paracetamol and water. The voice inside me won't settle. It continues to boil with America and the backlash and the broken promises of a digital age, and I'm struck by the sudden, automatic thought that not even Iceland with its midnight light and angry men and strange beer has quite succeeded in shaking America from my dreams.

Taking off for a walk I return early, intimidated by the familiarity of the streets. My head hurts. My eyes misinterpret the shapes of everything – the shops, the church, a woman jogging with her dog – but my brain still knows what the eyes see. And though I'm disoriented, my common self makes sense to me here in some deep way requiring no proof. This is, after all, the place I was born, the England I can take for granted, the sweet, contrary England, too proud to decline with grace and yet too timid to look ahead, the England so overwhelmed and sustained by history that to catch the future's gaze would be to flirt with its own demise. Poor England, busy running backwards, a place without a plan. Just Eng-land, the land of Engs.

Returning to the Apple Mac after all this time, I feel as though I'm stripping off in front of a parent. It has seen me change from the person I was to the person I am. It has felt the sting of my first disillusionment. But of course we are both proud and neither of us is prepared to admit that things are not the same. The machine displays the same prompt screen it has always displayed and gives no hint that anything is different. As for me, I move through the same almost unconscious list of commands. We don't make any kind of contact, but the contact is already made for us. I don't love my Apple as I once did. And however it has come by the facts, I am certain that it knows this. It senses that for all my resolve to pluck something grand and lastingly optimistic from the first mad flush of the digital age, some inaccessible corner of my psyche still exists in a state of thin foreboding. What if? My mind whispers. What if the entire digital diaspora of broad-band info channels, of satellite links and instantaneous connections, of digi-cash and image flows, serves to do nothing more than flood the world with factoids, to weigh us down in the tide of trivial choice? What if it leaves us dazzled and dependent, common conscripts marching to the deceiving tune of money in some electronic re-boot camp, some world-wide Holy RAM-on Empire? What if it finally drowns us in its data?

In a sudden burst of protectiveness, I think of Mac. It's a strange, disembodied thought too, little more than a patchwork of phrases and a feel for his voice, but it persists with stubborn resolution. It says: Welcome to the post-modem world.

There are three e-mail messages waiting for me. The first is from a friend on the WELL asking if I'd have any objection to having virtual sex with him. A German TV company is making a documentary about technology in the Bay Area and wishes to film my friend having sex across the wires with someone (evidentally I'll do) in Europe. I mail back to say no, then modify my answer to maybe, but only if there's money in it. The second message is from Mac:

>I've missed you. Please phone.

This makes me smile. Sweet, stubborn Mac. I'll call him the moment I've read the final message waiting for me, an anonymous mail sent through the anonymous remailer at the hacker group

HacTic's offices in Amsterdam. This is odd. No one I know would send an anonymous mail, except, perhaps, Mac, and then only in the early days. I move the mouse to its header and click the message open:

>We have good reason to believe that you are involved in unlawful, harmful, hateful, threatening behaviour and/or harassment, particularly relating to minors. We will be watching you.

Harmful, hateful behaviour? I search my memory. I scan my mind for evidence of an enemy, find none. I'm both puzzled and disgusted. Could the whole thing be some kind of joke? It certainly doesn't *feel* like a joke. Who could possibly hate me enough to send such a thing? Who would be so crass as to find it funny? I think of everyone I know at the WELL. No one even remotely hostile springs to mind. I consider my friends, the people I've met through my involvement with technology. Daniel? Thor? Michael from MIT? No no no. Then who? The longer I consider the message, the angrier I become. How dare they? And why? Before long, I've convinced myself that this unwanted, hateful piece of correspondence is not simply an irritation but a violation of my privacy, if not harassment in itself. What kind of creep would send such a message unless it was his intention to intimidate and disarm? And what exactly might he mean by unlawful behaviour relating to minors? What if the sender actually believes his lies? That thought sends a nauseous ache to my guts. I consider the probabilities. They are all awful.

Any thought of speaking to Mac has vanished. My WELL friend e-mails back in the evening, saying that the German TV company are not prepared to pay us to have virtual sex for their cameras, but they are promising to broadcast the show on German national TV. What a scintillating opportunity! Do sex on the wires, get fifteen seconds of fame in Duisburg. Roll the cameras. When *do* we start?

A vile suspicion burrows slowly into my mind, like some malevolent creeping thing. Could the anonymous message have been sent by this WELL friend? And if not, who? I don't know. But I feel I know less and less. Disillusionment is so ugly.

FRIDAY

Another message arrived this morning, or rather, a reiteration of the first, sent through the same anonymous remailer at HacTic. This message was doubly strange; it was signed by the Guardian Angels of the Internet. Why go to the trouble of sending a mail via an anonymous remailer only to give your name and e-mail address? I discover why after typing a reply and receiving the following response from the Guardian Angels:

>We are not the senders of this message. Nonetheless, we are concerned that our name is being used by another party. If you discover the identity of the sender of the message, please let us know.

So my e-mail stalker is using a false identity. But why?

Scrolling back through old correspondence files, I find nothing hostile, but I'm incidentally shocked by the number of people who could be responsible, the number of electronic passers-by who have swapped e-mail with me over the past few months. It's such a promiscuous form of communication. I've had dozens and dozens of e-mail partners and for the most part I've long since forgotten who they are or what we talked about. I'm left to draw the conclusion that speaking to the world is not enough without having something to say.

Perhaps I'm beginning to unravel, as though all the effort of holding off the backlash is slowly blowing me apart. Maybe it's the effect of the hangover, but I don't think so. My thoughts turn to Nancy, who knew me before and knows me now. Nancy, the girl from Ipanema with the wide swing. Six thousand miles away. I'll e-mail her in California. As for England, I suppose I can still count on Mac to be an anchor, the sole survivor of better times, but I'm in such a bad, stringy mood I can hardly bear to call him.

So I pass an evening on the Web, clicking myself into a state of altered consciousness.

SATURDAY, SUNDAY AND BEYOND
Hello reality

Mac calls. He's worried about me. Can we meet? How about this afternoon? The instant the phone goes down a horrible flutter starts up in my stomach and a voice whispers: 'What the hell are you doing?' Mac is nineteen. The year Mac was born I started senior school, bought my first record and fell in love with Donny Osmond. Mac was born the year I first menstruated. While Mac was milk-fed, I could have been a mother. Nonetheless, I tell myself, this is what I have waited for. This is what I want. Flesh on flesh, breaths mixed, something more than modem to modem.

I wash my hair. Mac is fifteen minutes late. I clean my teeth. Half an hour. I rub baby lotion into my legs. An hour. Pluck my eyebrows, clean my teeth again, rub baby lotion into my . . . and then, of a sudden, just as I'm about to give up on Mac, the doorbell shrieks. I run up to the first floor, find a chair and peer through the stairwell window out onto the street. A puzzle. The man standing at the door is not the tall dark man with blue eyes who stood behind me at the queue for the ferris wheel. Not the man who was Mac. This man is shorter and heavier set. He has mouse brown hair. He is wearing a thick sweater and a pair of jeans and though he *is* Mac he is not – how should I say this? – he is not the Mac exactly I'd anticipated. But he has beautiful eyes. Deep lush irises and lashes so long you could twist a rope from them. Irises the colour of conkers. Beautiful eyes and a long sweet blush of a smile. Say hello to another Mac. Hello to reality.

For some reason the whole meeting is very awkward. We hew and ha for a while over a cup of tea (a cup of tea!), reconstruct past e-mail messages, laugh nervously over our few misunderstandings, compare notes on each other's voices (before discovering his age, I had imagined his as darker, whereas he thought mine would sound older). We see-saw through the usual geek initiation rites: Apple Macintosh vs IBM, the RISC chip over Pentium, Microsoft meets the Universe. He does look terribly young. We play a game of Doom; he wins. I make another cup of tea. He inspects my bookshelves. I pretend not to notice him staring at me over the teapot, but as he's heading for the bathroom, I'm watching his back and imagining the front, and telling myself that the body may only be nineteen, but what comes out of the mouth is much older, more considered and mature. We get talking about my record collection and though I try to dazzle him with my new flourish of techno CDs, he insists on rooting around among my most embarrassing old LPs and reading out the sleeve notes. After that he reassures me that there will be an early eighties revival sooner or later. Then he turns his attention to my books, fishing out paperbacks and asking me what they're like, and of course, he chooses the very ones I haven't got round to reading, leaving me no choice but to pass comments like 'Hmm, moving', 'informative, as I recall' and 'very nice'. We pick through the books, and for some odd reason I get a sudden attack of nervous giggles and the sun stabs though the windows and Mac suggests we go for a walk on the Common, and somehow the walk elongates and becomes a tremendous hike round South London and we fetch up in another park and Mac says he'll show me a few of his aikido moves and we each feel the other's heartbeat quicken and he throws me over his back to demonstrate a move and with the tiniest hesitation fails to back off quite as quickly as he might, and sensing that I have also failed to back off as quickly as I might, he draws me closer and closes those beautiful eyes and kisses me. And I'm so frightened of the excitement that I forget to breathe.

Kiss me quick Mac.

Sunday morning I wake up with the sun on my skin and I realize that, yesterday excepted, I've barely been outside in a week. The light is picking out the blue veins in my hands, the first few fragile knots and lines, the slight slack around the waist. I watch Mac sleeping at the edge of the bed and even though I'm smiling at his grassy eyebrows and the brush of his lashes and his quiet lips, a splinter of sadness slowly worries its way under my skin and into the flesh. There he lies, my new lover, just risen from child-hood, and here am I, long-adult with my blue-white flesh just at the edge of age and I know then that this thing will never do. The realization sinks me. I feel used up and alone, as old and frightful as the sun.

The next thing I'm aware of is the sound of the phone ringing. Mac has already gone. Assuming it's him, I run to pick up the receiver before the answer machine catches the call and mouth 'hi' in my best throwaway voice, but it's not Mac – it's Daniel.

'So did you meet anyone younger than me?' Daniel never announces himself at the beginning of a phone call. 'In America I mean? Anyone doing techie stuff. Anyone successful?'

'How old are you again?' I ask, collecting myself.

'Eighteen now. Hahaha.'

I think back.

'Well in that case yes, I did.'

'Shit.' In the background I can hear Daniel's little sister begin to chant: 'shit, shit, shit.' Daniel puts his hand over the receiver. A muffled whisper. 'You mustn't say shit, it's rude. Well I know I did, but that's different.' Then he lifts his hand and returns to me.

'I s'pose that even if I did a Bill Wyman and disappeared for twelve years in a haze of booze and drugs, I'd still only be as old as you when I made my comeback.'

'Thanks for pointing that out, Daniel,' I growl in return, feeling like some sad monument to days long gone.

'Hahaha,' sniggers Daniel.

My breath smells of the blood on my lips. I boil up a cup of cold coffee left over from the night before, and reach for the newspaper on the doormat. On the front page is an article about Soul Catcher 2000, a British Telecom project to 'download' the memories of entire lives onto computer chips, and I'm reminded of Adrian T. I wonder if memory is the store of context and meaning in our lives and whether those without it are condemned to live in a loop of shadowy ephemera.

A hand-delivered parcel clunks through the letterbox. Inside is a video tape and a note from Mac saying 'Watch first, eat later.' Until now I'd never seen his handwriting, never scanned across the particular pattern of his hand. Until now, at least so far as the written word is concerned, we've only ever talked in typing.

The tape contains one of the strangest sights I've ever seen – near complete footage of a series of cosmetic surgery procedures performed on the face of a French performance artist called Orlan. In the first procedure the surgeon inserts a pair of silicon cheek-bone implants into the woman's forehead, transforming her face into something from a fifties scifi film. As the scalpel unzips the skin from her ears and the surgeon's hand is inserted and the skin of the face is prised from the muscle below, Orlan, under local anesthetic, provides commentary on the theory and practices of medical technology. As the muscle of the cheek is exposed to the camera, the bone just visible under the rube of rolled-back flesh, Orlan discusses the creation of the post-human body. It's an ugly, prurient show. I'm taken aback to think of Mac being taken *in* by such inverse vanity. But maybe he isn't. What a peculiarly inappropriate thing for Mac to give me, considering what we've just done.

The afternoon is spent at a PC warehouse, lusting over various intricate pieces of hardware with glamorous names and impossible claims. Software is such a letdown by comparison with the glossy plastic thrills of circuitry. The marketing people know that when you purchase a gigabyte of data, you want it to look like a gigabyte (you want it to be *big*), but they can't come up with anything to make it big other than outsized boxes full of polystyrene. So you pay £50 for your outsized box, all sealed off in shrink wrap, and you get it home and bingo, two tiny floppy discs or a single data CD tumble out. And you feel strangely cheated.

Next to the Bon Jovi official screensaver on aisle twelve lies a drab little container called 'Great Bear's 101 Love Letters', which immediately draws my attention. It turns out to be a software package of themed love letters. Angry in Love, Secret Admirer, Love Can't Wait, Friends as Lovers, AIDS, Disease and Love (*Disease* and love?) The box blurb says: 'You simply choose the category, select the perfect letter, personalize it by using easy, fill-in-the-blanks steps and you are ready to print, e-mail or modem your words of passion . . . Because everyone needs a little love.' 'Great Bear's 101 Love Letters' is produced and manufactured by the Commando Corporation. There are no letters to cater for 'Inter-generational Love', 'Internet Love', or even 'Impossible Love'.

Nancy replies to my e-mail of Friday:

>Two episodes of American history come to mind, she writes:

>First. When Raleigh and his men moored off Roanoke Island and began to paddle ashore in landing boats, the Indians, not having seen such boats before, refused to believe in their existence and supposed that Raleigh and his men were walking on water. The Indians thought they were gods.

Second. When the Spanish came to Mexico they brought with them an old Moorish legend about the existence of seven golden cities, the Cities of Cibola. In 1549 the Moorish slave Estevan crossed into what is now Arizona, and spotting what he hoped was gold, but was in fact mica, a glinting, slate-like stone the Indians used for building, he sent word to his boss that he'd seen the Seven Cities. By the time another expedition arrived in Arizona to find Estevan, the slave and all his party had been killed. And no one found any gold.

In other words, I know how important it is to you to be upbeat about all this new electronic stuff, but at what price?

WEDNESDAY

No word from Mac. I rang a neurologist friend to find out more about memory. She said people with no short-term memory like Adrian T often display signs of *latent* memory. No one quite knows how this works, but the research indicates that latent memory is somehow akin to the unconscious. Impressions, conversations, sights and feelings can all be stored away without our having access to them, or even being aware of their existence. For every memory you can recall, you may have a thousand you can't. Millions of little bytes of information, your whole unconscious history, can remain hidden from you forever, because without conscious memory, the brain stores remembrances unconsciously, automatically. And though these unconscious memories can't be remixed, sampled, distorted consciously, they can nonetheless mark a person, change him and bring to his life a history.

So, according to my neurologist friend, though Adrian T may have few conscious memories beyond his sixteenth year, it's quite possible that his latent memory is perfectly intact and, if that's so, then he can learn from experience, albeit in a limited way. His latent memory will continue to sculpt him in ways he can neither control nor fully perceive. And though his recollections of a more recent life are dim, Adrian T will not be forever frozen in adolescence. Slowly, just like the rest of us, he will find a way to grow up.

SATURDAY

Ten minutes before Mac is due to arrive, I've arranged my newly bathed self in a picturesque manner on the sofa before a copy of *Generation X* and a cup of mint tea. We don't bother to pretend to want to talk. Mac opens his arms and I fall into them and we pass the afternoon sliding about the bed, breaking off only when the muscles in our limbs demand it, but otherwise lost in the thickness of sex and sweat. By the evening, the bedroom is rank with the odours of rawed flesh and bright blood and semen. We dress and tumble out onto the common, where we suck on giant ice creams and apply their coolness to the grazes on our chins. I lead Mac down to the bog, far from the games pitch and the dog-walking tracks, far from the patch where the gays hang out, far from the bandstand and the café, and we hide under a hawthorn tree. A fat German Shepherd digs us out a while later. I want to sleep out under the light pollution, but Mac insists on going home.

I tell my lover about my travels over sour black coffee. And although he nods and passes the occasional comment and is sweet enough to laugh, it's clear that Mac is barely listening and an absent glaze wets his eyes. For a while I'm able to convince myself his inattention is tiredness, but I know that the truth is otherwise. E-mail merely gave us the illusion of commanding each other's absolute attention but it's now plain that Mac is too much pre-occupied by his own inner world to want to pass much time exploring mine, inner or outer. He isn't interested in my real-life stories. For Mac, adventures happen in the world beyond the wires. I suppose everything else must seem to him to be some lesser reality.

About the anonymous messages: Mac suggests I e-mail the system administrator at HacTic, who replies a few hours later by saying that he doesn't really understand the problem. So what? Some nut is accusing me of child molestation. Mac has sunk into my sofa and switched on the TV. He says he can't see what the big deal is either.

MONDAY

William Gibson is in town tomorrow to promote his new novel.

TUESDAY

Feeling like a vampire

The crowds are phenomenal. Every techie worth the name owns a piece of timeshare in Gibson.

The writer shows up as scheduled looking beaky and thin. His voice is smooth, but for some reason I quickly lose the thread of what he's saying and find myself drifting along in an atmosphere of associations during which it occurs to me that people's imaginations, their inner lives, are also a form of virtual reality, which leads me to wonder whether, say, cats have imaginations and, if they do, whether they create interior worlds from their dreams, and whether there exists such a thing as cat VR.

Waiting in line to get my copy of his novel signed after the talk, I overhear Gibson saying something about the info-agoraphobia of modern life, the tidal rush of white electronic noise which competes for our attention and I wonder whether that is why he felt compelled to re-imagine cyberspace and why also he can write about it without seeming banal or over-literal. In any case Info-agoraphobia's a meaty phrase and I make a mental note to remember it.

While he's signing my book, I ask Gibson about his childhood and he recalls that as a pensive child in a nowhere sort of town, he'd been obliged to live in a fantasy world of scifi comics. This secret world had kept him sane, but it had also kept him apart, he confessed, and I said: 'Do you think the Net means the end of the outsider?' And Gibson said, 'Well maybe it does, you know.' And without drawing any comparisons between us, we agreed that, had the Net been around during our respective childhoods, we might have ended up on some Internet Relay Chat channel exchanging opinions about Nike Airs with kids in Sydney and moaning about our parents. And Gibson might never have written a line.

Info-agoraphobia. *One banana two banana three banana four.*

After the talk I discover that someone has broken into my Nissan and run off with the radio. What they couldn't have known is what a terrible radio it really is. I sit in the driver's seat and imagine the thief hunched over his newly rifled kit fiddling with the tuner and banging the thing about in a desperate attempt to pick up something other than the London country music station. And destined forever to fail.

I mention the radio to Mac when he rings later that evening. He says he used to steal car radios himself when he was a kid. All the boys he knew who'd grown up in London during the eighties went on nicking sprees. It was just one of those things.

Nancy comes to mind. Whenever I feel lonely, I wish she were here with me. I wish she were my sister. I wish she were my *fantasy* sister. But she is not my sister. She is a distant friend, who, by technological trickery, sometimes feels near.

> >Dear Nance,
>   I think I need your advice, but I'm not sure how to explain what I have to ask. I expect you'll have worked out that Mac and I are lovers. He has come to represent something important to me though I don't quite know what. I do know that it's destined to fail. Because? Simple. He's nineteen and I am, well, you know how old. He's too raw. Something is missing. What can I call it? Some shared sense of life, perhaps. A backstory.
>   A while ago I had the idea that Mac and I were indivisible. Two halves of one soul. Oh god, I know that's corny and in any case I haven't thought it for a long time. But e-mail is full of tricks that way. But now I feel I am a vampire, drinking his youth, using the life up.
>   What should I do?
>   Love
>   M

Only once it's sent do I realize that this is my first electronic *letter*. 'Dear Nance' and 'Love M' seem to make the words more intimate and more demanding of a considered response, just like faxes used to be ten years ago.

The remains of the day are spent watching TV and floating in and out of consciousness. Sometime during the night I stir myself from the sofa, down a couple of antihistamine tabs and stagger to bed before dissolving into a dizzy universe of dreams.

WEDNESDAY

I'm woken by the postman bringing two parcels – a tape from Daniel and a pile of the latest technoculture books from Nancy – plus four bills, six items of junk mail, the advertising flyers for three Indian takeaways and a pizza-to-go place, and a Time-Life instant scratchcard. I spend an hour or two skimming through the books and munching chocolate, ticking off keywords in my head, when some spark of a nerve reminds me to call the police and report the stolen radio. The policeman on the other end of the phone asks if I've ever considered investing in a fully lockable, detachable, pump-primed, quadraphonic, security-coded, alarm-ridden model. I thank him for his help and reassure him that next time I find myself with a couple of hundred pounds lying around I'll give it serious thought, only will it bring me a cup of tea in bed?

In the evening an e-mail arrives from Nancy.

> >Darling
> Nineteen-year-old men are specifically conceived, designed and manufactured for thirtysomething women. All resistance is useless. You mean your mother didn't tell you? Oh really, stop being so serious. You'll get bored of each other soon enough.
>   PS Did you get the parcel? Discovered Hot Java yet? I forgot to ask - how was Iceland?

She's right. I resolve not to think about Mac for a day or so and chew him over once the skin has settled, so to speak. Since we don't e-mail with the frequency we once did, the task is easier than it might have been six months ago.

Daniel calls. This week he's been commissioned to compose TV music, he's started writing for the *Wire*, been screen-tested for a new computer games show and become the technology correspondent of *Harper's and Queen* . . . Then there are ongoing discussions with Mo'Wax, Ninja Tune, R&S Records and the possibility of some collaborative remixes. This and that. He wants to know if I've seen the new Sony Playstation, or come across a beta copy of Virtual Racer and whether or not I'm aware that ambient jungle is about to become the next big thing or that Slam City Skates skateboarding shop has another sale on? Oh, the rise and rise of Daniel P.

Nancy is online when I write to her. She's burning rubber up the Infobahn, scattering roadkill on the data tracks, hot-rodding along the Information Superhighway. Well, it *is* her office lunch break.

>Like I said, she replies, in answer to mine. >All resistance is useless. Now tell me about *Iceland*. Did you meet the president?

>I forgot.

>*Forgot?* So what *did* you find out?

>Not much, to tell the truth.

(Which might have something to do with the fact that I drank enough alcohol to burst a brewery.)

>No encounter with dour Viking programmers, then?

>I didn't meet anyone remotely dour. Icelanders don't take themselves seriously enough to be earnest, even.

I make a vague attempt to draw the subject to a close. Nancy appears to take the hint:

>Not like Californians, then.

>No.

>Tell me, would you say a culture of technology is developing everywhere? I never seem to make it out of the Bay Area.

The phone rings, cutting the connection between us, but whoever is making the call hangs up the moment I answer. I wander back to the screen, reset the modem and wait for the dialler to re-establish a connection to the server. In answer to Nancy's question, I'm beginning to suspect that technology merely moulds existing cultures, rather than creating new ones all its own.

Technology + business = the information economy, downsizing, global markets, instantaneous price adjustments, world products, niche marketing, surveillance.

Technology + popular culture = syndicated TV soaps and live news broadcasts and four trillion terrestrial channels and five million cable channels and home shopping and instant access to Internet Relay Chat.

And so on. Mac comes to mind, with his huge working knowledge of mixing, sampling, re-ordering, matching, revising and distortion, his can-do mentality, his vividly felt connection to the world. For a short moment I'm envious of him. Then other thoughts invade the space. The more I think about the idea of global culture, for example, the less I like it. Global markets and global corporations muscle in at the same time as there's huge political and social fragmentation. Is that a co-incidence? I don't think so. And what are we to expect as a result? A world no longer divided into Japanese, Russians, Haitians, or even into Asians, Africans and Australasians, but into the Slavic Christian Shoppers' Club and the Death Penalty Supporters' Consumer Group, which moneyed little microtribes will in turn be opposed by the largest tribe of all, the undifferentiated global poor. And if that's the future, how the hell is it going to be any better than the present? I type:

>On a macro level all the digital revolution's really going to do is concentrate power in the hands of the owners of global capital.

Nancy replies:

>On the other hand, without it, we wouldn't be talking now! Hey, by the way, I'm eating wheatgrass juice and a veggie sandwich. I've cut out the crap, which must mean I'm happy again, right?

I think of the baked beans, fried eggs, chips and chocolate cake I've got lined up for dinner, and sense a dark depression coming on.

THURSDAY

Some statistics about technology and national habits, gleaned from the pages of *Newsweek* and the *Financial Times*:

> *The average British household spends 8 minutes per day on the phone. The average American household spends 24 minutes.*

> *4.5 per cent of Japanese homes are hooked up to cable TV. In America, it's 60 per cent of homes.*

> *In the US there are 34 PCs per 100 citizens, in Britain there are 22, in continental Europe only 10.*

> *66 per cent of American households rent at least one video per month. Only 22 per cent of European households do.*

Data, statistics, information, knowledge, research. Comforting, but what does it all mean? For me? For Nancy? For any of us?

SATURDAY

A special e-mail has arrived from Larry T, with details of his son's memory problem. Trouble is, it's all in some encrypted code. Beta 64 I think. Mac says he's never heard of Beta 64. No one seems to know how to decode it, except Larry T himself, of course, but I'm too proud to mail him and ask. Net users love a newbie to patronize, but once you reach a certain level of Internet experience something changes and you're suddenly expected to be an expert. Intermediaries are not welcome on the Internet.

There were local elections last week, and Mac refused to vote. He appears to be very bitter about politics, says that everyone in the UK under the age of twenty has been forced to stand by while an effective one-party state (sixteen years of Conservatism thus far) has steadily dismantled young people's opportunities and sabotaged their education. He's seen five or six general elections pass, but the politics has always stayed the same. Voting is for losers in Mac's world. Politics is just a matter of Doing It Yourself.

With this in mind, my unsuitable lover has invited me to a roads protest. I find this anti-car mood of his slightly odd, because he's always seemed so fond of machines, but this is also the first time he's asked me to accompany him anywhere and I've no mind to turn him down.

According to Mac, the anti-roads movement began when an assortment of young people – unimpressed by Thatcher's baubles – set off in convoys of ancient vans and decommissioned buses in search of a new lifestyle, only to find themselves moved on by police wherever they stopped a while. It seemed to these new nomads that what little common land remained in Britain effectively belonged not to the people but to whoever was making the rules in parliament. Before long the tabloid press got wind of the convoys and the myth of the smelly, scrounging New Age traveller was made. Then to make things worse, the government introduced the Criminal Justice and Public Order Act, which made it a criminal offence for six or more vehicles to gather on a piece of land with the intention of remaining on it. And at the same time the government thought it might as well criminalize a couple of other alternative youth lifestyles too, so it also became a criminal offence to hold an unauthorized party with more than one hundred people listening to amplified music in the open air. Neo-pagans, hippies, young travellers, back-to-the-landers and party goers were suddenly united in a common bond of resistance and the do-it-yourself generation was truly born.

My unsuitable lover says he doesn't want any kids of his to inherit a giant smoggy car park in lieu of countryside and that's why he wants no more roads. Funny, but at Mac's age, I never gave kids a thought.

Mac shows up carrying a large parcel wrapped in white linen. The brown hair, by now familiar, the usual chunky sweater I've grown to like, the lolloping gait. A book of photography and an assortment of treasures from his childhood emerge from the parcel: a balsa-wood boat, a ball made of rubber bands and a guide on how to put up a tent. Mac's gift reminds me of everything that first drew me to him. The generous spirit, happy-go-lucky ease, the self-involvement. I can't recall when I was last so touched by any gift. A swell of protective affection hits my throat and I cup his chin in my hand and stroke the corner of his lips with my thumb and smile. His face softens and he grins at me and I crease my eyes and stare into those brown beads of his, and I'm *almost* able to convince myself that the throb in my throat and the tightness in my chest are something to do with love.

'Let's go to bed,' I beg. 'Please?'

Mac shakes his head, adamant we head off to the protest. 'It's all meat and no potatoes with you,' he moans.

'Can we drive to the protest?' Mac can't believe his ears and heaves with impatience and contempt. 'You just don't take this seriously, man.' But he does agree, reluctantly, to allow me to drive him to the nearest tube station and during the car journey takes it upon himself to harangue me for my lack of moral fibre.

'Look,' I say, 'Political causes are generational.'

'Right.' This from Mac, with bitterness in his voice. 'So I guess that, like, invalidates them.'

'Don't be ridiculous.' The atmosphere between us is sour as ferment. 'It's just that people your age seem to have fixed on anti-roads.'

'And hunt sabbing, and ethical shoplifting *and* animal rights *and* squatting *and* environmental stuff *and* the CJA.'

We've had this conversation once already, but it looks as though we're about to have it again.

'You people only care about the Criminal Justice Act because it restricts raving and squatting and hunt sabbing and the travellers' lifestyle. It's all self-interested. You don't care about the fact that, say, a suspect's silence during police interrogation can now be used as incriminating evidence against him in court . . .'

We turn into a side street and scan the road for a place to park.

'And you do?'

'Of course,' I say, backing up into a space between a VW Beetle and a Jeep Cherokee.

'So why the hell are you letting "people" like me do the protesting for you, then, *Saturday Night Fever*?'

Mac knows exactly when to pull his punches.

We arrive at the protest just before midday. About five hundred others have already gathered, and are being handed posters and anti-roads placards: NO V'ROOM TO BREATHE, PEOPLE NOT CARS. The plan is to occupy a central London street, close it to traffic and party away the afternoon, thereby demonstrating to the locals how much richer their community might be without the roar of trucks and the billowing fumes of backed-up cars at traffic lights.

Mac and I lose each other somewhere between the meeting place and the tube station. I hang around by the ticket machines hoping to spot his orange T-shirt moving in among the crowd. It occurs to me that he might have run away deliberately and that I might even be an embarrassment to him. British Transport Police and the Met are out in force inside the tube station, running up and down like cornered alley cats and delivering little homilies through their loudhailers on the punishments to be meted out to fare dodgers. A tide of fare dodgers breaks over the ticket barriers and tumbles down into the bowels of the station. Five hundred protesters, destination question mark. The police don't like the look of that at all. They've positioned spies to report on anything they overhear. All over the station anxious policemen are busy filing misinformation back to HQ. 'Caucasian male, mid-twenties, heard shouting something about Hampstead, sir. Oh no, wait a minute, correction. Party's destination is Rio de Janeiro. The one in the southern hemisphere.'

The human tide heads south to Camden Town, then descends en masse from the trains. Someone shouts, 'Don't make any trouble with the police' down a megaphone, and a man near me volleys back, 'We don't have to make trouble. The police *are* trouble.'

Out on the street near Camden Market, where consumerism in the form of cheap street fashion and ethnic jewellery masquerades as counterculture, the protest's organizers, Reclaim the Streets, have blocked the route to traffic by setting a couple of wrecker's yard jalopies in the middle of the road and wiring up a sound system to blast house and reggae out into the street and make the tarmacadam shake.

'Party, you bastards,' shouts someone.

At that moment I think I can see Mac, weaving in and out of the crowd at the margins of the road, banner in hand, but the moment I move towards him, he's gone again. Protesters are laying down cloths and tarpaulins on the road, setting themselves in circles about. Some begin to dance while a group of bemused Italian tourists pose for pictures under a banner reading KILL THE CAR, RECLAIM THE STREET. The air of celebration has less to do with the rush of disobedience now and more to the fact that a large group of young folk are set on having a good time. It's not that the protesters aren't genuinely angry about their cause, it's that their anger concentrates the atmosphere and makes each protester feel closer to the comrades by their side.

A TV news crew has appeared to film someone spraying FUCK SISTOM on one of the charabangs, a Talbot. The police have finally arrived and are turning away the traffic built up on either side of the street party. A wiry-bodied teen is taking a baseball bat to the Samba's windscreen. A spray of splinters hits the road and the crowd instinctively ripples back. The kids who had been romping over the machines a minute before now strain at the periphery in wonder. Two TV crews move in, followed by two or three of the protesters and the kids, who set about smashing the car lights and tugging off the chrome fixtures. One man takes a wrench to the Talbot's front door, and suddenly three or four men are inside, ripping out the upholstery, peeling back the plastic cladding. The crowd begins to chant 'Kill the car, kill the car', and the children plunge in, egged on by the presence of the cameras and each other and set to the cars with stones and other weapons. 'Kill the car, kill the car, kill the car.'

Note: As teenagers my generation didn't protest against cars. We always thought the world would be blown to fragments long before it was stifled by petrol fumes and overlaid in asphalt. When we protested, which wasn't very often, it was usually about Thatcher, the miners' strike, Nicaragua or cruise missiles.

I didn't have much of a social life until I'd learned to drive. I cycled to places, but it was a long way to anywhere much and scary in the dark. There were no buses around. My dad was in the car business then, and he'd sometimes bring an extra motor home from work for us to use. Consequently, by the time I reached eighteen I'd driven all kinds of different cars. I was always so terrified of wrecking them it took the pleasure out. Dad was fierce. One time I drank too much and sped up the wrong side of a dual carriageway at two in the morning. The car came to a standstill in the middle of a roundabout. After that I had two rules – never drink and drive, and always be first off at the lights.

There was a patch of dual carriageway with a roundabout at the end near the village where we lived and the boys would steam up the carriageway in their dad's cars, or whatever, and try and make it all the way' round the roundabout at the top in one handbrake turn. No one called this joyriding, though, because the term hadn't yet been invented.

If the notion of a car culture had ever occurred to us, which it hadn't, we would have associated it with America and with words like megalopolis, conurbation, freeway, turnpike, toll-road, drive-through. All the modern words. America. Am-er-i-ca. *Onebananatwobanana*. Oh I know it's half a dream, but I miss it all the same.

A flash of orange catches my eye and is lost in the rumbling roll of protesters, market shoppers and tourists. I move away from the carcasses of the cars and find a spot to sit on a piece of tarpaulin up by the bridge over Regent's Canal. A couple station themselves nearby, the woman leaning up against the iron bridge and the man rolling a cigarette against the crossroads of his knees. In the midst of the throb and song of people I'm overwhelmed by the urge to lay down my head and sleep. The man finishes his cigarette and begins to doze. I feel my eyes darken and I wake to find the day worn on and the sun dumping its last-ditch remains in bright columns onto the paving stones of Camden Town. The couple next to me have gone. South of the ruins of the cars, the crowd is dancing. Cans of Tennant's Extra and bottles of cider litter the street. The banner KILL THE CAR, RECLAIM THE STREET, hangs limp between two telegraph poles. Camden Market's stallholders have begun packing up. A good day for them. I wander down to the canal, past Dingwall's Club, and back up Chalk Farm Road, but Mac is nowhere to be seen. At the phone box by the bridge I call Mac's number. There's no reply. Some small remnant of defiance prevents me from giving up and returning home, so I buy myself a beer in a café and scrutinize the thin trickle of protesters slouching towards the tube.

An hour or two passes before I call Mac again. Still no response. As evening takes over from afternoon the police begin to move in closer, forming a phalanx between the protesters and the underground station. And at seven, or thereabouts, someone throws the first bottle.

I get through to Mac from the phone at home. He answers on the fourth ring.

'Hey,' I say, 'were you there at the end? It all got out of hand.'

'Yeah.' He sounds deflated and impatient.

'It's a shame that . . .' searching for the word, 'we lost each other.'

'Yeah.' A second's pause. 'I looked for you . . .'

'And I looked for you . . .' I surprise myself with the bitter tone.

'So what did you think?'

A shimmer of hostility passes between us. 'I thought it was a pretty desperate gesture, car fetishism in reverse. Smash it up, or deify it, you're in thrall either way. Take the Unabomber.'

(Take me, for that matter.)

Something in my tone puts Mac on the defensive:

'Every time more roads are built, they generate more traffic. It's a waste of money.'

I spot a parallel:

'Maybe exactly the same thing will happen to the Net,' I say, modulating my voice in the struggle to change the subject. 'As the bandwidth gets bigger, it'll fill up with more and more corporate advertising and virtual shopping and porno pics and snapshots of people's holidays. And eventually absolutely everything in real life will have its counterpart on the wires.'

'At which point,' says Mac taking up my cue, 'real life can simply be replaced by representations of real life.'

'And planet earth, its history and everything in it can be reduced to a magnetic strip on a smart card in the hands of a single superior intelligence.'

'Oh God, it sounds like the BT project.'

Mac laughs and I laugh, and neither of us quite knows why.

Much later, in the middle of the night, I'm lying awake and alone in bed and something Nancy said suddenly comes to mind. 'The networks will be built in a day,' she said. 'They already are. In a year's time you'll hardly remember life without them.'

ONE MONDAY

Autumn has arrived. The cat has a new coat and the first of the fallen sycamore leaves twists about in the wind on the common. Mac and I see less of one another. Less and less. It's the way things go, I guess.

Daniel calls today. He's been asked to contribute to *Wired* magazine and he's talking through some kind of record deal with 3D of Massive Attack. And since ambient is almost certainly dead, he and Ben are about to set up a guitar band.

'Daniel,' I say, secretly envious, 'don't you *ever* stop?'

'Hahaha,' replies Daniel, which presumably means no.

THE FOLLOWING DAY

Re: data, statistics, information, knowledge, research.

I wake up early, get in my car, put my foot to the metal and drive two hundred and fifty miles to a technoculture conference. Heath is already there. We smile and wave at each other over the banks of plastic chairs.

The cultural studies departments of universities and colleges really have found their motherlode in digitalia. It's the perfect topic for them. No sooner have they got their hands on something than they're decoding it. X signifies Y, this means that, black is actually white when you look at it closely enough. And the digital world offers endless possibilities for decoding because the digital world *is* code.

Lecture One: Arthur and Marilouise Kroker, a husband and wife team of technotheorists from Canada discuss the will to virtuality. I read Arthur K's book back in the spring. Today though, the couple canter incomprehensibly through cyberheroes, recombinant flesh, haikued souls, pull into telematic data, then gallop ahead with hard-wired bodies, human remnant, techno-euphorics, crash and burn, virtual roadkill, geek-flesh, gene splicing, hypertext, and finally, at the finishing line, 'Nietzsche has a modem'. Arthur says: 'We'd like to conclude our presentation with some speed spasms to explore the deep digital music for cyber-ears and hypertext bodies.'

After the talk, I look about for Heath, and, not finding him in any of the obvious places, I wander over to the bookstall and pick up a copy of Arthur K's book, *Data Trash*. 'Data trash loves living at the violent edge where total human body scanning meets an inner mind that says no, and means it. When surf's up on the Net, data trash puts on its electronic body and goes for a spin on the cyber-grid.' It's strange to think that I was once bold enough to imagine I understood this. I hold out the book to the bookstand assistant.

'What is this exactly?'

'Oh,' she says. 'As I understand it, it's a collection of virtual stories for the flesh-eating nineties.'

During the break a man and a woman, both serious-looking, are standing drinking tea over the sugar bowl. The man is saying: 'The sociological stuff interests me because it says so much about . . .' waving quotation marks in the air with his hands, '"one's own career."'

'And one's area,' adds the woman. 'But more than that, one's *category*.'

'Just look what happened to Foucault,' says the man, helping himself to another sugarcube. 'So restricted.'

'True,' agrees the woman, bleakly, then, brightening, adds: 'but he was a Marxist, a liberal and an anarchist.'

'So I guess that does make it better.'

Coming out of the cubicle in the ladies' toilet I spy Marilouise Kroker powdering her face. I mean, actually powdering her face, with *powder*. I didn't know anyone used that stuff any more.

Heath is nowhere to be found. Not in the cinema, the lecture theatre, nor wandering about the concrete walkways. He must have left at some point during the first lecture. From now on, I'm on my own.

Mid-afternoon I'm strolling along one of the concrete walkways, avoiding a lecture, when the bent figure of a man appears in view, until from a few metres distance I'm able to make out the prostrate form of one of the panellists from this morning's Q&A, who appears to be pulling something from the ground. Hearing me approach, the man looks up awkwardly, abruptly straightens himself and with some embarrassed haste strides off in the opposite direction muttering to himself like the White Rabbit. It's not until I actually reach the spot where he was standing a minute before that I see what the panellist was pulling at. Someone has glued a twenty-pence piece onto the walkway. I give it a little tug, but it's stuck fast. For the next half-hour I stroll around the pathways with new eyes. There's a coin stuck onto the surface of the concrete every fifty paces. Once the afternoon tea break is announced, there'll be a stampede. The pavement will be black with panellists picking pennies. Who's idea of a joke is this? And where *is* Heath?

At four I sit in a plenary session entitled 'Replicunts and Cyberfeminism' in which an Australian woman called GashGirl *and* Puppet Mistress distributes nudie pictures of herself and discusses in detail the sado-masochistic episodes of her six-month Net sex career.

Lying in the foyer just before the start of the post-tea-break talk are a few bundles of leaflets put out to accompany the day's lectures. Picking two at random: 'Techno: Psychosocial Tumult', and 'Pronoia and the Jilted Generation: A Technomadic Manifesto', I head into the lecture theatre. Up on the rostrum a couple of technicians are wiring up a sound system watched by the gathering audience in the pit, and by a boy-man standing at the side of the rostrum with a bottle of beer in his hand and a smoking rollie caught between his lips. Curious, I flip through the first couple of pages of 'Techno: Psychosocial Tumult', read: 'samplers are the hyper-concentrated representation of the subjective experience of time, with possibilities for time travel through stretching, combining, looping, compressing and reversing sounds. Sequencers form new desires for composing, connected to the breaking up of an individual into a collection of experiments. Drum machines and synths are tools for survival against mediocre audio programming and the restrictions of commerciality, fashion, competition and self-promotion. Routes constructed between music studios and the dance floor circulate into resistance against unacceptable states of mind.'

And some time after that, I climb into my Nissan, put my

foot to the metal and drive the two hundred and fifty miles back home.

THURSDAY

Mac comes round in the evening. I return his Orlan tape. Go on, take it. I insist. Trash it. Shred it. Waste it.

I feel as gnarly as a redwood tree.

> *Fee, fi, fo, fum*
> *I smell the blood of an Englishman*
> *Be he alive or be he dead*
> *I'll grind his bones to make my bread*

Stomp, stomp, stomp. Mac decides not to stay.

The sex is . . . *nice.*

FRIDAY

Daniel calls. He hasn't given up on the guitar band idea, but he's now thinking of living in San Francisco for a year after school. He'll cut some tracks, compose a film score, do a spot of DJing, file for half a dozen magazines, remix some stuff, make a video, write a book (only joking about the book, hahaha), generally chill out.

SUNDAY
Ugly, shop-soiled, disillusioned

I'm leaving London for Wales. Travelling at about the same speed as my jalopy is a dumpster truck carrying a skip engraved with Heath's raiding insignia. Three TV monitors, a modem, and four keyboards.

It's dark by the time we reach the Severn Bridge. The Saturday night crowd has gathered in McDonald's in the centre of Newport. I walk past the pool hall, a chapel, across the road and into the chippie, order a box of fried chicken and ask the owner if he knows where the nearest B&B might be. 'Try Stow Hill,' he says. So I begin the trek up Stow Hill, licking the chicken from my fingers as I go.

The woman at the B&B is watching the TV when I ring on the doorbell. She opens the door. Curiosity plays about her lips.

'Visiting someone?' This in a Welsh tilt, lifted at the end.

I smile in return. 'Some friends are having a party tonight at the Brewhouse.'

'Oh, well.'

'Not friends exactly. We met on the Internet. The Way Collective? They're holding a WebJam, whatever that is.'

The Collective, a group of ex-students from Newport College of Art have set their hearts on a technomadic lifestyle, roaming the country with computers in their bags and mobile phones in their pockets, picking up graphics jobs here and there. A CD cover, a rave flyer, a festival poster. If only there were graphics jobs. If only they had enough money for computers and mobile phones. If only they could roam. In the meantime, they imagine setting up a WayOut Internet training school in Newport, and WayOut Internet café cum bustling arts centre at the Brewhouse pub and a WayOut Nomadic Research Centre. This in a town where a good night out is fifteen pints of Carlsberg and a Happy Meal.

'I wouldn't know, love,' says Mrs B&B. She waves her hand about the room. 'There's hot and cold water in the bathroom at the end of the corridor. Tea and coffee facilities. And what time will you be wanting breakfast, then?' She hands me a photocopy of a map.

Later, I walk back down Stow Hill, through the shadow cast by St Woolos Cathedral as it rises over the terraces like a rocket at the launch pad. From my vantage Stow Hill gives way and falls towards the River Usk, whose pitted waters are lit by the safety lamps from the cranes on Bristol Packet Wharf. Across the other side of the river the estates of Summer Hill create a bauble of brightness, the thinly illuminated vein of the M4 motorway is just visible beyond. There is no sound except the occasional play of metal on metal and a faint rush from traffic headed east on the motorway towards the English border. Back on Stow Hill, two cars pass by at speed. A blare of noise follows them upwards. On the corner of a terrace of early Victorian houses a woman spills out of a Hindu Centre and heads off rapidly down a side street. A boat wrinkles the water at Liverpool Wharf, drawing a faint slap from the waves. Closer up, the river smells of dank, sour water, rusty with industry.

Britain's down, but it's not quite out. The scene fills me with a rush of fondness and I'm suddenly remembering what I love about the country. Its quirkiness, its dogged and misplaced self-reliance, its mesh of people, its lovely bloody-mindedness. A mawkish little tear starts down my cheek, then another, and another still, a whole tender flood, bringing with it such an unfamiliar feeling I wonder if something alien has invaded my psyche. A laugh comes out, followed by more tears. And then I'm crying for something else, though I don't know what. Everything.

I take out my pocket mirror and inspect my eyes under the light of a street lamp. They are puffed and veiny. My cheeks are red, my mouth bumpy. I look like a tomato. I turn around and make my way back to Mrs B&B and her tea and coffee facilities. Later, with one eye on the TV and a cup of instant hot chocolate in my lap, I find myself writing out the story of my technolife:

> *Woman falls in love with America.*
> *Gets tangled up in technophilia. A brief period of wonderment follows.*
> *She returns home (which never felt like home). She champions the cause, in her usual inefficient way.*
> *No one much is interested. A nineteen-year-old boy is all.*
> *So she runs back to America but finds everything changed.*
> *She stiffens her lip. Or tries to. Typical Brit.*

Returns home (which still doesn't feel like home).

She is ugly, shop-soiled, disillusioned. Stiff-upper, stiff-upper, stiff-upper self-pity.

She thinks: what now?

MONDAY

Newport looks less romantic in the light. At some point in the late seventies, the planners got to work, sowing the town and its surrounding countryside with a dismal crop of distributor feeds, one-way bypass loops, overhead walkways and out-of-town retail parks. And then the money ran out.

The BBC want the Way Collective WebJam for their new *CyberWales* series, but they won't pay the crew weekend rates, so the Way Collective have agreed to restage last night's party again today for the benefit of the cameras. A film crew is already stationed outside the Brewhouse pub. Paul and Helen of the Way Collective introduce themselves, point out Jenny, the director on *CyberWales*. Paul is chemical white. Helen seems cheerful, but is not. The atmosphere is dark.

'We appear, as you can see, to be locked out,' says Jenny crisply. Helen lets out a sigh.

'Sorry.' She takes on a beaten air. 'Sorry, sorry, sorry.'

One of the film crew appears with a tray covered in foamy cups.

'And, uh, look, you missed the cappuccino run,' says Jenny to me, taking her mobile phone from her pocket and calling London. 'Hello, hello, yeah, get me Mike.' In her black vinyl bomber jacket and tight leopardskin top she's a tiny replica of Tina Turner in *Mad Max 2*. Only white.

Some minutes later the Brewhouse owner appears with the key, and we all file in. Downstairs looks like Central Park after the Rolling Stones, knee-deep in ground butts, beaten-up cans and used bits of Wrigley's. Upstairs is worse. There is vomit on the floor. Helen goes off to find a broom, while Tiny Tina and I work up what passes for a conversation in the hope that it'll get us out of the clearing up.

'You live in Wales?' I say to TT.

'*No, of course not*,' TT replies. 'I live in London.' Sensing some burr in my voice she hesitates a moment. Then continues: 'Although, *obviously*, I'm red hot on all this techie stuff, I deliver aesthetically and I have a fucking good rep, or I wouldn't be doing the show. Plus I had an amazing Welsh childhood.'

Part-way through the morning, TT decides she needs a pre-shoot meeting, calls Helen and Paul to her table.

'I'd like to discuss the representation of the Way Collective on TV,' she says.

Helen: Fine. Paul: OK, man.

'We're really going for an *East Enders* audience here with *CyberWales*. So . . .' She holds up a wedge of tweedy material, stuffed like a car seat '. . . we've had this fantastic cuddly soft computer made from Welsh wool.' A conspiratorial tone creeps into her voice. 'We don't want any of the housewives watching to be intimidated, do we?'

'What about a wool modem?' asks Helen. Jenny loses her smile.

'No, no, no, that really wouldn't look right.' Jenny tosses her crop and addresses herself to Helen:

'Trust me, you're talking to a *Nettie* here.' Helen and I swap glances and the smallest of titters.

'Nethead,' says Helen politely.

And with that the figure in leopardskin and leather stomps off to 'rig up'. Paul wonders if they'll all be stars once the show is broadcast. 'Just think. We could get funding to set up a Techno-madic research lab, a vast, global nomadic think tank. It'd be like pronoia.'

'Except Steve Roberts already set up the Nomadic research labs in San Diego with a ton of sponsorship money,' I say, meanly.

Paul shakes his white dreads and smiles: 'Yeah, probably. But

I'm gonna leave the country anyway. I reckon I can do better somewhere else.'

'Like where?'

He shrugs. 'I dunno. Somewhere like Mozambique, maybe.'

Escape. The full force of it lodges deep inside my head. Somewhere beyond the hype and anti-hype!

By eleven-thirty the cameraman has finished setting up the lights and Helen has done the sweeping and clearing. Gareth, the presenter of *CyberWales* zooms in, puts a hand out, slaps backs, squeezes palms, grins like a speeding goldfish. All 'hey' and 'hi' and 'Let's get it kickin' in here'. And whaddya know? Gareth *also* had an amazing Welsh childhood.

Around midday TT gives the signal to begin the shoot.

'OK, I want to do a vox pop about the Internet with some regular Newport types. Then we'll "do" the party.' She stripes a couple of quotation marks in the air. 'So – will you, you, you –' she points to a group of students, me, the owners of the Brewhouse and the stills photographer – 'go down into the street and we'll ask you on camera what you think about the Net.' We shuffle out of the pub into dazzling sunlight and begin our vox pop rehearsals with Jenny as coach, marking each of us in turn. 'You say something like "The Internet? Never heard of it." You say: "The Internet, sure, I use it all the time." OK, everyone, OK, quiet now, we're going to roll with this. Number one . . . GO!' And at that very moment a real Newporter with a face as raw as a flayed pelt staggers up the street and onto camera singing, 'Where's my fucking giro, where's my fucking giro,' to the tune of The Conga. *Cut!!*

By three, Jenny's had the Brewhouse dry-iced and she's filming Gareth wearing camouflage trousers and wrap-round shades thudding bare-chested about an 'interactive' dance floor with the art college extras. Rave graphics spin about the ceiling and a row of computers spews out hip images from the Web. The beat goes ta-tata-ta-tata. Gareth whoops and favours the camera with his better side. Someone is pretending to capture the thing on a palmcorder. For the TV cameras of course.

I have been exiled to a table at the other side of the room with a journalist from London who's about to be interviewed for *CyberWales* on the subject of children, porn and the Net (for god's sake dads don't let your daughters . . .)

'I can't believe this crap,' I scream above the beat. A sudden surge of anger rises up in me. 'All these tired media cyberclichés; wrap-round shades, dry ice, cool Web pages, club clothes, porn. Who gives a shit? Not Wales and not me.'

MONDAY

I'm still unable to crack Larry T's encrypted message. There is news over the radio announcing two more anti-roads protests over the weekend, arrests made.

The Apple Mac and I aren't getting along particularly well right now. Some weird little bug in my e-mail program is leaving its calling card all over my messages. I type in:

>**Dear Mac**

and the bug adds about a hundred lines of:

>**???*!!!%%%@§§5\$ &&+!!!**

and promptly dispatches the mail. Remembering New York Thor's prowess with the mails, I send out an electronic SOS and get no response. I wonder whether Thor had finally kept his promise to himself, and is living somewhere so remote that not even his SkyTel pager works. And is happy. A small shimmer of hope curls up my spine.

THURSDAY

A shameful discovery! Cat has been sick through the ventilation holes of the Apple Mac's CPU. I noticed when I pulled it out to reach for something behind, but it must have happened some time ago. Leastwise, I guess it was sick. In any case, it's no wonder the thing was behaving weirdly. Now I feel guilty about all the A.I. cracks, of course.

SUNDAY

Roddy rang this afternoon. He got beaten up in a skirmish between the police and some young people on the Marsh Farm Estate in Luton.

Did I mention Roddy before? We met for the first time at the anti-roads protest. He was filming the whole thing for an alternative news video called Undercurrents. I bought him a cheese and spinach pasty because he didn't want to leave his post and I wanted someone to talk to.

'You look tired,' I said. He'd been working the nightshift at Heathrow airport the night before, monitoring the data-backup tapes. 'Do you do this often?' I gestured about. It sounded like a come-on, but Roddy didn't take it that way. 'No,' he said, smirking, 'I started as a paparazzo. Can you believe it? Hanging around at three o'clock in the morning at Harry's Bar waiting for Don Johnson to come out. Now look at me.' We began eating our pasties. Roddy said he'd just had enough of pointless celebrity pics. He'd seen some documentary on the TV about badger-baiting and decided to join the animal rights lobby. At that time everyone in the lobby was talking about the CJA and the poll tax riots and the anti-roads protests and Roddy was converted to the DIY movement.

We swapped phone numbers, and I rang him a few days after

the anti-roads march to make sure he hadn't been hurt in the bottle-throwing and police charges. After that he sent me a tape of some of his work. Footage of cherrypickers pulling protesters from trees at the site of the M11 extension in northeast London, of hunt saboteurs being arrested, mounted police charges, riot shields. All in the name of public order and safety, of course. One time Roddy took his camcorder into the Houses of Parliament, wandered about completely unchallenged and filmed the Mother of Parliament's most private parts. He opened filing cabinets, taped the contents of wastebins and MPs' desks. No one stopped him, not once.

Yesterday his camcorder was smashed to pieces. He said he was intending to file a complaint against the police. I asked if the disturbances at Luton had anything to do with Exodus. A couple of years back a collective of young homeless people squatted a disused pig farm on the outskirts of the town and persuaded local businesses to donate wood and tools which they used to renovate the farm and make it habitable. They set themselves up as the Exodus collective. After a while, they began putting on free parties round and about, using donations from the partygoers to keep the farm running. At their height, ten thousand people were turning up to these free parties, which the police didn't like at all. Tension between the two got worse and stayed that way.

Roddy, like Mac, belongs to the Digital Generation, the first true inhabitants of the world of CCTV and Internet and computer disks and VCR and electronic billboards and the last batch of adults to be produced by the twentieth century. Images are the Digital Generation's hard currency. Without images they are lost. Roddy once said: 'I only ever get frightened when I take my eye away from the viewfinder, because then I'm actually a part of it.'

A sweet and cheering e-mail arrives from Nancy, leaving a charge of restless energy in its wake. I walk down to the Common and pick up a tin of spaghetti and a McDonald's apple pie for supper. Two glasses of Jim Beam, three cigarettes, two Unisom later, I'm sleeping like a baby. At three-fifteen I'm woken by the sound of

Cat scratching at the door. An orange spear of light is coming in from the street lamp outside. I pull the duvet up over my head and close my eyes once more. Mac comes to mind. I roll over onto the other side and try to hum myself to sleep. Within seconds I've drifted off, only to be woken minutes later by snoring, presumably my own. After an hour of intermittent humming I resolve to get up and do something productive, so I fetch myself a cup of tea and walk out onto the roof terrace from where I can admire the Big Dipper and watch the wind wrapping the moon in clouds.

A man wanders down the street, sees me standing there with mug and sweater, stops momentarily to stare. Spell of the night broken, I creep back inside the house and log onto the Web and flip to Daniel's webpage and notice a shadow of myself on the screen. I finger Mac's e-mail box, register that he has twenty-two messages waiting, feel a trace of guilt for keeping tabs on him and cut the connection.

All sleepiness gone, I wander out to the terrace again and wait for the light to come up, leaving the stains of the Big Dipper in the sky. Over the roofs of South London, TV aerials are slicing up the dawn like prison bars, spotted with the black-hole shadows of satellite dishes and, though I can hear nothing, I know that each dish and spoke is quivering with silent messages, the white noise of our existence. It's like this every night. Whilst London sleeps and its screens are grey and lifeless, a gargantuan roar of energy still gushes from aerial to aerial, from receiver to receiver and from dish to dish. The flow of life fills me, standing there, imagining the billions of images hurtling past me then through space as radio signals and microwaves and light, their currency now void and their power dulled, the great sea of images that is our whole century's history washing out through the solar system and into the Milky Way and beyond. It's the twentieth-century's magic. I consider the kind of creature or machine, a million light years distant, which will bear witness to the weather chart for Chicago on 13 January 1972, and a soldier dying in a trench, the *I Love Lucy Show* and John F. Kennedy's brains in Jackie Kennedy's hair, a family filling a shopping cart at K-Mart in Cincinnati,

Ohio, and another family eating a McDonald's Big Value Meal and two kids abducting a little boy in a shopping mall in England, Roddy's tramp through the Houses of Parliament and the view of a smart bomb hitting a home in Baghdad and Brazil winning the World Cup and an advertisement for Mighty Morphin Power Rangers and Michael Jackson's *Thriller* video and a downloaded slice of a criminal's brain and a virtual sex store and my mother and father and Mac and Daniel and Nancy and me.

And then the days begins, as it always does, with Cat insisting on his breakfast.

SATURDAY (NEARLY A WEEK LATER)

Something has happened.

Mac and I had been together in the afternoon. I'd lit a Camel and was propped up on cushions, smoking. With his back to me, Mac was stroking Cat. We were talking about the weather. Even though it wasn't winter yet I was longing for spring. Mac, who has a habit of reiterating his position five times together whenever it differs from mine, replied: 'I like winter,' running his hands over Cat's fur. 'Winter is fine, winter is good, winter is better than any other season.'

'Well *I* don't think so,' I said bluntly, taking a long drag on my cigarette, reminded suddenly of the first time Mac told me he liked the rain, way back when.

'The summer's for, like, flakes,' reiterated Mac, picking up Cat and thumping him into his lap.

'Cat doesn't like people's laps,' I said, although it wasn't true. With typical feline treachery, Cat had started up a motory purr.

'Yeah, like, right,' said Mac. I scrabbled about for some response that was adequate to my anger, but my mind had cut off. All I was thinking was how much I hated him. We sat in horrible silence for what seemed like an hour and was probably an instant, and when I opened my mouth a stream of bile spilled from it and I shrieked:

'I *despise* all your "like" and "man" crap. Just who the *fuck* do you think you are? Some American kid from the Projects, or what?'

'Just listen to yourself,' Mac replied, as though whatever I had to say was suddenly beneath his contempt. He turned about for an instant and shot me a look. The sight of those turned-in eyes made me loathe the stuff that lay beneath them, all those parts of him I didn't have access to any more, all the pieces of his self that he had given me in e-mail and was denying me now.

'The sex wasn't all that good anyway.' I lit another cigarette, noticed how shaky my hand was, registered the fact that Cat had run away.

'Yeah, right,' he said. Something else snapped then. I looked at him, in all his youngness and careless arrogance and I felt as though he, and only he, was the reason I could never get back to the kid I once was with Nancy on Venice Beach. It was as though he was sucking out the happiness. And I realized I didn't even know him well enough to hurt him much, and I leafed through the index of spite in my head and all I could think of to say was: 'You didn't even think to use a condom, for God's sake.' (As though the whole thing was his idea.) 'I thought everyone your age understood the risks. And you could have fucking killed me.' Or killed me, fucking. I heard myself bellowing like a wounded, crusty old wildebeest.

And Mac simply looked down at me and laughed. There he was, standing now, squat and brown, not the tall black-haired man with blue eyes who had stood behind me in the queue for the big wheel, but Mac, laughing, with his stupid soft cock jigging up and down in rhythm with his diaphragm. For an instant I wanted to howl with laughter too. And then I wanted to make him cry.

'Oh come on, man,' he said. 'The risks are tiny.' I could see him quelling his anger, refusing to be moved. It made me want to punch his lights out. He put his trousers on. 'Any case, what about me? You've had way longer to pick up diseases than I have.'

I gave him a look but he refused to acknowledge the gaze. I felt my face flush with bitter, thwarted tyranny, as though suddenly conscious of the other's power.

'Look, if it makes you feel any better, I've only slept with, I dunno, fifteen or twenty people, OK?' Mac was about to go, but I couldn't let him.

'Fifteen or twenty? Not even nineteen or twenty, but some casual guestimate?' I screamed. 'That's just about one for every year since you were a *foetus*. Fifteen or twenty post-AIDS generation people, a pyramid of millions. Jesus, Mac, somewhere along the line we've probably slept with *everyone*.'

'Plus some one-night stands,' said Mac, pensively. 'I don't remember how many.' I could tell he was softening, and I knew I had him.

'You'll just have to have an AIDS test, then,' I said calmly, twisting the knife.

He picked up his football shirt, stumbled to the door, murmured 'whatever' and was gone.

Calmed by a draught of Jim Beam with a hot chocolate chaser, I e-mailed Nancy begging her to call.

Mid-afternoon the phone rang. Thinking it was Nance I ran to it and garbled 'Hello!' with such sad excitement it took me back. Then I remembered that it was the middle of the night in Nancy's world.

'I'm in Whittington Hospital, waiting for the results,' said Mac.

I felt an overwhelming rush of guilt.

'Do you want me to come over?'

A sly laugh slipped down the phone line. Then something happened. Mac's breathing changed.

'It's fucking horrible,' he began, his voice sounding full from the effort of staving off tears. 'I had to go in and talk to a counsellor before the test.'

'Did you tell your parents?'

'What do you think? Of *course* I bloody didn't.'

'Mac,' I said, too late for it to count, 'I'm sorry.'

I felt him stiffen.

'Yeah, well, I'll let you know.'

The phone fell silent and the empty signal followed it.

I spent the remainder of the afternoon pacing about the flat, conscripting Cat into acting as my companion and picturing Mac sitting out his punishment in some waiting room at the Whittington, flipping through ancient copies of *Cosmopolitan* while some technician two floors above trawled microscopically through his blood. I found myself imagining the slow curve of his buttocks, his sweet-faced grin, the pull of life in his body.

He rang again at some hour in the evening, brusque this time.

'It's negative.'

The relief spun through me like a sword. I found myself coughing up a string of guilty sobs.

'Happy?' he added. I swallowed sputum and felt dead.

'Can we meet?' I said, sounding pathetic, even to myself.

'I'm going to Amsterdam.'

The phone went down.

Later, I remembered that the HIV virus has an incubation period, and told myself not to be so paranoid. Nancy did not call.

SUNDAY

Daniel is poking through the fridge in the kitchen at my flat. We're discussing the music video he's about to make. It'll be filmed at night, and feature Daniel playing air synthesizer on top of Tower Bridge. The music will be clipped from a long composition of his called 'NeoTokyo', and he's hoping for a post-apocalyptic paranoia feel. He's going to do some fast-cut urban sequences and he wants the whole thing to look kind of Sam Raimi.

'Where are you thinking of filming the urban sequences?'

'Uh . . .' He looks pensive. 'East Molesey?'

I cut a slice of bread and drop it in the toaster.

'Daniel, East Molesey is a middle-class 'burb. The high street is full of antique shops, for God's sake.'

'Well?' Daniel is on the defensive. He cuts off all the crusts on his toast. 'East Molesey is my 'hood.'

This elicits a giggle from me. I'm sorry but I can't help myself.

'Honest,' says Daniel, now in playful mode. 'Hahaha. East Molesey can be really hard.'

Daniel is now drinking alcohol. He's had his hair buzz-cut and put on some weight. Other things have changed also. He's suffered his first real setback. Sussex University has turned down his application to join their media studies programme. An appeal has failed.

'I'm not some sixteen-year-old protégé any more,' he sighs, scraping off the burnt bits on his toast. There's a note of nostalgia in his voice, as though he's suddenly become conscious of what he's given up and is no longer certain that it was all worth it. Maybe he's sensing that adulthood isn't necessarily a freedom.

'Up till now I've been like a mascot or something.'

Though I'm so used to Daniel's face that it's hard for me to figure changes in it, a new kind of uncertainty seems present in his eyes and a new determination about his mouth. We sit and eat our toast. Thinking back over the months of our friendship, Daniel and I have actually taken great pains with each other. I wonder why his youngness and naïve vitality brought out a fond protectiveness in me when I am so easily threatened and disordered by the same in Mac.

'I went to the Cold Cut studio today.' Daniel scrapes his toast scraps into the bin. 'They asked me to jam about on the keyboards and I did this riff which sounded just like the Doors.' He heaves an enormous comedy sigh. 'It was just like being a pop star.'

After Daniel's gone I make myself a cup of tea, switch on the electric fire and log onto the Net. Outside the wind hoots round the corner of the street taking with it the carcasses of leaves and all the mess of the pavement. There is no mail from either Nancy or Mac. When I call Nancy, I am put through to her answering service. A feeling of utter isolation steals over me. It's not an expansive, exhilarating kind of isolation, but a pinched-up, compacted little knot of sadness.

I f-feel so lonely I could d-die.

THE FOLLOWING SUNDAY

This is suicide Sunday.

The larger part of a cardboardy Filet o' Fish lies half-eaten on the table at McDonald's. Outside the sky is low and brackish, and the ruined remains of the late autumn light fall onto the greasy breezeblock towers of Charles Square. Four kids on the verge of adulthood are sitting on a new wooden bench in the square, sucking rollies. There are stains and rifts in the concrete and an odour of damp and piss percolates through the air. At the feet of one of the kids is a Staffordshire bull terrier on a rope of leather. A skateboard is balanced on the left side arm rest.

Charles Square was supposed to be Bracknell's town centre, but these days the centre is assumed to be McDonald's. All edge towns are like that now.

Inside McD's the Sunday Sweep progresses. Young families are strewn about the ground floor, parents looking harassed, kids running their free plastic promotions along the tables. Teenagers are on the floor above, taking up the afternoon with french fries and a Coke. At the front of everything is a flower bed planted with sprigs of green stuff. The dead remnants of Happy Meals are threaded in between and the whole bed smells vaguely of benzene. The most striking thing about the place though is its hive rhythm, built from the throb of softened voices, the slow churn of number-less people processing from door to counter to table to waste bin, to toilet to door. It's the soft swag of Billions Served, the humming buzz of humanity.

Those four kids squeezed up on that single homage to a public space remind me, now I think about it, of the bench in the park near my flat, which went up in the summer. Attached to it is a plaque, with a boy's name and dates and the legend: 'He took his own life.' Whenever I walk by, which I do often, I feel as though I'm slinking past a crack in the world, leading down into the deep core. The bench is always surrounded by kids and their dogs, showing off and larking around.

I call Teena from the phone booth outside McD's.

'See you at Hope Cottages, Mount Pleasant around two-thirty,' she says, confirming our arrangement.

'How do I get there?'

'It's on the outskirts of the town. Just ask.'

'The edge of the edge,' I say, but she has already hung up.

It's difficult to know what the town planners were thinking when they built Bracknell, back in '49. I wasn't there. I suppose it must have seemed like a good idea. Nice new housing estates, no slums, only an hour or so from the capital. A future place, or a place with a future. Only the future isn't here yet. The future never arrived.

Out in Charles Square one of the bench kids has taken to leapfrogging an old washing-powder box on his skateboard. His dog bounces yelping behind, his mates are feet up on the bench, laughing. It has begun raining in earnest.

Suicide. I considered it once or twice, when I was a teen. Everyone does. Only later did it come to seem like a serious proposition. You can't feel mortality when you're fourteen. You have to imagine it. How many pills it takes, the psychedelic twirl of blood in the bath, the drowning panic, the white light at the end of the tunnel, what you'd wear. Marilyn Monroe, Jim Morrison, Sylvia Plath, Kurt Cobain. Day-dreamed scenes against a Joy Division soundtrack, and a title sequence listing the people who'd be sorry . . .

The suicide rate has risen by 71 per cent among men between the ages of fifteen and twenty-four in the last ten years. Isolation, unemployment, bullying, no prospects, no role, no role models come to that, always pressure. Pressure all the time. Pressure to succeed, have sex, get a job, a life. What's gone wrong? Father-lessness, extended adolescence, the fantasies peddled by youth culture, the feminization of the workplace, violence, insecurity, divorce, AIDS. Everyone has a theory.

I walk to Mount Pleasant in the rain, through the empty bus station, past the old folks drop-in centre, under the bypass and across a tub of dead petunia plants buried in the concrete of a roundabout. Each node on the journey is a little drabber than the last. A local newspaper headlines with the story: 'Mounted police patrol estates'.

Teena, twenty-one, answers suicidal e-mails from a computer terminal at Hope Cottages, as a volunteer for the Samaritans.

'We take it in turns to log on, download the messages and compose a response.' (Think about the people who love you. It won't always seem this way. Why do you feel so lonely?) 'Sometimes people reply, sometimes they don't.'

The Samaritans receive e-mail messages every day in several different Englishes and a number of foreign languages too. Anonymous e-mails arrive from an anonymous remailing terminal in Finland, fragmented messages are despatched in bits and bytes of code, some encrypted, others not. From time to time an incomprehensible trail of keyboard characters arrives. Most times, though, it's the usual mix of self-justification, confusion, resentment, terror. A thousand cries for help. The lonely crowd in the global village. Consider this, says Teena:

'Before people kill themselves they could easily make a video or a tape of their message. But they don't. They write a letter.'

'How do you know that what you're doing helps?' This in the gloomy tone that has become habitual now.

'How do you know it doesn't? It's hard to say. You hope to make a difference, that's all.'

The Samaritans don't advertise their e-mail service, occasionally it's mentioned on the Internet, which is where I came across it, but in the first year of the service they received well over a thousand e-mailed messages. By their own estimates fewer than half the people phoning in or visiting the Samaritans' drop-in centres are in serious danger of taking their lives, but three-quarters of their e-mail correspondents are genuinely suicidal.

'An e-mail is different from a phone call,' says Teena. 'An e-mail is final. An e-mail is the written word.'

From Hope Cottages I make my way back to the railway station, past the sump of petunia plants, under the bypass, then through the empty bus station and along the side of McDonald's to the greasy breezeblock towers of Charles Square and finally to the bench with the skateboarding boy and the dog with the sharky eyes.

v: THROUGH THE LOOKING GLASS

'Berlin is completely fucked,' my new friend gasps and he should know, he's been here since the wall came down. He tamps his rollie on the bar top. 'No special status, no government grants, no jobs, nothing.' We are sitting in a basement dive somewhere east of where the wall once stood and where its rubble still lies, talking and drinking German beer, which, although not as strange as Icelandic beer, is at least considerably cheaper and better-tasting. By some strange quirk of the brewing process, the more German beer I find myself drinking the closer it comes to the Reykjavík kind. H and I are keeping warm and drunk down here. It's a freezing night and the buildings all around us, still burdened by the sooty grime of their past, are clattering with the noise of new graffiti. Ahead of us the freakish light of the Fernsehturm shines like a nuclear eye obliterating the night around.

H stops to call a friend from a public phone outside the bar. It's one in the morning and the air is so punishing cold that ice clings in crystals to the hood of the phone booth. The coin box has been part-pulled from the wall. H goes off the idea of calling his friend. We work our way down the street towards a group of potheads lounging about on a bench. The pavement appears to shift at an angle to the road, like a piece of toffee set on a slant.

'Where's the nearest bar?' asks H. A German-sized woman in hippie clothes points to a door behind us. Her boyfriend offers us a toke.

'We'll have a drink,' says H, 'and then we'll go to the Bunker.'
'Right.' The Bunker is a techno-club, H's favourite.

'I have something to say,' declares H, considering the label on his bottle of beer.

'Go on.'

'Techno music is like a symbol for freedom in East Berlin.' H is in philosophical mood.

'Vorsprung durch Technik.' My beery breath washes over H. It doesn't seem to bother him. In fact, he pulls his barstool closer and, leaning a hand quite casually on my shoulder, continues:

'What I'm saying is, Germany's love affair with machines is all so *German*.'

I stare at the mattress of foam floating at the top of my glass, trying to get this to sink in, but its precise meaning eludes me. So I go 'Wow,' which seems to satisfy H. He puts an arm around my neck and compresses my shoulders together – which is somehow both erotic and slightly nauseating – then tosses me a fine smile. He gazes at his glass, and struggles with some thought.

'There wasn't any dance music in the East before. There wasn't any disco or hi-energy or electro pop. There wasn't anything. Then the wall came down and whoomph, in came techno, like an avenging god. And the kids went mad. For the first time they felt part of the world. Connected. It was like a new way of being.'

'A new way of being,' I repeat, wondering vaguely if I'm falling in love or merely drunk enough to feel big feelings.

Back out on the street the hippie woman and her boyfriend have been replaced by a group of skinny teens with all the hallmarks of junkies. A posse of leather men billows past checking out the junkie boys and heads off towards the Spree. En route to the Bunker on Albrechtstrasse we pass by ten or fifteen building sites, their cranes lit up like radiating mantises. H suggests we count them. One, two, four . . . or is that three? And do you count a road repair? Or is it only new buildings? Men in uniform stand guard inside the fenced perimeters, holding back their German shepherds. Steam rises from everything.

H and I swallow a little speed to help us to remain upright

through the queue outside the Bunker. We're at the head of the queue before I notice I'm holding my hands like fists and my knuckles are white.

'I feel like beating something up,' I say to H, wondering if that's a line from a movie.

'OK,' says H, sounding like he's on for that.

'Only I'm too bloody scared,' I add, thinking I might be feeling sad about something or whatever. Not caring much.

H wipes the side of my face with his glove and we stumble into the Bunker.

Inside it's one-eighty beats a minute. Hardcore. Gabba. Tension. Techno. Boom, boom, boom, boom, tinkatink, tinkatink. Ku'damm, Ku'damm, Ku'damm. We spill along a warren of dank corridors dripping with the condensed sweat of dancers, tension techno racing through like fast blood. The smell of pheromones and chemical paint is inescapable. The whole scene here is like watching the violent spewing and pumping of your own body from the inside, at three beats a second.

'Fucking great.' H jabs around on the dance floor like a leg bone on a trampoline.

'Yeah.' Tikatink, tikatink, dom, dom, dom. The noise makes you want to peel off your skin and stomp around flesh free.

And later we seem to be in H's flat, smoking dope and coming down and I'm secretly wondering if we're going to crash together before we actually fall apart. And the light outside is flabby and grey like left-over porridge and there are crews of Irish, Scots, English, Turkish navvies lining up in front of the building sites and the blokes in uniform are still there, keeping everything orderly. And H says:

'You should see the scene in Dresden. It's bloody hardcore.' And there's a moment's silence in which we're considering our erotic possibilities but are too stoned to do anything about them. And then the S-bahn rattles by, leaving an empty noise behind it, and everything, including me and H, feels suddenly angry or sad.

And with bitterness in his voice H says:

'Ten years ago, those folk in the Bunker were just kids, kids being spoon-fed Marxist dialectic and the inherent contradictions of capitalism. And now they're suddenly expected to believe that the equilibrium unemployment level is 10 per cent, the market creates its own demand and the West is our friend.'

Below us, a van pulls up at the side of the street and the driver delivers a bundle of morning papers to the newsagent.

TUESDAY

The Berlin train draws into Dresden and I'm running through a list of excuses for not getting off. It's too late in the day, we're halfway to Prague already, my bags are too full, my head too heavy. All excuses, whereas the truth is guilt. British guilt. Dresden is the city the British wasted, razed, blew to bits. The train screams to a halt. I sit tight and stare at my toes and eventually the driver pulls off the brakes and the carriage begins to crawl away from the station and out into the suburbs, and in no time we're rushing southwards towards the Czech border where the countryside begins to close in, throwing up huge rocky crags. And by the time we've reached the border we're following a slow procession of black barges tugging down a dark river and all about us are high sandstone cliffs, the glowering sky and naked middle European castles. Looming pines cut gloomy silhouettes into the cloud, and below us the river begins to run a little faster. Before long a man in a cheap polyester uniform wanders down the aisle to check our passports and we're suddenly sliding through the Czech countryside like some sly metal snake.

PRAGUE, THURSDAY AND ON TO THE WEEKEND

I'm installed in a disused army barracks which has been given a sniff of paint and laughably renamed the Legion Hotel in one corner of IP Pavlova Square in the southern section of Prague

New Town, about ten minutes walk from Wenceslas Square. The district was actually established in 1348, according to my guide, but much of the original, medieval New Town was demolished and rebuilt in the nineteenth century in the Art Nouveau style, so strictly speaking, I suppose it should now be known as the old-new nouveau old-new town. Prague hasn't developed in a muddled, organic way, like most ancient cities, but in discrete steps. Medieval, *fin de siècle*, Republican, Communist, New Order.

The Legion Hotel is Communist era. Clues: the rooms are dingy, the showers bracing, the rations meagre, the staff stony, and it's going to be that way no matter what you pay. The general squalor seems really to enrage only Germans and Americans, though, and the foyer is seldom empty of some frustrated soul from Essen or Iowa going ballistic over the freezing water, breakfast spam and ripped sheets. Naturally the staff don't give a hoot. In common with much of the rest of Prague, the Legion's sole concession to the new order aside from a coat of gloss paint has been to triple the price of everything four times over, and then to double it again.

So here I am, unravelling out over Eastern Europe like a card of sour, unwanted wool.

Every ground space larger than a pocket handkerchief is currently being dug up by gypsy navvies, imported guest workers from Slovakia. Telephone cables, sewage outlets, fibre optics, electric ducts, water pipes, fire hydrants, service tunnels for the underground. The whole city is in the process of having its clunky communist veins removed and new and leaner veins inserted in their places. The pedestrian crossings here tick like crazy cartoon bombs, their red and green men blacked out by blown fuses.

H had heard a rumour that Prague was about to receive what will possibly be the least-needed edifice in Eastern Europe; a multi-media space: 'underground' gallery, alternative English-language bookstore, Internet café and cool ex-pat hang-out to be called the Terminal Bar. A little piece of @ abroad.

The moment the Iron Curtain came down in Prague, half America turned up to peer in at the window. About forty thousand people living in Prague are Americans. Over the past couple of years the features pages of the Western press have brimmed with stories of expats in Prague under such titles as: 'The New Bohemia' and 'Slackers in Paradise'.

The Terminal Bar isn't operational yet, but I manage to find the number of the planning office and the chief, Chuck, invites me to swing by, sit in on the staff meeting and check out some of the plans.

So I wander down towards Wenceslas Square, past the city's first sex shop and along a cobbled alley running parallel to Zitna Street. Eventually, I burst out of an alley halfway down Wenceslas Square, opposite the Europa Hotel and next to the delicatessen where tourists buy their souvenir sausages, and from there along a narrow cobbled street, lined with wedding-cake buildings filled with Bohemian crystal and Czech garnets and other nicknacks, down into the Old Town Square, with its bizarre agglomeration of gothic pubs, rococo palaces, churches and Art Nouveau offices. The Terminal Bar team work out of a slip of a room at one end of an apartment in the Old Town Square overlooking the fifteenth-century astronomical clock.

At the Terminal Bar staff meeting Chuck and his team discuss who got the most stoned the previous night and how cheaply you can buy draw and where, and whether or not to put Ortega y Gasset's work on dialectical materialism on order for the bookstore. Staff meeting conclusions: none. Chuck then repairs to another room and brings in some architectural drawings of the Terminal Bar-to-be. There is a press release, but it's not quite finished yet, and no one remembers where they last saw it.

'When do you plan to open?' I ask, inspecting the drawings.

'In April, maybe. Approximately in April.'

I hand back the plans. 'Can the infrastructure handle T1 connections?' The plans call for high-speed fibre optic cables connecting the café's computers out to the main carrier at the university. Chuck either fails to register the question, or chooses not to respond to it.

'We're gonna have cool stuff all over the walls. Like posters by the Residents. And we're gonna have all these amazing videos like the footage of the Prague Spring and Eraserhead and, you know, books like Burroughs and Bukowski and so forth.'

Another of the Terminal team interrupts:

'And loads of cyberpunk stuff and future culture and . . .'

'And, like, cool magazines.'

A small silence falls. One of the team breaks it with a lazy belch.

'The point is, the Terminal Bar doesn't want the Czech public to get caught up with the idea that Western culture is all about Barbie dolls and *Dynasty*,' says the belcher.

'And hey,' sparks Chuck excitedly, clutching a new idea, 'how's about we invite the Red Army Faction to the grand opening?'

'Totally *cool*.'

'Or the Baader-Meinhof gang!' brainstorms Chuck.

I spend the remainder of the morning stamping around the Powder Tower, one of a zillion tourists in town. The last time I came to Prague, in '85, the rows of Art Nouveau apartment buildings were caked in desiccated diesel fumes and the streets in last-night's vomit. No one seemed to do much other than work and queue and drink. But now the streets have been cleaned up, the Art Nouveau murals repainted and the stores filled with Bohemian crystal and hand-carved gypsy kitchen utensils and everyone now finds themselves working, queuing, drinking *and shopping* in the authentic spirit of the Prague of the *belle époque*, minus a few small details, such as Jews and horse dung.

Something tells me I'm not going to be here as long as I'd first imagined.

Towards night I fetch up at the Radost Club, trying to track down Linda Ladida, who, according to H, is one of the pivots of the

Czech Republic techno scene. Radost is beginning to fill with the sparkly young things of the bright new order, the sons and daughters of Prague's all-of-a-sudden fat-cats, its free-market shuffle-bags, import and export fixers, its currency launderers, minor league hoodlums and speculation scum. And a heavy turnout of expatriates.

The barman points Linda out to me. She's one of the DJs at Radost on Thursdays, techno night. A teenage face. Luminous skin, thick white hair, wells for eyes, lips the colour of summer rhubarb.

'Cosmic Baby was playing a set tonight,' she says, 'but he cried off. They all do it.' She shrugs, lights a cigarette and pauses with her drink. 'The *idea* of playing in Prague is cool, but there isn't any money in it.'

A fourteen-year-old in a silk dress and feather boa brushes past, followed by a boy in Stüssy. Prague's new privilegentsia.

'At least Radost pays its DJs, I suppose, but I don't like it much. The moment I play anything hard or, like, jungle, the floor clears.' She offers me a cigarette, lights it with hers. Some animal sense passes between us. For an instant she fixes me with a stare, as though trying to see through to the other side. She begins to say something, hesitates, then backs off.

'On the other hand, Radost is also the only club in town with a decent sound system. An American expatriate owns it. How long are you here for?' she's shouting now above the tinketytink of chart hits.

I shrug and put on a vacant smile.

'Come and see me. Here or at Planet Alfa.'

She delves in her pocket for a piece of paper, signals to the barman for a pen.

'And if you're really interested in the Czechno scene, go here.' She hands me the paper, on which she has written the word 'Slunicko'.

I begin a question, but she already has her back to me and is headed off towards the DJ's box.

Up on the street, a gang of gypsy navvies has begun digging

up the pavement leading to I. P. Pavlova underground station, working from the dim hue of a sodium lamp. By tomorrow the square will be filled with the same strange circus of screeching pneumatic drills and wavy plastic bunting as the rest of the city.

Next morning Morgan, the technical manager of the Terminal Bar-to-be, and I wind up drinking weak coffee together at the Hotel Europa on Wenceslas Square while a pianist fingers his way methodically through the Burt Bacharach songbook. Morgan interrupts the pianist's second rendition of 'Little Apples':

'Come to Radost this evening. The expatriate literary scene meets there every week for a poetry evening called Beef Stew.'

'Will you be there?'

'Sure.' A knowing grin spreads over his cheeks and up into the chalk blue of his eyes.

I confess: I took to Morgan the moment I first saw him. Even there, at the Terminal office among the Baader-Meinhof Gang and the black polo-necks and Ortega y Gasset's materialist dialectic, Morgan never quite managed to suppress an air of optimistic energy. And optimism seems pretty exotic to me right now. Exotic, erotic, exotic, erotic. And anyway, I can always go on to Slunicko after Beef Stew.

Someone has let themselves into my room at the Legion and run off with my salami and seven cans of beer.

The man down at the registration desk doesn't seem too interested.

'English no good, sprechen sie Deutsch?' Two Germans are carrying on over some money dispute next door.

'Stolen,' I repeat. 'It must have been the chambermaid.'

'English no good.'

'Listen, Mr Man, Salami is gone, OK?'

The man shrugs and turns away.

'Wurst, dammit,' I persist. It's no good. I speak no Czech and barely a word of German and besides, salami is Italian.

★ ★ ★

I arrive at Radost late and in a grisly temper, sit through four odes to the sunset and come to the conclusion that Beef Stew is actually little more than Dog's Dinner.

Afterwards a dozen or so members of the Beef Stew literary chain gang, plus me and Morgan, move to a non-stop bar near the metro station and sit ourselves down on four wooden benches around a central altar of beer glasses and begin the serious business of poetic vivisection. I try to engineer a seat next to Morgan, without it seeming too obvious, but end up sitting between Jonathan and some amiable-looking guy in a tired velvet jacket.

'Only a few years ago,' says Jonathan, as an opening gambit, 'this place would have been packed with dissidents wrestling with philosophy.'

'What happened to them all?'

'Capitalism,' reflects Jonathan, brimming with portent, as though certain that he and his friends are all that remains between Kafka and barbarism in the Czech Republic.

Beyond him shine the teeth of a dark-haired woman, her face in shadow.

'So what are you doing in Prague, Jonathan?'

'I guess you could say I'm a painter in verse, a citizen of the globe and a travelling storyteller.'

Well, yeah, I think to myself, I certainly could say that, but I don't suppose I will.

'Been here long?'

'Oh yeah,' Jonathan lifts his hands in the air and smiles sagely. 'Like, nearly two years. Really, it's time for me to move on.'

'Oh? Back home?'

'Home?' Jonathan looks as though he's suddenly been faced with a new concept.

'Well, yeah, you sound like you come from the US?'

'*Oh that.*' The sage smile again. 'I haven't been there for *years*. No, I'm thinking of moving to Tbilisi. I just read an article in the *Herald Tribune*, which referred to Tbilisi as – dare I say this? – the new Prague.'

The thin man in the velvet jacket mentions having visited Tbilisi the year before.

'There are apparently cafés all over,' observes Jonathan, 'with artists in.'

'It seemed pretty poor to me,' says Velvet by way of a contradiction, 'from what I could see. Picturesque though.'

'Ah, so there might well have been cafés,' says Jonathan, 'but you didn't necessarily *see* them.'

Velvet shrugs and smiles in a pliant way.

'And when you say picturesque . . . ?' My eyes dart over to where Morgan is sitting. Velvet explains that Tbilisi lies hard up against the mountains and that beyond them lies the Black Sea.

'So, no Soviet-style Projects or anything, right? Nothing nasty to look at.'

Velvet concurs. So far as he recalls, the town is built of wood. He doesn't remember any high-rise building at all.

'The *Trib* said, like, one in every two people is an artist.'

Velvet looks into his beer.

'But how does anyone make a living?' I ask.

'*Art*,' insists Jonathan, offended.

We begin to pay particular attention to the froth on our glasses of beer, a bitter little trio, trapped in the here and now, with one another. The dark-haired woman, who had been seated next to Jonathan, is talking in animated fashion to Morgan. What's more, they are both grinning.

Jonathan lights a cigarette from Velvet's packet.

'What did you think about the metaphor of a Chinese shawl in Al's poem about the transport system?' asks Velvet, scanning the room for an escape route.

At about midnight I wander over to Naprikope Street and, following the sound of banging, fetch up at Slunicko. Inside, several hundred Czech kids are pumping around to hardcore, stamping out the beads of sweat on their bodies. At the centre of the dance floor groups of skinny skinny boys jump up and down towards the lights like performers in a flea circus, gasping in the heat and heaving for breath. A strong smell of salt ricochets off the walls and a stench of piss and vomit has collected around the entrance where the toilets are. Thin things wander about wide-eyed. In the flickering light the whole club appears disordered, chaotic and as violent with threat as a dark, malignant diamond. Something scary is going on at Slunicko and for a long, wild moment I feel an urge to be a part of it; to be drawn into the same rough carnival as the skinny boys: to be sucked in and spilled out, to be made helpless by the racing energy, to have passed through the mouth of matter to the other side; to be annihilated, gone, destroyed. But a sudden smallness creeps through me, and in my sudden smallness, without Morgan or H or Linda Ladida, I'm stupid with fear.

Back at I. P. Pavlova the same gang of gypsy navvies is peeling back the tar and shoving in more veins.

The next day at lunchtime I head down to the Planet Alfa record shop. A bulky man is standing at the sales desk.

'Are you looking for Linda Ladida?'

I nod and wonder how he knows.

'She said to tell you to wait for her.' The bulky man speaks in a German accent.

'Are you the manager here?'

The man laughs. 'I own this place.'

He watches me flicking through the racks of CD covers for a few minutes, then says:

'What did you think of Slunicko?'

I turn around and look at him, but his face gives nothing away.

'I thought it was very weird. Everyone looked really wired. It was as if the whole place was about to go off.'

'That's the superspeed. The teens all do it. There aren't any real drug laws yet.'

'Superspeed?'

He shrugs: 'It's just like speed but about ten times stronger. And it's cheap. But anyway, Slunicko's no good now. They carpeted the place, and put the woofer under the stairs. American money probably. It's as bad as Radost. The real good scene is at the warehouse parties. Up at Ladronka, for example.'

At that moment, in walks Linda with purple hair, smiling at the German owner of the store.

'Hello,' she says to me. 'I thought you'd come.'

'I went to Slunicko,' I reply, for want of anything better.

'Yes,' says Linda as though she's already familiar with the fact. 'Who was DJing?'

I mention a name.

'He doesn't like me,' she says, motioning me to a seat in the corner of the store. 'I can count my friends on one hand.'

'I'm sure that's not true,' I demur. Something in Linda's manner has changed since we met at Radost. She's less relaxed, spikier, as if something she had always taken for granted has suddenly begun to trouble her. 'They're jealous of the way I look, and the fact that I get booked to DJ in Germany. And because I'm a witch.'

'A *witch*?'

'Uh huh.' It suddenly occurs to me that this is what Linda wanted to tell me all along, right since the moment we first met by the bar at Radost.

'And my mother is a witch too.'

'Is that why you dye your hair all those colours?' I ask, rather feebly trying to change the subject. Linda smirks and pulls a purple strand.

'Nooo,' she says, tutting with feigned indulgence, 'that's the Swiss. They think I look dangerous, and just to prove it, they dye my hair purple . . .' She shrugs. 'But I make enough money.'

'Enough money for what?'

'To buy techno records, of course, so I can be a good DJ.'

'Do they know you're a witch in Switzerland?'

She shakes her head and giggles. An image of a warty woman in a black pointed hat comes to mind and makes me giggle too.

'They know here, though. That's why they don't like me.'

'Then why don't you just go and be a DJ somewhere else?'

Linda wrinkles her nose and throws me a pitying look.

'Because I'm Czech, of course.' The conversation is beginning to unsettle me. I'm thinking back to Slunicko and wondering if Linda was there after all. I force my mind to imagine blanks and regain its equilibrium.

'Well in that case,' I say, joking again, 'why don't you just conjure up the records from thin air?'

'Because a lot of my powers are gone. I used them up doing something bad.'

I'm trying to draw a sense of Linda's mood from her face, but there is nothing written there other than a general sort of gravity. One part of me wants to turn away, another is magnetized. I hesitate long enough to give Linda encouragement:

'I was at hairdresser school. I had this terrible teacher. I hated her. She was always shouting at me, telling me everything I did was wrong. I hated her so much that I cast some spells and put a curse on her. The week after she got ill and went into hospital. They said it was cancer. It had grown so quickly there was nothing they could do. She's there in the hospital now. Everyone says she's going to die.' Linda looks up at me. 'You think I'm horrible.'

'No, Linda' I say, with genuine awe. 'I think you're very very . . . *interesting*.'

'Can I play you one of my techno sets? Very hardcore.' Brightening, Linda Ladida beckons for me to follow her into a back room, and begins to pull white label records out from a stack on the floor.

'The only time I'm not thinking about anything else is when I'm playing techno,' she says. Tikatink, tikatink, tikatink, dom, dom, dom.

'How about coming for a drink?' I say.

MOSCOW, RUSSIA, ONE WEEKEND NEAR CHRISTMAS

Maxim Presnyakov has been up for two nights talking to a girl from Omsk on the network. He is removing his fur hat and wiping the pate beneath. Some people's lives camp out on their faces. Maxim Presnyakov is one of those people. His eyes are as dead as the air. A film of sweat shimmers over the pale green skin of his face. A milky way of whiteheads plays over the sagging cheeks and inky smears about his eyes mark the place where anxiety has drowned in drink. The toll of booze and sleeplessness make fifty of the twenty something years of Maxim Presnyakov's reedy body as it strobes a harassed path through the crowds at Proletarskaya station.

We stop to catch our breath on a bank of disused ticket machines, dating back to the days when kopecks still had value. Four or five years ago, perhaps. A whole era in Russia. Seeing us stalled, a woman in cheap clothes approaches and tries to foist a kitten in a sock on us. It's the second or third kitten in a sock we've been offered today. Unable to move in its swaddling, the poor little thing blinks and mewls. Maxim doesn't speak. He is already drunk, but that's not it, because he speaks even less when he's sober.

The floor at the entrance of Proletarskaya station is grimy with diesel oil and melted snow. Maxim slips and has to grab a nearby vendor to steady himself and the man, taking advantage of his captive audience, clamps his arm round Maxim's and starts hectoring him to buy something. Some faked papers, or maybe a passport. The smoky fluorescent light blading in from the street outside obscures my view. In any case, Maxim brushes the vendor off without buying whatever it was he had to sell, and catches me up. We slide the soles of our shoes in synch across the slush towards the stairwell.

Up in the street the sour smell of cheap sausage wakes the gripe in my stomach. We pause to put on our gloves and scarves and fur hats. Maxim retrieves a cloth from his pocket and wipes away the beginnings of a nose bleed. Avoids my gaze. Clutching a bottle from one of the kiosks lined along Nizhegorodskaya we make our way slowly along the ice towards the apartment. A fist of icy wind, caught in the gully between two tower blocks, rushes along the road, beating up the line of matt brown cars parked at either side. Max and I pause again for a moment, stilled by the opposing wind. Great liver-coloured apartment buildings with crenellated peaks tower over us, pitted with yellow light and covered, now that advertising has arrived in Moscow, with tackily painted billboards. Filthy mud-coloured traffic rumbles bumper to bumper, spouting geysers of carbon monoxide. 'This is the Russian interpretation of civilization,' shouts Maxim against the roar of a diesel truck. When he does speak, it is generally to make some droll and bitter little statement of the obvious.

The Marlboro Man hangs above the entrance to my apartment building, cut off at the waist, but otherwise remarkably unfazed in his thin shirt and bolo tie, given that it's twenty below zero. Were he not part-amputated, he would dip down into the door-way of apartments 456 to 474 and the tips of our hats would tickle his buttocks as we entered. Inside, a dirty rim of ice crystals glimmers on the inner window frames where the draught pours through and a pool of mud has settled on the tiled floor. Max and I silently agree to walk up to the fourth floor, following the stink of cheap disinfectant out from the hall to the stairwell. A lost kitten bleats from somewhere inside the broken elevator shaft.

This city is the worst place on the planet. Hell's own internal hell. The end of the end. But it's also the future the Net might make – a vast global anarcho-capitalist web, deregulated, dynamic, dispersed, de-centred, a shape-shifting reticulate world of naked profiteering; a world where each is connected and alone, drifting about in the web in accompanied isolation; picking up and drop-ping contacts, colleagues, lovers, enemies as casually as the days. Waiting to eat or to be eaten.

Later, I take the metro to Dzerzhinskovo and wander along Marska Street towards the Kremlin, whose crenellated walls and onion domes and capped minarets lit in lurid multicoloured light loom through the tissue of mist like some sinister, ill-omened Disneyland.

Later still, clumping through the snow outside McDonald's with its lines of guarded limousines, Tania shouts over to me:

'My problem is I don't know how to work the system.' She's

complaining about the complete cessation of government funding for any kind of alternative arts.

I shout back across the biting air. 'What system?'

And Tania laughs bitterly. There's no system in Russia now, only varying degrees of hustle. We buy some more vodka and two pots of dehydrated noodles in one of the private booths outside Kaluzhskaya station in the south. We're visiting Volodya, who never has any food at home, according to Tania. He spends all his money on electronics, doesn't eat much.

The object of our visit pulls back his front door an inch and, seeing Tania's moon face, waves us in. Outside, the common parts of the apartment building smell of decaying greenstuff, but Volodya's flat is faintly perfumed. In the light of the room, Tania's eyes are coal black with bruised moons beneath. Volodya's too.

Tania slips past us into the kitchen with the noodles. Volodya and I smile shyly at one another. He offers me a pair of Chinese slippers in broken English. English the Russian way, with no articles. 'Weather is cold. You like slippers?' He doesn't want his room messed up with dirty snow from our boots.

Sitting down on Volodya's floor waiting for Tania to reappear, I arouse myself with the thought that Moscow is like a game of Sim City gone wrong. You start with the archetypal metropolis: broad blocks zoned into commercial, residential and industrial areas, bounded by jugular avenues and six-lane boulevards. You scatter gargantuan boxes of apartments with their tiny, imbecilic windows, you carve out parks and public squares, you encourage the masses to play. And then you begin to have some fun. You pull funding from the infrastructure, you cut off the electricity supply, you make the water sour, you demolish part of the transport system and watch the population improvise. You close down the police force, put the hospitals into bankruptcy and sell off the city's public utilities. You build rows and rows of shops hawking fatty sausages and Versace suits. You let factories bleed their chemicals into the air. You blacken legitimate enterprise and create a cash economy instead. You make it easy to evade taxes, jump the system. You ignore racketeering, bribery, and the omnipresence of violence and threat. You make life intolerably tough for almost everyone and obscenely luxurious for a tiny few. And finally, in a last magnificent gesture, you rename everything and insist that history be forgotten. And there you have it. Moscow at the end of the century. Sim City gone bananas. *One, two, three bananas.*

While my mind has wandered, Volodya has been beckoning me to his computer screen in a corner of the otherwise empty room in shy sentences, half-English, half-Russian. I call Tania over to explain. The gist of it seems to be that for a number of months now Volodya has locked himself away with his machine – which is borrowed – and rendered in almost insane detail 3-D images of rubberized monsters, she-devils, demonic machines, pornographic robots, apocalyptic towers and strange minarets. He has a talent for programming paranoia and his current paranoia centres on an absolute certainty that the Soros Foundation are about to repossess his machine and thereby render him mute and helpless. Volodya *has become* his machine. Without it, he is a void.

I miss Mac. I miss everyone.

We sip the noodle soup in silence, stringing out the two pots between the three of us, Volodya not so much eating as day-dreaming with his tastebuds. The noodles are stale, but Tania and I are hungry. Volodya soon disappears back into his electronic life.

Perhaps Volodya knows that the only depths left to plumb in Russia are imaginative ones, for crooks and hustlers have all the others fully covered. Perhaps that is why his machine is his lifeblood.

That night deep sleep evades me. In the hours before dawn, I dream with great lucidity of the stub-faced thugs and fur-clad floozies drinking themselves into their seats at the metro station, but everything else in the dream is strangely altered or distorted. Psychedelic whorls shift about the ceiling and smoke as thick as dry ice oozes from the windows. I wake from the dream only to fall back into it. This time the passengers at the station have gone but their luggage has come to life and bred, like a pack of abandoned dogs, filling the aisles and seats and overhead lockers of the train with a surreal family of animated cork sausages, glass cameras, fur-bound VCRs and living circuitry. At dawn I clamber from my cave of mattresses and duvets exhausted by the night and brew up a cup of dusty Russian tea. A crust of ice has collected inside the windows of the flat, and from somewhere deep in the building the lost, cold kitten begins to yell again.

Max, Yevgeny and I meet at the St Petersburg station, beneath the departures board. It is ten in the morning and a small crowd of minor Mafiosi is already placing bets at the cockroach racing booth by the side exit. Maxim is green, silent, a little drunk and so raddled from lack of sleep that Yevgeny, young and tender-faced, looks almost preternatural walking beside him. Yevgeny is nineteen, seven years younger than Max, though the difference between the two Russians might as well be seven decades, for Max's face has already gone to seed, whereas Yevgeny's isn't even planted yet. In fact, this boy-man possesses the disconcerting aura of a foetus; instinctual and otherworldly.

Maxim presents his lips, misses my cheek and lands a kiss of sorts on my jawbone. All three of us giggle and go red. Then we wander across the marble and out towards the market where rows of trestle tables, selling pirated software and pirated porn and pirated everything else, have been sunk into the snow and are guarded by the dead-eyed little men and women of the provinces. Across the road, Kazan station is already tin-can tight with east-erners waiting for their trains back to Tajikistan, Kazakstan, Siberia and the Chinese border. At the sausage stand a girl, maybe fourteen and as pie-eyed as junk can make a body, brawls about in the cold, screaming about being ripped off, Yevgeny says. No one is really listening.

We end up in an expat bar down an alleyway not far from McDonald's, Maxim and Yevgeny both skulking, having disagreed over our destination. Yevgeny wants to head to some gay bar, while Max favours a non-stop lock-up dive on the other side of town. And since it's too cold to fight it out in the open air, and since every warm place in Moscow with the exception of the metro charges a sack of bullion just to enter, the argument is resolved pretty quickly and, as so often happens when two people have opposing views, the least best solution is the only one the parties can agree upon, which is in this case the expat bar in the alleyway not far from McDonald's.

They say that Moscow is the third most expensive city in the world, after Tokyo and Osaka, the difference between Russia and Japan being that in Moscow your money doesn't buy you anything worth having (unless, of course, you're a fan of fatty sausages and Versace suits), which is presumably why the Russian rich (read Mafiosi) have put down roots in other countries and like to think of themselves as internationalists.

Anyway, we order three glasses of Guinness at $15 a pop at the bar and on the third or fourth Guinness, his tongue loosened by cigarettes and alcohol, Yevgeny begins to tell us the story of his life and the history of his future. The long 19.3 years of it.

This is Yevgeny's plan: he's decided to study stock and bond dealing at the Moscow Finance Academy, after which he's going to earn his fortune on Wall Street. There is a contradictory sentiment here. Yevgeny stayed in New York state for a year on a student exchange programme and hated it, found it boring and bland and the students his age charmless and superficial, but America remains his goal. For America was an Aladdin's Cave of kit and Yevgeny returned to Russia wondering how he might get himself a piece of it. Some day he'll make enough money to move out to California and set up a research lab and discover the secret of physical immortality. And then he'll live secure and forever in America, the ringmaster of his own circuitboard circus of futuristic skylines, freewheeling techno-kings and opportunity pie.

Maxim Ivanovich's ambition extends only to a job at Sun Microsystems in Silicon Valley. So Maxim Ivanovich thinks his friend is mad. Programming, systems design, even administration. But Wall Street and immortality? Ha! His friend's head is full of stupid pubescent pipedreams. Ha! Ha! Ha! But then again Russian reality cannot hope to make a dent in the bewitching American dreamscape of gadget goons and software barons.

It hardly seems fair to judge Yevgeny for his dreams. What else is there in Russia? The standard of living fell by 17 per cent last year. And things are getting worse.

Sitting through Yevgeny's tale, I am taken back to that summer evening in New York when Thor disgorged his life's story by the blue light of the movie set on Greene Street. In so many ways, the Russian and the American have led one life, from child programming whiz to porno-geek to empty screen-shell. Only Yevgeny isn't disillusioned yet. Yevgeny is still listening to German industrial bands. Yevgeny is still inspired by *The Hobbit*.

I look at Max and Max looks at me, and we recognize the same thought. We're thinking that the future isn't ours any more. We've been written out. The future belongs to those who have yet to question its promises. What was it Thor Simon said? That the moment you pick on something whose process does not enchant you is the moment you begin running your life backwards, forever in awe of some goal set an eon before. Thor recalled Gatsby. I wonder if Maxim Presnyakov has read those words?

'Gatsby believed in the green light, the orgastic future that year by year recedes before us. It eluded us then, but that's no matter – tomorrow we will run faster, stretch out our arms further ... And one fine morning – So we beat on, boats against the current, borne back ceaselessly into the past.'

This isn't the future. This is somebody else's present.

Eating late lunch with Maxim at a canteen in the centre of town, it would be easy enough to pretend nothing has changed. Here are the same dreary queues for plates of leaden dumplings. Here are the monstrous babushkas in their nylon overalls slopping soup into plastic soup bowls. Here are the dusty Technicolor pictures of the party faithful, and the smells of cheap booze, watery food and exhausted, sodden lives. Here is the same reek of nostalgia that Russians love so well. This is how the past makes the people its prisoner and leaves the present beyond their reach. This is how the retro-future does its dirty business.

Maxim reaches the bottom of his bowl and begins sopping up his gravy with a piece of dry bread:

'Yevgeny makes viruses,' he notes.

'Computer viruses?' (As if it were possible to make any other kind.)

Maxim returns to his meat without giving a response.

Yesterday the metro fare was one thousand roubles, today it is fifteen hundred. The last time I was here, a one-way ticket cost five kopecks. A dollar was equal to a rouble at the official rate, and to fifty on the black market. Two oranges now cost as much as twenty back home. Rows of country women travel fifty miles to sell handfuls of dates, and strings of mushrooms and bunches of dill. Back out on the street, four men huddle inside a photo booth drinking vodka and a thick-set man is beating up a thin boy for stealing something from him. A crowd looks on, as if curious about the outcome and in that moment Moscow feels as frozen as the planet Pluto – and as remote, come to that.

That evening in the mafia bar, Andrei is drinking weak beer and serial-smoking Gitanes. I know him by the OS/2 WARP badge pinned to his rabbitskin hat. Andrei speaks only programming English, and I don't speak Russian and there is a limit to what we can say. While we are waiting for Max to arrive the words disc, fix, yes, no, index, sort and copy pretty much describe the limit of our mutually comprehensible vocabulary. So in lieu of conversation we exchange polite snippets of programming protocol.

'Computer,' remarks Andrei, smiling vigorously. 'Copy computer virus.'

'Yes,' I grin. 'Maxim computer.'

'Maxim, yes, stop,' smiles Andrei.

Maxim is later and later, damn him.

After a while Andrei and I learn to avoid one another's gaze by feigning complete absorption in our surroundings. And what surroundings! An etiolated rectangle of a room painted deep purple with floor to ceiling mirrors and a black plastic bar with beer in wood-style barrels, its patrons bull-necked men with heavy jewellery and their spike-heeled, slap-happy molls. The whole place giving off the stifling, furtive, mutely violent air of a Scorsese set. The barman, a heavy man in his forties, does not like the look of us at all. He can't place us. Andrei is too young and cheaply dressed to be a hood and I'm neither young nor glamorous enough to be some hoodlum's piece of arm candy. We can only be troublemakers. Just to be safe, he beckons Andrei and me to lean over the bar and offers us a brief glimpse of his handgun.

'Gun,' nods Andrei.

'Gun,' says the barman.

And the two men roar with nervous laughter. I'm about to turn round to pick up my bag and get the hell out when in stumbles Maxim, bringing with him a cloud of diesel and cheap booze and a spray of filthy snow. Swaying up to the bar, he and Andrei exchange iron grips and bear hugs, like two lost soul brothers, in the Russian way, while I fork out another thirty dollars for a round of watered beer.

'Andrei has been wanting to tell you about his big computer skill,' says Maxim. 'Andrei asks are you spy?'

'No, of *course* I'm not a spy,' I growl. 'Why, is Andrei a spy?'

The barman looks up and appears to take note. Leastwise that's what I see, but I suppose I might be imagining things. In any case, how could Andrei be a spy? Andrei is a cybernetics student at the technical university, and a member of one of the four hackers' groups currently active in Russia, two of which are in Moscow, one in St Petersburg, and the other, more shadowy, which operates out of Omsk in Siberia, where the Russians conduct a part of their military intelligence operations. Andrei's off-duty speciality is making viruses. But I don't imagine that makes him a spy.

'Andrei says he's given up viruses,' says Maxim, betraying a giggle. 'In his spare time he only make systems utilities.'

'Maxim,' I say, peevishly, 'if you're going to start playing your weird little games you can forget the free beer.'

'OK, OK,' says Maxim, capitulating. He jabbers something at Andrei and the two enjoy a dark cackle, no doubt at my expense.

'Andrei still says he's given up writing virus,' says Maxim, 'but he lies.'

Poor Maxim. He looks so worn and yellowing. Being droll is probably all the fun he gets, aside from the girl from Omsk, of course.

The former Eastern bloc is full of virus writers. Hundreds of programmers were trained in military computing, and then once the Cold War ended, left with nothing to do. In the old days, the KGB would arrive on the doorsteps of computer whizzes with examples of the latest Western gizmo, and the whizzes would be expected to examine the equipment and suggest a way of replicating it.

'Andrei write virus to damage all programmes in C, because he hate C. His virus made people crazy,' says Maxim, draining his beer and calling for another.

In the late eighties Andrei programmed viruses out of teenage spite and fury. At that time the new, bully-boy breed of Russian businessman was beginning to buy PCs, without having a clue how to use them. Cutting-edge equipment would sit on the new desks in the new offices of the new fat cats of capitalism. And as a fifteen-year-old in love with the hack, a boy who had to beg for access to a machine, a boy for whom the very word computer was an act of magic, Andrei hated the fat cats.

Still, he would probably have given the whole business up sooner if he hadn't found a way of making money out of it. He used to invent viruses to order. He'd be working for the corporations who put out anti-virus software. It was a sort of worldwide computer protection racket. The big corporations would pay up to $500 for a really good virus so that they could write (and sell) the anti-virus programme for it. A couple of the corporations on Andrei's books were even willing to pay him to release new viruses into the computer systems of competing corporations. At one time it was an international business.

The virus-writing business dried up as corporations installed better firewalls and more sophisticated computer security, and by the early nineties, a group of young Russians were left knowing how to write viruses but no longer able to earn a living from their craft. A reasonably skilled worker employed by a Russian company might be taking home $50 a month. The price of a good computer in Russia is $1000, twenty months' salary.

'They get very frustrated,' says Maxim, shaking his head, 'so they make more viruses.' Maxim Ivanovich swallows a long draught of beer.

'Andrei says hackers in Omsk are making worm.'

'A *worm*?'

'Internet worm.'

'How does he know?' Maxim looks embarrassed. This whole strange meeting is beginning to feel like some out-take from a James Bond movie: barmen with gun drawers, floor-to-ceiling mirrors lined with Mafiosi, virus protection rackets, Siberian worms.

'Omsk worm will completely destroy Internet.'

'Could that be true?' But Maxim Invanovich simply shrugs his shoulders and assumes an enigmatic grin.

We pour out drunk into the Moscow night, and crunch through the frozen snow towards the metro. Andrei slides off into the darkness. Outside the entrance a woman is selling packets of frozen peas from a plastic trestle table. A huddle of men exchange cloudy vodka breath inside. Beside them, unregarded, lie a couple of *bomzhi*, Russia's new homeless class. Otherwise, the metro is empty.

We push open the door and enter. The air is sultry. Up on the mosaic wall, lit by a deco tulip lamp, a gilt and marble clock reads eleven forty-five. I feel a pang of hunger. Maxim is already some distance ahead so I slide over the slush and catch his arm just as he's about to push a metro token into the barrier machine.

'What time does McDonald's close?' I ask.

He shrugs, withdrawing the token. 'We can walk there and see.'

'Yes,' I say, glancing at the clock again and realizing all of a sudden how much I'm looking forward to a bite of McDonald's apple pie.

*   *   *

>**Abort, retry, ignore?**
>**Retry**

A blink takes me out to the other side. In Moscow the air smelled of diesel fumes and fatty sausages. Here the scent of orchids meets the breeze. It's sumptuously warm. The pavements have never seen snow or filthy slush. The city is plush with greenery. Well-dressed men and women walk by looking as though they have somewhere to go. Everything works, every light bulb and vending machine and metro train goes about its quiet business. There's a kind of precision here. Market stands and street stalls are set in regularly ordered rows. The traffic runs in neat metallic stripes, while below it metro trains shoot from point to point. Buses float about the roads, more like brightly painted brigantines than the bilge wagons on Moscow's boulevards. People are calmly waiting at bus stops, making orderly lines at the cab stands. Looking across the bright clumps of new office buildings towards the swell of sea it feels as though all those dismal, sorry-looking bars and creepy barricaded stores were fragments of some unlovely dream from which I am now released. And I am left standing wide-eyed in the midst of another future and wondering if my travels have finally ended.

This is Singapore on New Year's Eve and I am at a party, alone.

A throng of people lines the rails along Boat Quay and gazes out over the river to the clock tower at Marina Park. The warm breeze of the old year is tugging at their hair. It is 11.05. I am standing on the terrace of the Boat Quay Internet Café, with a hundred or more of Singapore's new generation of high-tech sharp-suits, who are braying and whinnying about in a polite manner and swirling their Chardonnays and swapping their business cards. The future will begin in fifty-five minutes. Where I'm standing a gentle kind of calm has settled. Further along the barrier separating the café from the promenade a couple of boys are leaning over the ropes and inspecting the steady flow of people filing up a set of concrete stairs onto South Bridge. The three of us are simple in the crowd.

Feeling suddenly lonely, I shuffle closer. One of the boys turns briefly to smile before returning his eyes to the scene ahead. A pink floodlight dazzles the old City Hall, ripening the leaves of the palms at either side of its chalky dome. Another gust of wind lifts my hair and dries the sweat beneath it and a string of dirty white boats shuffles up and down the slow brown sauce of the Singapore River, scooping up the reflections of the lights on Boat Quay. Perhaps I am dreaming that. I've been away on my own so long I hardly know what's real and what's imagined any more.

We watch on. The boy peeps over his friend's shoulder and pretends to be looking out towards Raffles Quay.

'Hi,' I venture.

The boy points to his chest, as if to say 'What, me?' A look of mild panic predominates. His lips wave about like a pair of stranded eels. A nervous tic detonates under his right eye. He elbows his friend, shoots another fast glance at me and spills the contents of his wine glass onto the quay. Both boys begin to giggle. A minute or two of shaking, squeaking, ticking and shooting follows. Then the duo gather themselves and draw in two cavernous, courage-raising breaths.

'Hi,' they mutter through their hands like speak-no-evil monkeys. Tic, tic, squeak, quiver.

'So, do you work here?' I ask, for want of anything better to say.

'Oh yes,' grin the boys, shuffling just close enough to hand over their business cards. It's clear that they're not boys after all, and not quite men either, but something in-between. Technical administrators at the Internet Café.

Our introductions somehow preclude further conversation. I fix my eye on City Hall. The shorter of the two boys, Gerald, lets out another embarrassed giggle. Silence falls. Harold starts to hum. Gerald vanishes.

'Well, this is nice,' I say. 'A private party. Singapore's first Internet café . . .' I heave an involuntary sigh. 'New Year's Eve.'

'Are you from England?' Harold blurts, his eyes on the river beyond. 'I was at university in Colchester a few years ago. British TV is very good.'

Lights bounce off the glass towers along Raffles Quay like coins.

'The *Sun* newspaper has rude pictures in it,' adds Harold.

So, the *Sun* has rude pictures. *Rude* pictures? No one says *rude* pictures. At least, not since the fifties. The conversation peters out again. What's so bad about being on your own on New Year's Eve anyway? I'm about to move away when Gerald returns with a tray of wine glasses. Harold struggles to explain himself:

'We don't have the *Sun* in Singapore. But I thought it was funny – because it was so rude, you see.'

Gerald senses a certain unease.

'Oh no,' he says in a solemn voice, 'Tsk tsk. No *Sun* in Singapore. It's like satellite TV. They wouldn't allow it, you see.'

'No, no,' confirms Harold, shaking his head.

'So what about the Net then?' This from me. 'There's all sorts of stuff on there.' I motion towards the café and almost immediately, as if out of nowhere, a waiter appears with a tray of canapés.

'Oh yes, yes.' Gerald is smiling now. 'Very rude.'

'There will have to be regulations,' adds his friend. 'This is Singapore, you see. We don't like rude things here. This isn't America.'

No, I'm thinking, this definitely isn't America. Nor Moscow either. This is Disneyland with the death penalty, so William Gibson said. But it may well also be my final stop-off point. I am ready to go home. It has been such a long year, busy with discovery. It has been such a long, long day. I feel I've lived a lifetime today. A part of my past has fallen away. In its place I am sensing a brooding, unfamiliar stillness.

Leaving the Y early this morning, knowing it wouldn't do to spend New Year's Eve staring at the ceiling fan in my room, I began to wander towards Orchard Road. At Chinatown, where they were cooking rice congee and pork buns for breakfast, I stopped and ordered Nescafé and a murtabak and whiled away a few minutes watching the fast flow of new cars rushing from the suburbs into the city centre.

Up on South Bridge Road I discovered a shopping mall for Russians. Though hardly homesick for Moscow, I was nonetheless curious enough to wander in. The place was full of bull-necked Russian men, dragging bags of purchases or standing in groups talking and thumbing through their rolls of US-dollar bills. I hovered by the entrance. A bull-neck passed by, loaded to the chin with a stack of plastic objects. He winked at me in a condescending way and disappeared out into the street, leaving a Singaporean storekeeper smoothing out the wad of $50 notes he had left behind. I asked the storekeeper what the Russian had carried away.

'Wafers. You want wafers?'

Wafers are the printed circuit boards from which motherboards are made. I shook my head and said that I'd supposed such things were readily available in Russia. The storekeeper shrugged.

'Russian don't know what he's doing,' the storekeeper said in a sly tone. 'He buy two hundred empty wafers. He don't know there's no chips. He think the computer work without chips.' He tittered.

Oh well, I thought, they have always been a nation of hopeless hubrists, the Russians.

I'd made up my mind to visit the botanical gardens, but a feeling of apathy stole over me and I couldn't raise any enthusiasm for the trip. I wandered out of the Russian shopping mall towards the metro and my eye was drawn to a bond-trader console standing in the window of a computer store. Its features were noted on a sign beneath: six phone lines, private switchboard, automatic stock updates, voice silencers, recorder, CD-ROM player and a dip in the leather for a coffee cup. That machine, and others like it, are really the iron lungs of Singapore, pumping money through the city's needy body. I looked about the street with its broad blocks of glassy buildings and the whole scene seemed to melt into an indistinguishable morass. A quick, needling spur of panic pricked me. It was as though I had found myself at the centre of a maze whose every turn led to the same blind alley. I waited until the feeling had passed and a sense of freedom overtook it. I began thinking how *nice* everything was. So I decided to go shopping.

I floated down into the metro station and stood in front of the ticket machine, feeding in coins until a brightly-coloured smart card spewed out. Clutching this I crossed the marble floor and slipped onto the escalator down into the bowels of the place. It was quiet, though busy. Thin, compact women stood immobile on the tread of the steps, burdened down with shopping bags. Almost everyone appeared to be carrying some new purchase and I guessed that by that ritual they recognized each other's lives.

The metro was bristling with information. Instructions everywhere, in Chinese, Malay, English, other languages. Toilet here. No photographs. Tickets there. Buy a season card. Payment zones. Last trains. First trains. Mind the doors. No durians. No photography. No pushing. Stand here. Wait there. Exit A to street. Follow signs. Exit B to street. In the event of fire no running. For security reasons . . . It was so quiet that the black flare of instructions jarred.

On arrival, the train stopped at precisely the point where the internal doors of the station platform met those of the carriages. I wondered how that happened. Was it automatic, computerized? We bundled on and took our seats. No one stared, except a few kids, but no one avoided eye contact either. The air was so cool from conditioning that it hurt my nostrils. More instructions flowed out of the train's speakers, statements of the obvious or reminders of etiquette and decorum. 'The next stop is Orchard.' 'Please take all your bags with you.' 'Do not obstruct the doors. This causes delays and can be dangerous.' Now, most subway trains in most countries require certain rules to be met, and issue certain instructions, but the ones in Singapore give explanations too. It's all very rational. In New York they'll say 'Stand clear of the closing doors' and in London, 'Mind the doors', but they don't tell you why. In New York pieces of old gum line the seat rims. In London the upholstery is slashed and filthy. In both cities gangs get on the trains and steal your stuff and it's been known for weirdoes to push innocent commuters onto the track. But none of these things occurs in Singapore, because very few Singaporeans ever bother to break the rules. In fact, the only real social problem on the Singapore metro is how to fit in all the shopping bags and still have room for the people. The only engineering problem is how to keep the train running under the ballast of Gucci and Versace totes.

Singapore isn't the shopping capital of the world for nothing. It's the shopping capital of the world because there are more shops per square metre of space here than anywhere else on the planet and because – at least since the spice route days – Singapore has been a trading hub linking Asia, Australasia, the Americas and Europe, and also – importantly – because there is absolutely nothing else to do.

So, still overcome by the niceness of everything and hungry for a piece of consumer pie, I got off the train at Orchard Road and leaned on a bus stop a while to get my bearings. A line of four-storey shopping malls disappeared off into the far distance. Even at the vanishing point there were shopping malls. And people. The red-brick pavement was full of people, here and there interrupted by some groomed tropical planting of palms and orchids. Insects danced about too. I thought that if ever the street really was an orchard of trees, it was now most definitely an orchard of stores, each a fulfilment of someone's idea of paradise, each so heavy with harvest all you had to do was to pick and pay.

Christmas having only just come and gone, giant plastic friezes of Santa and Rudolf the Red-Nosed Reindeer remained stuck on the facades along Orchard Road and Christmas songs blared out from the shopping malls like calls to prayer. *Santa Claus is coming to . . . have yourselves a merry little . . . I'm dreaming of a white . . .* I stumbled into Orchard Plaza, a vast dome of sparkling lights and brilliant chrome, replete with designer jeans, quadraphonic speaker sets and Belgian chocolates. I felt like an Eloi going down into the Morlock's den, doomed but perfectly content all the same. The air hung as it does in cathedrals. For a moment I felt quite giddy with pleasure. To me in my numbness the place seemed a grand culmination, the end result of generations of human dreaming, a place you could wake up and discover that what you'd dreamed was true. Like California. Cal-i-forn-I-A. They were comforting, those stores, all piled up with promise, piled up with purchases, little reasons for going on. Stocked with buyable little futures. They'd even gift-wrap them for you if you asked nicely.

I moved from Orchard Plaza into the mall next door, but it was the same. So I walked a block further to a set of brass revolving doors but that too was the same. I walked on to a set of smoked glass doors which gave onto a large atrium filled with all kinds of shops and boutiques and little experiences and shopping events. I clambered to the top floor, in the hope that everything would look different and clearer. But it didn't. Down below, the crowds flowed by just as before. They tramped from store to store, drawn upwards in silent shafts through corridors choked with shopping opportunities, descending heavy with trinket bags into the basement food courts, scoping in and out of the nooks and corners, pumping along the escalators, emptying bags, filling others, signing forms, producing plastic from their wallets, curling through the vastness like the smoke from a discarded cigarette, lost in the formless whirl of stimulation. Shoppers everywhere, the lifeblood of the vast machinic project that is Singapore, gushing along the corridors and racing through everything. And the odd thing was how calm it all was.

Harold, Gerald and I help ourselves to some dim sum. A pager begins to chirp. Gerald pulls it out of his pocket.

'My parents. They want to know if I will be home soon.'

'Don't they know you're at a New Year's party?' I ask.

'Of course,' says Gerald, nodding vigorously, 'but usually I go home straight after work, you see.'

We stare into our Australian Chardonnays. Gerald picks at the enclosure rope.

'So.'

'So,' nods Harold. A warm breeze passes through us. Further along Boat Quay a dance band has started up. People are pressing along the steps and onto South Bridge, leaving a kind of blunt excitement behind them. Everyone is smiling and I'm reminded, though I don't know why, of the soft smell of Marin, of eucalyptus and gasoline. The blue of the ocean, as it appears from the plateau above Muir Woods. It seems strange, now, that California felt like the future, with all its frenetic reinvention, its ruthless energy disguised by casual friendliness, its innovative eccentricity and ambition, because here in Singapore another future has arrived. A calm, conforming future. A future with all the bustle taken out.

I meandered back to the YMCA and stared out over the cranes and quays of the world's busiest port to the flotilla of cargo ships and tankers in the distance, churning the matt grey swell of the South China Sea. From my vantage I could see the world's bounty floating by and the fingers of Singapore reaching out to touch it. How Mac would love it here, at the centre, I thought. How in thrall he'd be to the shopping malls, how turned on by the rows of camera bits and fish-eye lenses and software and monitors and keyboards and mice and modem cables. I pictured him wading along the shelves of utilities software and cutting swathes through the corridors of consumer durables. The thought brought a smile to my lips. He'd be in his element here, for Mac is a true geek, in the nicest way. A man forever fascinated by the detailed possibilities technology brings, someone who likes to reach beyond the real world, beyond the confines of bodies and the mess of human interaction, to the stillness of machines. A man, like many men, who strains for the open sea, where the water is no longer churned to foam.

There on the terrace of the Y, I began to admit to myself that Mac and I would never again be lovers. Oh, we enjoyed the anticipation, the lust, even the futurology while they were fresh, but the thrill had gone for both of us. And in any case, I had begun to feel tired of never-fulfilled fantasies and hopeless projections. I had come to the conclusion that it was finally time I grew up.

I left the Y. It seemed too sad to stay. Being by now both hungry and thirsty, I followed a flight of marble steps into a flood court at the basement of a nearby shopping mall and, picking up a root-beer and some Singapore fried *mee*, I stationed myself at a table near the entrance, just beyond the pull of the air conditioning but protected from the thick soup of heat outside. A giant polystyrene snowman bobbed about like some swamp thing in the foyer, to an accompaniment of thrilled gasps. Today's copy of the government paper, the *Straits Times*, lay on the table top and my eye fell on a New Year's Eve statement put out by the Singaporean Prime Minister, Goh Chok Tong. 'Some Singaporeans still behave as if they were in the stone age,' he wrote. 'They litter . . . park motor vehicles indiscriminately. They vandalize library books. They push and shove for free used text books. They even pilfer or damage orchid displays.' The article rambled on about the number of *kiasu* in Singapore these days, who seemed 'determined always to win, grabbing everything, jumping queues, keeping coming back for more, looking for discounts, never minding what others think, rushing and pushing to win the race with the winner taking all!' I glanced about at the decorous crowd of Singaporeans lining up for their food or sitting neatly at their designated tables, keeping themselves to themselves, and felt utterly bemused.

I thought about the Internet and it struck me that, whatever is written and said about the uncensored unpoliced space of Wiredworld, the actual experience of most of the people who use it is really very different. The large service-providers, the CompuServes, America On Lines, Prodigys are every bit as highly policed and controlled as Singapore society, and the signs are that this will be the way the networks develop. No one is to blame. The rewards of conformity have always been great. I had only to look about me to see the truth of that. And I had only to think of Moscow as it was ten years ago when I first went there – grey, uniform but fed – and as it is now – chaotic, atavistic and hungry.

In Singapore, on the Net, everywhere. Prosperity, social cohesion, safety, *politesse*. All there. The only price, conformity, a certain careful, managed blindness. For information is not in itself subversive, and knowledge is not necessarily power. On the contrary, information can be used to manufacture consensus, and ignorance is often more powerful than knowledge where it means not having to act. If Singapore is a model of the virtual future, as it is a model of the real tomorrow, then there will be no disagreement, no individuality, no non-conformity, no rebellion, no politics, no freedom of speech. For if democracy and debate can be defeated by the store here in Singapore, then it can happen anywhere. And it is happening, slowly but inexorably. Even on the wires. Call it consensus, call it consumerism, call it multi-national corporations, call it the global village, call it what you will.

I had been walking while I was thinking this, and I found myself hard by South Bridge. The air was wet and warm and my head had begun to pound. Looking about, my eye was drawn to the Internet café and I suddenly felt famished for news from home, from Nancy, from anywhere. But the café was closed. I peered through the glass door into the room beyond, looking for signs of life. The monitors of a dozen Sun workstations blinked back like exotics in a zoo. We had been staring at each other for some time when a man dressed in black broke from a door at the back of the room.

'I'm sorry,' he shouted from behind the door. 'We're closed today for a private party.'

My spirits sank. I'd already imagined some loving message from Mac, and anything at all from Nancy. I wanted something of my old-new life back, the life of e-mail and electronic enchantments, and now, at the whim of this man, I felt denied. A dull rage came over me, like the dark bursts in the mind of a child shut out of a toy shop.

'Can't I come in and pick up my mail?' I cried.

The man had his back to me, and wheeled about.

'We're closed,' he said.

'But I've come all the way from England . . .' The man

hesitated momentarily, then began to wave me away again. He could sense my desperation and didn't like it.

'. . . and I see you have Sun workstations,' I added, in an instant's inspiration. It worked. The man stopped in his tracks, screwed up his nose and crumpled. The lock slid out of the plate-glass door.

'Oh,' I said, breathless with admiration. 'Just *look* at those machines.'

The man hew-hawed, proud as a well-turned soufflé and I felt a mild pang of guilt.

'I've never seen Sun machines in an Internet café before,' I said. Sun machines are notoriously expensive, grand and complex.

The man chuckled. 'We're pretty well capitalized here in Singapore. And everyone seems to be into the Internet right now.'

We might have been sitting in a café in Northern California only a year or so ago, having the same conversation. It would have been almost the same. The same blonde wood, the blinking kit, the black-clad man, proud to be on the cutting edge of things. He fetched a basket of popcorn and asked how I was liking Singapore. He was unaware that my mind was already six or seven thousand miles away, scrolling through the welcome page at the Whole Earth 'Lectronic Link in Sausalito, California. He persisted, politely.

'Oh, *Singapore*,' I said, wrenching my eyes from the screen and conjuring a smile. 'Terrific. Yes.'

Just then a message appeared on my terminal.

>You have no new mail

Damn, I thought, I must have typed it wrong. Or maybe the software screwed up. I typed in

>mail

again and the computer at the WELL in Sausalito, California, began to search through its mail files.

Where have all the months gone? It seems as though my first e-mail arrived only a day ago, a few hours. The small miracle chipped off the block of miracles that was the Internet. It was as though I'd stumbled on a thick supply of electronic brothers and sisters and mothers and fathers – my future kin, a brood beyond.

I must have read every line of that mail a dozen times. Copied it to the text editor and played about with it, rearranged the order of the paragraphs and corrected the spelling. Finally, when I'd done everything I could short of deleting the thing, I laid it down to rest in my mailbox, and spent another hour and a half concocting a response. I could not have been more dumbstruck if a $100m 7-picture contract had suddenly landed on my doorstep. I didn't really care what was written in that message. I simply loved the fact of it.

During those first few months, I used to track the course of every electronic mail that found its way into my mailbox, and I'd while away hours imagining all the locations and all the computers it had passed through en route to mine. The University of California, across to Chicago, down into Delaware, through Duke University, up into the University of Minnesota, past MIT, through CUNY in New York City, across the Atlantic to London and finally to me. I felt I'd witnessed the pulse of the world. The dogged will of those messages amazed me. However many miles they had to travel, and however tortuous the route, they always found their way through. Such purpose! Like the Pony Express or sperm racing inexhaustibly toward the egg.

When I was a child, about eleven or twelve, and desperate for mail, I would write off to the foreign embassies, requesting their visa forms and tourist brochures. I also used to send off applications for every home-shopping catalogue I ever saw advertised. Reams of colour catalogues expounding on the delights of Tyrolean mountain climbing, the charms of Transylvania, the strength of Greek hospitality, the quality of home furnishings or the panorama of free gifts would routinely pour through the letter box, all addressed to me. Me. Sometimes I'd fill in the YES! TELL ME MORE coupons and mail them back, other times I'd scratch off all the lucky number cards, and despatch the order forms (without payment). If I was feeling at a particularly loose end I'd construct letters thanking the senders for their leaflets detailing 'Views of The Black Forest' and 'How to claim your free prize now,' and congratulating them on their presentation, typeface and on the selection of pictures. I'd even cut out the drab 'no thank you, please remove me from your mailing list' coupon and mail that back in a different envelope. Not once did I ever receive a response to my letters, but I didn't care. So far as I was concerned, I was pitching a stone into a pond in order to watch the ripples expanding to the edge. The loss of the stone mattered not at all.

Sitting in the Internet Café in Singapore, I realized that I'd fallen out of love with the Net some time ago. Somehow my real life had crept back in and stolen its thunder. Oh, there were *people* on the Net I still loved, for sure, but the Net itself had lost its pull. This realization made me feel uncomfortably released, like a freed animal still magnetized by the glint of metal bars. I keyed in another request for mail. A machine message appeared on the screen.

>You have no new mail

The man in black must have guessed at my disappointment, for he quickly left my side and fetched a printed card from a drawer by the cash till and handed it to me, saying:

'Please come to the New Year's Eve party we're having tonight. Just say you're George's friend. If you're not too busy doing other things, that is.'

I smiled and pocketed the card. Mouthed a thank-you. Busy doing other things. Ha! As if.

Harold and Gerald and I fall into a gentle silence. Gerald worries at the rope while Harold and I direct ourselves to the quiet light over the Singapore River. Every so often the plate glass windows of the café deflect the conversation of passers-by and send it rattling back towards us in odd little snaps and bites. The clock to the right of City Hall reads 11.30 now and above the heads of the people standing along Boat Quay a flock of champagne bottles appears in readiness. Somewhere further east the dance band has begun another set. They are playing 'The Girl from Ipanema' (poorly).

Our conversation idles along through favourite foods (prawns, oh yes!), pop groups (Queen, progressive rock is very good), Web sites (IBM and Sony), magazines (*Wired*) and books (*Hitchhiker's Guide to the Galaxy* for Gerald, *Advanced UNIX Manual* for Harold). We gravitate to hobbies. Gerald swims, Harold says he likes hanging out. They both write code for business utilities. Harold adds: 'That's what everyone does,' with Gerald nodding wildly in agreement. And Harold says: 'We like to upgrade ourselves. You see, everyone in Singapore wants to be like the man who developed the Soundblaster Card . . .'

'. . . and who's now one of the richest people in the country,' fills in Gerald, jigging his brain about.

By lunchtime, I was sitting in a cable car overlooking a cruise liner moored beside the World Trade Centre, and comforting myself with the thought that, should the cable break – and they always do in movies – I would plunge right into the liner's Olympic-sized swimming pool or, better still, directly into the cocktail bar at its side, which wouldn't be so bad at all. Not at all bad. I could probably live with death by dry martini. The sky over the Straits was woolly grey, and a thin breeze drubbed the cable car, causing it to list towards the sea. I was oddly excited by the small risk of danger presented by my situation. But in spite of its lurches, the cable car stayed on its course and dropped me at Cable Car Plaza in the middle of Sentosa, Singapore's playground, the satellite island given over to the city's R&R.

Sentosa has it all. Brushed beaches of imported white sand, five-star hotels, insect kingdoms, shark tanks, butterfly walks, waxworks of both the surrender and the liberation of Singapore during World War II, three Asian villages (Eastern-style, Southern and South-Eastern), the (newly built) ruins of a made-up lost civilization, and Singapore's only preserved nineteenth-century fort, augmented, of course, by a contemporary assault course, war games and a Battery Sergeant Major tour guide. The only thing really lacking in Sentosa is reality, but, hell, we all have quite enough of that.

Most of the population of Singapore seemed to have piped over to Sentosa for the holiday. There were queues at the bureau de change, queues both at the cable car entrance and exit, queues leading to the café. I headed off to the round-island monorail. A train soon arrived and the queue elbowed its way on, leaving behind a sticky trail of ice-cream wrappings and cotton-candy sticks like a lizard leaves its tail-meat in the mouths of predators. There was noise all around. Up on the plaza, a group of men squabbled over uniforms at the warlord photography booth and their kids strung out behind, hustling for ice-creams. Parrot calls issued from a set of speakers buried in the greenery. There were gasps of delight and frustration emanating from the butterfly walk, quarrels blasting from the café. And the train trundled on, pausing at the insect kingdom, then at the phoney ruins, where a tour group got off and began clambering over the fibreglass remains of a temple, taking photos as they went.

We picked up speed and floated noiselessly on towards the amphitheatre and food village, dazed by the procession of plastic birds, transplanted palms and spray-on smells. As the train slowed into station six a couple sitting opposite fought wordlessly for control of the family camcorder. The driver advised us to 'alight for the enchanted grove of Tembusu, Asian Village, Orchid Gardens, Central Beach and Volcano Land'.

Later, I was standing in the orchid gardens over the combed expanse of Central Beach, with its concrete-planted palm trees, and wondering in a vague way where they had brought the sand from. Australia? The South Sea Islands? My mind trailed back to Venice Beach. Was the sand as white as this? I stumbled down the path and onto the beach itself. The surface was soft as flakes, but beneath the surface ran some kind of hard layer, maybe concrete. I began to run, kicking sand behind me as I went. I recalled how, when Nancy and I chased along the beach in California nearly fifteen years ago, we left divots in the sand which the waves then rushed in to fill. I stopped running and looked out over the choppy water of the Strait. The days were very long back then, at least as long as this, and often longer. Endless sometimes. We waited them out, as a child waits out her childhood in awe and enraged by the adults telling her what she'll know and who she'll be in the years to come. But we weren't children. I'm not sure what we were but whatever stage we'd reached, we felt our future there. Our smiles were full of it, and so too were the looks we gave each other.

But never mind. The more you mind, the more you run your life back upon itself. And bitterness and regret are easy impulses.

I pushed the sand into two long mounds at either side of my arms. Then I hollowed out a nest for my head and I lay back and the sky fell down on me so I could feel the scorch of the sun. All of a sudden, a clump of wet grit landed on my belly, followed by another. Then a shell flew in between my feet and then a strip of seaweed. I sat up, and saw two children hurtling down to the sea, laughing, their shoulders shaking, as though it was the last day in the world for laughing. An image of my childself came into my mind and I remembered my first beach holiday in Brittany, and how I'd had to tie a plastic table cloth around my broken leg to protect the plaster of Paris from the sea, and how my enemy at school wrote 'shit' on the plaster's foot where I couldn't reach to white it out.

The children splashed about and pulled one another down into the waves. I caught myself thinking about kids and the future once more. They seemed so full of promise, those children, like small guarantees of tomorrow. Somehow, that made it all the more poignant. Kids don't have a sense of the future like we do. In a year from now, those children playing about in the sea will probably have no memory of today, existing as they do in a kind of magic limbo, a permanent and vivid present, an enchanted spool of day to day.

They must wait to become adults before they can take ownership of the world. Only then will their footprints begin to leave their mark. Only then will they be able to look over their shoulders and see their impressions lying there like divots in the sand.

Eventually the children came out of the sea and disappeared, leaving a nylon day-pack behind them on the beach. I went over to it and peered in. There was a carton of coconut milk and a blue plastic dolphin inside. I sat the dolphin on the beach and carved out a sea of sandy waves and ripples for it.

I thought about myself at seventeen, running along in the California sand, brimful. Back then it felt as though the future belonged to me. At that age you'll believe almost anything. I dug the dolphin further into its hot white sea. It seems so naive now, but then I believed it. I believed it because my time had come to believe it, and I wanted to believe it, but also because America itself seemed to confirm that it was so. The voice of America was whispering then what it always whispers. Promises. *It's yours, it's yours.* Promises. Somehow those whispered promises joined with the whispers already in my mind until all I could hear was the roar of the coming years, bold as the roar of a shell. *The future. It's yours, it's yours.* I let the sound wash through me like the bank of a wave and I felt winded and free, released from the bounds of mortality. Looking back now, I can say that this was the only time I have ever been unafraid of life or death. It was as though I'd been washed away from the world of little humans and had landed on the shores of big humanity. A reverse Gulliver. And I remember how happy I was.

Only the dolphin's fin stood above the sand now. From that angle it was indistinguishable from a shark. I tugged it, and the blue body emerged trailing sand from itself like a beach Niagara. There was still no sign of its owners. I laid it on the sand and let it heat up in the sun for a while, then tested out the temperature of the plastic on my skin. The dolphin felt livid and satisfying. Acts of petty masochism are often so calming. Dusting the sand off the thing, I put it back inside the day-pack and left both together on the beach. I felt quite bored and restless. When I got off the monorail at Cable Car Plaza I noticed the fresh red fish tattooed on my arm.

By the time I left Sentosa it was already dark and the lights of Singapore were casting patterns over the waters of the strait.

Ahead of me was spread the perfect cybernetic city; a city of controls and signals and routing switches which watched over and mothered the continual flow of commodities and people and traffic and data and money. Singapore, the binary world's most glittering prize, a hub of work-in-progress, a rationalized, siliconized, de-bugged, virtually perfect piece of code. Beautiful. A newtime temple of glass and chip and concrete.

From where I'm now standing it's becoming clear what this recent love affair with the digital world really meant to me. It was a nostalgia trip. A form of time-travel. It drew me forwards into the future and pulled me back into my own adolescence, into the orgasmic feeling of possibility I sensed on that Amtrak train speeding towards San Francisco. I've been trying to achieve the impossible – to hold my past close and comforted in the distraction of other people's futures. All this time, running my life backwards, as though the future still belonged to me; which of course it doesn't. For the future belongs to any of us only for the shortest while, from the instant we finally burst from our child-hood skins to the instant we are bound back inside adult ones. For the shortest while we transcend our own mortality.

All those months ago, when I made a promise to myself to hunt the future down, some unconscious need rose in me too. A need to grab that transcendent moment of adolescence, to keep it and never allow it to escape. To be released from the bonds of childhood and adulthood at the same time. For we are all of us afraid of death. Many of us are afraid of life.

For fifteen years I lived as an adolescent lives, in a stilled moment of dramatic portent. It's common enough these days. Without wishing to boast, I must say that I've had some measure of success. I've staved off many things. Commitment, responsi-bility, even love. Mostly love. I've lain in wait for the next new tool and style, floating from desire to desire, mesmerized by novelty, pulled in by its promises. I dreamed the future dreams. Promise. Promise. Promise me. Promise me. Promiscuity. Promise me promiscuity.

The Net is a Peter Pan machine, the screech and bubble of

the modem always promising some new identity, some novel reconstruction, forever hinting at the future and drawing in its feint outlines.

And so I went on, useless arms stretched out in front in order to reach for something far behind, an idea of the future which lay already in my past. And the present rocketed by unnoticed. When the backlash came it threatened me and I fought it. My nostalgia and my future-lust were contradictory. They left me confused and troubled. I felt pulled in different directions. I was afraid and so I lived by self-deception, defending an impossible utopian techno-future, a wired Wonderland which I already knew at heart could never be. Only our real lives can save us. Only here in the mess of things can we be redeemed. But I was afraid.

I can't pinpoint the moment I finally stood up to the terror of real life. Was it in New York or Newport? Over the years ahead it may become clearer to me. But I do know that from that moment, the future began to drain away. I panicked at that. I think I must have felt suddenly abandoned by the one thing I had most jealously possessed, most passionately defended, most consistently loved. This idea of a future I'd somehow picked up on Venice Beach nearly fifteen years before. The happy dream, a dizzy, carefree tomorrow wrapped in the close and welcome arms of America. Am-er-i-ca. Mad, generous, brave America. The America of the good life. I raged – as only a jilted adolescent can rage – with wild destruction. With sad, illusory promiscuity I ran about: from London to San Francisco, to New York, then on to Reykjavík, then back to London, then Berlin and Prague and Moscow, making a promiscuous journey from place to place, always in the hope of dulling the disillusionment and beginning again. *Promiscuity. Promise me. Promise.*

As the cable car lurched back into its berth at the top of Mount Faber, I felt I was finally making my own uneasy settlement with the digital world. And although I'm no longer so sure that technology will bring me closer to the future, I know now that the future isn't mine to have. I am no longer adolescent, but fully adult.

And there's something else too. I am a member of a transitional generation, a generation who may well be left out of the next century's concerns. Another generation of young adults have grown up behind us, and unlike us, they take the digital world for granted. They truly are the first generation of the twenty-first century. And we belong to the space between the old and the new. If you can call that belonging.

Standing at the railings on Boat Quay, a strong and steady calm comes over me. Perhaps I have finally reached the still point and if I have, it is because I have travelled about so much and hunted down the same story in every place, and found that it is never the same. I've learned there is no single future, but an army of futures. And I'm no longer compelled to possess the single bright tomorrow. For now I'm sure that there's no one techno-logical arrow, piercing through the heart of everywhere. There is no cosy global village. And whereas once I saw tomorrow in an Amtrak train as it rushed towards its destination, I know now that it had no single destination. No-one is waving from the track. I am free to watch a hundred futures develop and evolve. And that is another kind of promise. Another kind of promiscuity.

I make my way back to the café and take a seat at one of the Sun terminals. It is now 11.50. A plate of snacks arrives. The man sitting next door helps himself to a prawn satay and nods graciously in my direction:

'Live here?'

I shake my head and place a spring roll between my lips.

'Are you talking to America?'

I click on the mouse at my elbow and telnet over to the WELL in Sausalito, California.

'Of course,' the man continues, picking up another prawn satay from the plate, 'we'll never be like America here.'

A message from Nancy scrolls up on the screen:

>Sweetheart, I am *so* sorry not to have replied to your e-mails, but I'm here now, so Happy New Year's Eve. Is it snowing in London? We had a weird storm here last night.

I guess the Mac thing has probably resolved itself by now. That older woman/younger man double ticket never holds good for long. No-one's to blame. Would you like me to send you the Shaving Ken? Anyway, here's the big news. Dave and I have finally got it together. And - don't tell anyone - I think it might be ... L.O.V.E.
Have a wonderful New Year, sweetheart. I know you will.

The man next door continues talking, but I'm no longer listening. A sudden rush of happiness fills me up. I type:
>Greetings from Singapore

And then, realizing how long Singapore will take to explain, I press my thumb on the delete key and begin again.
>Hello Nance. I type. >Congratulations and Happy New Year from London.

Outside, the polo-necks and suits have moved up to the rope, anticipating the first moment of the New Year. I worm my way back to Gerald and Harold.

'At eleven fifty-nine everyone counts down the minute and at exactly midnight they let off fireworks,' says Harold, thoughtfully warning me of the protocol.

Fifty-nine
Fifty-eight
Fifty-seven

shouts the temporary population of Boat Quay.

Fifty-six
Fifty-five
Fifty-four

Central Singapore looks as pink as a Turner painting.

Fifty-three
Fifty-two

Tourist boats bump by like clots in pink blood.

Thirty-one
Thirty

A yellow light appears at the top of the Raffles Tower.

Twenty-nine
Twenty-eight
Twenty-seven

Harold and Gerald are drumming the numbers on the enclosure rope with their fingers.

Eighteen

Seventeen

A helicopter bursts from the clouds above the port.

Ten

Nine

Eight

Gerald and Harold are counting down the seconds on their wrist-watches.

Seven

Six

The moon is as rosy as the soap your grandmother kept.

Five

Four

Three

And I am hoarse from hooting and hawing.

Two

One

And . . . BAM! A brilliant yellow fireball detonates over City Hall. And Gerald and Harold and I are shaking hands, shouting 'Happy New Year', and batting each other on the back. A blue star is falling, trailing a litter of white wires. Four yellow rockets are screaming into the sky. The smell of gunpowder is spiralling back down to earth. Harold's pager is bleeping. He digs it out of his pocket and tips it to the light. Above City Hall a helix of phosphorescent pulses whirls about then fades.

'Parents say Happy New Year,' says Harold.

'Oh yes, very, *very* Happy New Year,' giggles Gerald.

And a delicate mist rises over the river.

Acknowledgements

This book is the result of four years' experience. During that time many many people have made conscious or unconscious contributions to it. To those who were conscious my heartfelt thanks, and to those who were not, thanks too, and sorry it had to be that way.

IN THE USA
West Coast:
My great thanks to B. Alexandra Toole who more than anyone else made this book possible. Thanks also to Greg Pleshaw, Matisse Enzer, M. Normal, Gareth Branwyn and Howard Rheingold for their early inspiration, and to Matisse in particular for setting up my WELL account and kindly forgetting the fee. Many thanks to my friend, Paul Spinrad, who came in later, but has been no less influential for that. I'm particularly grateful to Paul for agreeing to read the manuscript for technical glitches, though any that remain are entirely my responsibility. My thanks go to Sheila Hayman, who very kindly put me up in LA, and gave freely of her ideas, experience and inspiring self. Isaac Dziga and Dee Flanagan taught me a great deal about the future. Many thanks to Larry and Adrian Treadgold and to Neil Hersh. I'm also grateful for the help and advice of David Pescovitz, Zoe Mapes, Doug Rushkoff, Mimi Ito, Jonathan Moore, Cynsa Bonnoris, Robin Templeton and the staff of Unplug; Rolando and his crew and Mike Boone of the music programme at the Glide Memorial Church in the Tenderloin district of San Francisco. Thanks are due also to Bart Decrem, Nathan, Benjamin and the staff of Plugged-In, to Marc Sabah and others at Palo Alto High School; Clare Boudreux and her pupils at Berkeley High, Bob Albrecht, James Gonzalez and the pupils of Piner High in Santa Rosa; John McLeod of Visionary Stampede, Wayne Gregori of SFNet, Peter and Alex Rothman, Desmond Crisis and the Otaku Patrol Group, Barry Kort, Chris Kryzan and all the teenagers at AOL who e-mailed me about being gay and on the Net.

East Coast:
Many thanks to Thor Simon for giving his life story to the book, and for showing me where I was going wrong. I'm very grateful to Gene and Margaret Kilik for lending me their beautiful loft, to Ian Jackman and Cara Welsh for encouragement and to Chuck Ocheret for his enthusiasm and help way beyond the call. Thanks also to Rose Platt and Kevin Morrill who gave me the idea (and some of the material) for the Intermission.

I'm indebted to Anne Hunter, Nancy Gilman and Amy Bruckman at MIT, and to everyone at the Students' Information Processing Board of MIT. I'm also grateful for the advice of the staff at the Clubhouse in Boston's Computer Museum.

IN ICELAND:
Thanks to Johnny Triumph for setting the whole thing up. Thanks too to Einar Örn Benediktsson, a good man and a great Viking, ditto Thor Eldon, and to Heiða, Torfi Frans, Simmi Gudmundsson, Eythor Arnalds, Gudjon Gudjonsson and Lára Stefánsdóttir for helping to make Iceland one of the six strangest experiences of my life.

IN MOSCOW:
Thanks to Andy Day and Tom Lassika for their faultless advice, to Maxim Presnyakov, Edward and Tania Detkina for tramping around the streets with me. I'm indebted to Ira Tsymbal for organizing my accommodation and to Zamir Gotta for his invaluable help in advance. Many thanks also to Dmitry Altuhkov, Andrei Kozhemyaka, Yevgeny, Volodya and the staff of Nikita Games Company.

IN PRAGUE:
Morgan Sowden, wherever you are, ta. Also the staff of the Terminal Bar-to-be, Chrisophe Klug, otherwise known as Mr Czechno, Honsa and Sasha. And last but absolutely not least my thanks go to Linda 'Ladida' Stepnikova, who has now, I hope, converted to white witchery.

IN BERLIN:
Thanks to Mark Reeder and Dave Rimmer for their advice and company. Thanks also to H, without whom Berlin might have bombed.

IN SINGAPORE AND MALAYSIA:
I'm grateful to Harold Jean Chin Chia and Gerald Quek, K. Ragavan and the staff and pupils of the Institut Megatech in Kuala Lumpur; to Malik Abdullah, also to Zaidbun Siraj and the pupils of the Ngee Ann Polytechnic, to pupils and staff of the Singapore Polytechnic, to the staff of Adroit Innovations, Georges Cardona and Sembawang Media.

IN THE UK:
Thanks to the staff and pupils of Burnham-on-Crouch High School, Walthamstow School and to Mike Burleigh and the pupils of Cedars Primary School. Vicki Merchant and Sgt Phil Stockford were very helpful on the issue of Net porn and David Collier at Trip Media, Richard Darling at Codemasters and Andy Johnson and Mark Langerak at Sega Europe helped me to understand what it takes to make a great video game. My grateful thanks to Heather Barker and Teena at the Samaritans, Julie Fawcett and the children of the Stockwell Park Friday Club, to Tim Leighton-Boyce, Paul Sanders, Adam Braimah, Lokesh Soni, Matthew Flanagan, Alistair Kelman, Professor Stephen Heppell at Ultralab, Ravi Chopra, Jane Hewland and the staff of Hewland International; the staff of Funland at the Trocadero, Mike Paradinas aka Muziq, Annaliza Savage, Robin Rimbaud aka Scanner, Martin Kavanagh, Paul Sargeant and Helen of the Way Collective, also to Angela Humphries of Research Business, Sue Fisher at the University of Plymouth, Mark Griffiths, Peter Robinson, Roddy Mansfield, Jamie Hartzell, Cory, Paul and everyone at Small World. Ta very much to Caroline and Robert Daykin for lending me their flat in the New Forest, and to all those people who sent enlightening e-mails over the years.

Paul Wilmshurst has seen this project through from start to finish, and brought to it his keen eye and even keener intelligence, as well as giving support and inspiration. Daniel Pemberton has kept me cheerful and provided many of the best lines. My fond thanks to Ben Russell for the book's title and for his encouragement, and to Tai Bridgeman and Camilla Finn for reading various drafts and telling the truth about them. My gratitude goes to my editor, Philip Gwyn Jones, who saw the book when it wasn't ready to be seen and managed in spite of it all to remain enthusiastic; to Karen Duffy, Lee Motley, Matt Herring and Anne O'Brien at HarperCollins. Thanks to Pauline Downs for helping me with transcriptions. And also to my agent, Gillon Aitken, who continues to support my work.

Thank you to Heath Bunting for showing me round his manor, and finally to William Gibson, who had absolutely no idea he was contributing to this book.

NOTE ON THE TEXT

In order to keep things running swiftly I have compressed the experiences of a number of years into the course of twelve months. A few names have been changed for reasons of privacy. Nancy is a composite, but all her parts are real. The intermission is a work of fiction. The title, *Hard, Soft and Wet* is shorthand for hardware, software and wetware, wetware being us.

Finally, I take sole responsibility for any technical bloomers in the text. Though the last few years have taught me much about technology, and even more about myself, I remain remarkably ignorant of Pascal, C++ and *even* Windows 95.